CONTENTS

C000224603

Printed by Belmont Press. Cover image from Craigentinny Telferton Allotments taken by Philip Gillespie
Maps produced by Alan Palfreyman Graphics @APalfreyman. Contains OS data © Crown copyright and database right 2019.

Scotland's Gardens Scheme, 2nd Floor, 23 Castle Street, Edinburgh EH2 3DN
T: 0131 226 3714 E: info@scotlandsgardens.org W: scotlandsgardens.org

CHAIRMAN'S MESSAGE

"I must go down to the seas again, for the call of the running tide" these words from John Masefield's poem 'Sea Fever' remind me of the deep connection that many of us have with the sea; something celebrated throughout 2020 in Scotland's Year of Coasts and Waters.

For me this pull to the sea is like my love of gardens, deeply rooted in childhood. A time when both provided opportunity to explore nature, play, learn and grow. To this day they still offer me the gift of space and time to think, walk and enjoy the wonder of wildlife; simple pleasures important for health and wellbeing. Be it the sound of the sandpiper at dusk, the discovery of orchids in the dunes or the smell of sweet peas and the delight of eating the freshly pulled baby carrots in the spring; all are deep-rooted reminiscences that still bring a smile to my face.

Sadly, today the natural world including the biodiversity found within our gardens and coastline is challenged by climate change, pollution and plastics or perhaps worse, simply by being misunderstood and undervalued at times.

Gardens are important teachers, a lens on the environment, barometers of change with a special ability to highlight humanity's relationship with the earth. For many individuals and families they provide an important accessible and intimate setting, one in which they can explore nature creating valuable memories. They are the ultimate source of wellbeing, providing food, environment, exercise and inspiration as well as a safe place to relax.

As Chairman I wish to thank our garden owners for their willingness to open and share these special places with you the visitor. I would also like to express my gratitude to the volunteers who give so freely of their time to support the opening of gardens for charity; without your help we simply could not function.

Gardens - Nature's Gift to You and Our Gift to the Nation – Please support our work by visiting our garden openings; remember that in doing so you will help ensure a better quality of life for yourself, your family and for communities across Scotland.

© Mario Testino

Sadly, in 2019 the Scottish weather reverted to its old self, with periods of stunning sunshine mingled with heavy rainstorms. Though disappointing for people visiting, some of the gardens and trees have flourished. Scotland's Gardens Scheme opened some 500 beautiful gardens in support of 250 charities, together with this year's good causes The Queen's Nursing Institute Scotland, Maggie's and Perennial, and welcomed many visitors, with and without umbrellas!

2019 was the year of 'Gardens and Health', celebrating the mental and physical benefits that gardening and garden-visiting can bring, and I am glad to say that more than a dozen gardens across the country hosted special visits from community groups and charities as part of this initiative. The Guest Charity bursary was awarded to Trellis, Scotland's network of therapeutic gardening, to help them develop workshops and teaching videos.

Indeed, in 2020 Scotland's Gardens Scheme will continue to celebrate 'Gardens and Health', but with a timely emphasis on healthy gardens and what can be done to enhance diversity and support wildlife. Every little helps: whether it be planting flowers to attract pollinators or using natural pest controls; making a garden pond or keeping bees.

Finally, as the proud President of Scotland's Gardens Scheme, I must thank every volunteer, organiser and garden owner for all the unseen work they do, come rain or shine, to open these wonderful gardens to so many visitors.

Camilla

VOLUNTEER WITH US

Our community of Volunteers has been raising money for charity since 1931 through their shared love of gardens. And our Volunteers are just as important to the charity now as they were in the very beginning. Everything we do relies on our incredible Volunteer Teams who help find our gardens, support openings with publicity and signage; and help on the day with admissions, refreshments and whatever is needed, even occasionally some last-minute gardening!

Our aim is to make volunteering *inspiring, rewarding* and *enjoyable.* We are currently looking for volunteers with various skills sets and experience, including PR, Social Media, Administration, Management, Accounts and Events. If you love gardens and enjoy working as part of a team – get in touch by email at **volunteers@scotlandsgardens.org** or call the office at 0131 226 3714.

'I love a challenge! Volunteering has brought me to fabulous gardens, including those that are still "a work in progress". I have made lots of new friends from the Garden Owners and my team of marvellous Area Organisers. '

Heidi Stone, Glasgow & District

'In Moray there are six or seven of us and I guess we have divided up the workload largely according to what people are happy to do as volunteers. Our aim is to enjoy the process of raising money for charity and we all have a passion for gardens whether herbaceous borders, strimmers or chainsaws.'

James Byatt, Moray & Nairn

Volunteers at Newtonmill House garden, Angus & Dundee

INTRODUCTION TO THE GUIDEBOOK

Let me tell you 'bout the birds and the bees and the flowers and the trees... in our beautiful gardens across Scotland. In 2020 we will continue to celebrate our gardens and health theme, but this year thinking about healthy gardens by celebrating wildlife. Our gardens and greenspaces are ecosystems that nurture a vast array of biodiversity including insects, butterflies, birds, small animals, earthworms and even beneficial bacteria. And these in turn benefit our gardens through pollination, improved soil structure and pest control, just to name a few.

Along this theme in this year's guidebook Simon Milne MBE, Regius Keeper RBGE, provides an interesting article about the very important contribution that our gardens make to the environment and climate change. And Jan Cameron, who liaisons with Trellis, this year's guest charity, discusses the very positive impact that working with nature can have on our personal wellbeing.

The Herbalist's Garden at Logie, Angus & Dundee

Our guidebook is again packed with garden opening and gardening information. We look forward to more that 500 gardens opening with us in 2020 with more new gardens than ever before. There are over 40 group and village openings with allotments (7), therapeutic (9) and community gardens (16) definitely on the rise. In late May (23-25 May) we will celebrate the bank holiday with a festival of garden openings across the country. Also, please don't miss the Angus & Dundee Garden Trail in June, featuring 17 new gardens opening across the county.

Our thoughts and wishes go out to the Jencks family who are mourning the loss of Charles, a brilliant man who has contributed so much to so many. Portrack, the Garden of Cosmic Speculation, will not open in 2020 but will return again in 2021.

Please join us and share our love of gardens with a visit – we've hundreds to choose from in the following pages. Soak up a bit of nature, and all its benefits, and help us to raise money for charity.

Terrill Dobson
Director

Private Clients   Financial Advisers   Charities   International Clients

Offices at: Bath Belfast Birmingham Bournemouth Cheltenham Edinburgh Exeter Glasgow Guildford Leeds Liverpool London Manchester Reigate Sheffield

Out of the Ordinary

Investec
Wealth & Investment

Wealth investment, help grow your future

At Investec Wealth & Investment we understand the potential of growth, that is why we have been sponsoring Scotland's Gardens Scheme, a source of beauty and inspiration, since 2009.

Like SGS, our heritage dates back over a century, providing exceptional levels of service to our clients. With offices in Edinburgh, Glasgow and across the UK, our local wealth experts can provide financial planning and tailor-made solutions to help you achieve your goals and secure your family's financial future.

With Investment Your Capital is at Risk.

To find out more, please visit
investecwin.co.uk/Edinburgh
investecwin.co.uk/Glasgow

Member firm of the London Stock Exchange. Authorised and regulated by the Financial Conduct Authority. Investec Wealth & Investment Limited is registered in England. Registered No. 2122340. Registered Office: 30 Gresham Street, London EC2V 7QN.

NEW GARDENS FOR 2020

Scotland's Gardens Scheme is delighted to welcome 89 new gardens opening across Scotland. We are so grateful to every Garden Opener and especially those braving a new opening this year. Please visit and help make their first open day successful.

Think you might like to open your garden for charity in 2021? We'd love to hear from you!

Photo by Philip Gillespie

By opening your garden, you are joining a long tradition of helping your community through both charitable funding and the pleasure of enabling the public to visit beautiful gardens. You will also benefit from our 89 years of experience in opening gardens, including our promotional support and even insurance coverage. We welcome all types, shapes and sizes of loved gardens.

Altries, Aberdeenshire

The Glassert, Stirlingshire

New garden entries are highlighted in green within the listing pages and with the NEW icon.

NEW GARDENS BY DISTRICT

ABERDEENSHIRE

Altries
Heatherwick Farm

ANGUS & DUNDEE

10 Menzieshill Road
Gardyne Castle
Torwood

ANGUS & DUNDEE GARDEN TRAIL

2 Whitewalls Farm Cottage
5 Glamis Place
6 Glamis Place
8 Leemount Lane
Balhary Walled Garden
Damside Cottage
Dundee Botanic Garden
Lawton House Walled Garden
Maggie's Dundee
Mains of Balgavies
Millden of Stracathro
North Lodge
Reswallie House
St Bride's Cottage
Templeton House Garden
The Doocot

ARBROATH COLLECTION OF GARDENS

37 Duncan Avenue
Inverbrothick School Sensory Garden and Forest Garden

BRECHIN GARDENS IN SUMMER

Andover Primary School Garden
Latchlea
Rosehill West

AYRSHIRE & ARRAN

1 Burnton Road
Underwood House

THE GARDENS OF FENWICK

2 Fulton's Crescent
25 Kirkton Road
5 Fowld's View
7 Raith Road
9a Maunsheugh Road

BERWICKSHIRE

Harlaw Farmhouse

COLDSTREAM OPEN GARDENS

Ladiesfield

DUMFRIESSHIRE

Craigieburn
Waterside Garden

DUNBARTONSHIRE

4 Cairndhu Gardens

EAST LOTHIAN

Longwood

STENTON VILLAGE

Tron House
Ruchlaw Walled Garden

EDINBURGH, MIDLOTHIAN & WEST LOTHIAN

2 Pentland Cresent
The Archivists' Garden
Jupiter Artland & Bonnington House
Meadow Place
Newhaven Heritage Community Garden

FIFE

Blebo House
Blebo Stables
Cambo Farmhouse

GLASGOW & DISTRICT

Duchess of Montrose Memorial Garden
Langside Gardens

KEW TERRACE GARDENS: BACK TO FRONT

15 Kew Terrace
19 Kew Terrace
20 Kew Terrace

INVERNESS, ROSS, CROMARTY & SKYE

White Rose Cottage

KIRKCUDBRIGHTSHIRE

Arbigland House

LANARKSHIRE

Auchlochan Walled Garden
Bothwell Village Gardens
Meadowhead

MORAY & NAIRN

Glebe House
No 3 Mains of Burgie

PEEBLESSHIRE & TWEEDDALE

Kirkton Manor House
Lamancha Community Hub
Prieston House
The Pines

GATTONSIDE VILLAGE GARDENS

41 Monkswood

WEST LINTON VILLAGE GARDENS

13 Fergusson View
16 Broomlee Crescent

PERTH & KINROSS

Fehmarn (also open with Bridge of Earn Village)
The Old Farmhouse

BRIDGE OF EARN VILLAGE

6 Balmanno Park
Earnbank

RENFREWSHIRE

Airlie
Garth House
Perch Corner

ROXBURGHSHIRE

SMAILHOLM VILLAGE GARDENS

1 Eden Road
2 Main Road
Barn Owl Lodge
Estate House
Field View
Macfarlane's Lantern
Pennyfield
Smailholm Farmhouse
The Granary
The Old Manse

STIRLINGSHIRE

Kilmadock House
Na Lagan
The Glassert

WIGTOWNSHIRE

Crinan

8 Leemount Lane, Angus & Dundee

SGS PLANT SALES 2020

When you buy plants that have been grown locally, you can feel confident that they will be happy in your garden. Our plant sales, held across the country by our Volunteers, are usually composed of plants which have been lovingly propagated from the local opening gardens. You'll also find plenty of local gardeners available to answer your questions about position, sun, height and spread. And, you'll help us to raise money for charity.

Merrylee Spring Plant Sale 2019, Glasgow & District

FIFE

Cambo Spring Fair outside Kingsbarns KY16 8QD

Sunday 12 April noon - 3pm

RENFREWSHIRE

SGS Kilmacolm Plant Sale
outside Kilmacolm Library, Kilmacolm PA13 4LE

Saturday 25 April 10am - noon

ABERDEEN

Leith Hall Plant Sale Huntly AB54 4NQ

Saturday 6 June 10am - 3pm

PEEBLESSHIRE & TWEEDDALE

Lamancha Community Hub Plant Sale (NEW)
Old Moffat Road, Lamancha EH46 7BD

Saturday 6 June 2pm - 5pm

ARGYLL & LOCHABER

Argyll Plant Sale (NEW) Kilmore Village Hall, near Oban PA34 4XT

Saturday 13 June 2pm - 5:30pm

ANGUS & DUNDEE

Angus Plant Sale Logie Walled Garden, Kirriemuir DD8 5PN

Sunday 21 June 2pm - 5pm

DUNBARTONSHIRE

James Street Community Garden Plant Sale Helensburgh G84 8EY

Sunday 6 Sept noon - 4pm

FIFE

Hill of Tarvit Plant Sale and Autumn Fair
Hill of Tarvit, Cupar KY15 5PB

Sunday 4 Oct 10.30am - 2.30pm

SNOWDROPS & WINTER WALKS

Scotland's Gardens Scheme is delighted to offer gardens open for Snowdrops and Winter Walks in 2020.

There's such an excitement when the first snowdrops emerge through the icy ground, pushing away the remains of the autumn leaves. These very first flowers of the year remind us that spring will return.

So this year, wrap up warm, grab your family and friends, and enjoy a brisk winter constitutional among some of Scotland's best snowdrop and winter gardens. Many of these gardens welcome dogs on leads, and some provide homemade teas.

Whether you're a galanthophile (snowdrop-lover), or just looking for a bit of fresh air, there are plenty of places for you to explore.

'In every walk with nature, one receives far more than he seeks.'
John Muir

Kailzie Gardens, Peeblesshire & Tweeddale. Photo by Kathy Henry

FIND A WINTER WONDERLAND NEAR YOU

Below are listings for gardens showcasing Snowdrops and Winter Walks 2020. Find out more in the listings pages or on our website.

Blair House, Ayrshire & Arran. Photo by David Blatchford

ABERDEENSHIRE

Laundry Cottage

ANGUS & DUNDEE

Dunninald Castle
Langley Park Gardens
Lawton House

ARGYLL & LOCHABER

Ardmaddy Castle

AYRSHIRE & ARRAN

Blair House, Blair Estate

DUMFRIESSHIRE

Barjarg Tower
Craig

EAST LOTHIAN

Shepherd House

FIFE

Lindores House

INVERNESS, ROSS, CROMARTY & SKYE

Abriachan Garden Nursery

KINCARDINE & DEESIDE

Ecclesgreig Castle

KIRKCUDBRIGHTSHIRE

Barholm Castle
Danevale Park

LANARKSHIRE

Cleghorn

MORAY & NAIRN

10 Pilmuir Road West

PEEBLESSHIRE & TWEEDDALE

Kailzie Gardens
Kirkton Manor House

PERTH & KINROSS

Braco Castle
Cloan
Fingask Castle
Kilgraston School

STIRLINGSHIRE

Duntreath Castle
Gargunnock House Garden
Kilbryde Castle

WIGTOWNSHIRE

Craichlaw

MAY GARDEN FESTIVAL WEEKEND

This year we're trying something new over the Spring Bank Holiday weekend, 23-25 May. We will celebrate this weekend with a number of gardens open to visit across Scotland. And we've also encouraged many of our gardens normally open only 'by arrangement' to join in. So, if you've had your eye on any of these gardens, have a look to see if they will be available for the Festival.

Forty-seven gardens have joined so far and are listed here. We hope to have more gardens available closer to the time, so please do check our website for updates. We don't anticipate these openings to be large, and most will not offer teas, but it should be a great way to explore lots of gardens over this May holiday weekend.

Photo by B Hutchinson

Photo by David Blatchford

BUILD YOUR OWN GARDEN TRAIL & VISIT LOTS OF GARDENS

PARTICIPATING GARDENS

ABERDEEN

Airdlin Croft

ANGUS & DUNDEE

10 Menzieshill Road

Inchmill Cottage

The Herbalist's Garden at Logie

Torwood

BRECHIN MAY WEEKEND FESTIVAL

9 Pearse Street

Bishops Walk

Brechin Cathedral Allotments

Kirkside of Lochty

Latchlea

Rosehill West

ARGYLL & LOCHABER

Braevallich Farm

Inveryne Woodland Garden

Maolachy's Garden

Strachur House Flower & Woodland Gardens

AYRSHIRE & ARRAN

Glenapp Castle

Kirkmuir Cottage

Townend of Kirkwood

GARDENS OF KILMAURS

27 Crosshouse Road

5 Kirkton Road

EDINBURGH, MIDLOTHIAN & WEST LOTHIAN

101 Greenbank Crescent

Redcroft

FIFE

Cambo Farmhouse

Kirklands

South Flisk

St Fort Woodland Garden

The Tower

KIRKCUDBRIGHTSHIRE

Corsock House

LANARKSHIRE

Covington House

Old Farm Cottage

St Patrick's House

Wellbutts

PEEBLESSHIRE & TWEEDDALE

Haystoun

PERTH & KINROSS

Bolfracks

Carey House

Cloan

Eastbank Cottage

Fehmarn

Rossie Gardens

STIRLINGSHIRE

43 Thornton Avenue

Duntreath Castle

Gargunnock House Garden

Kilbryde Castle

Shrubhill

WIGTOWNSHIRE

Balker Farmhouse

Crinan

Woodfall Gardens

ANGUS & DUNDEE GARDEN TRAIL

Running over the Thursdays, Fridays and Saturdays in June, the Angus & Dundee Gardeners are offering an opportunity to visit 17, not previously opened, gardens across Angus and Dundee.

The Angus & Dundee Garden Trail offers a flexible way to keep up your weekly dose of beautiful gardens, and is excellent value for money. These gardens are new to SGS and run from the west end of Dundee to the coast around Arbroath, over through Forfar to Edzell and down to Meigle. Visit a community garden, productive walled garden, as well as further private gardens of varying sizes and styles. The Dundee Botanic Garden will promote the trail with entry for trail ticket holders over the first weekend and Maggie's Dundee garden will also be available to visit throughout the trail. Our trail leaflet and tickets also feature local tearooms and plant nurseries to visit along the way.

Reswallie House, Forfar

A ticket for the
Angus & Dundee Garden Trail
makes a perfect gift
- and treat yourself as well!

5 Glamis Place, Dundee

GARDENS OPENING FOR THE ANGUS & DUNDEE TRAIL

GARDENS	THURSDAYS 4/11/18/25 June	FRIDAYS 5/12/19/26 June	SATURDAYS 6/13/20/27 June
Dundee Botanic Garden	4th only 10am-7pm	5th only 10am-7pm	6th only 10am-7pm
Maggie's Dundee Ninewells Hospital	anytime	anytime	anytime
St Brides South Kingennie		1-5pm	1-5pm
2 Whitewalls Farm Cottage Tealing		2-5pm	2-5pm
8 Leemount Lane Broughty Ferry	10am-4pm		
5 Glamis Place Dundee			11am-4pm
6 Glamis Place Dundee	9am-6pm	9am-6pm	9am-6pm
Forfar Open Garden Forfar			10am-2:30pm
Reswallie House by Forfar	2-5pm		
Mains of Balgavies by Forfar	2-5pm		
Lawton House Inverkeilor	10am-2pm		
Damside Cottage Leysmill	10am-2pm		
Templeton House Garden Arbroath	10am-2pm		
Millden of Stracathro Brechin		10am-2pm	
North Lodge Edzell		noon-4pm	
The Doocot Meigle			2-5pm
Balhary Walled Garden Alyth	3-8pm	3-8pm	3-8pm

CHARITY

Sixty percent of the proceeds will go to Maggie's Dundee with the net remaining proceeds to the SGS beneficiaries: The Queen's Nursing Institute Scotland, Maggie's and Perennial.

ADMISSION

£25 for entrance to all gardens (with £20 early bird price before 1 May). Accompanied children free. Pre-sale tickets available online at Eventbrite (search Angus & Dundee Garden Trail 2020) or from the local SGS committee members. Tickets otherwise available on the day at the gardens. Gardens can also be visited individually for £5.00 each.

CHAMPION TREES

Champion Trees are the widest, tallest, oldest or rarest examples of their species. Some examples in Scotland include trees that are 700 years old, have a girth of 11 yards or are over 66 yards tall. The Tree Register maintains a database of these unique trees which is updated by volunteers. Many of our gardens feature unique examples of both native and non-native species. We've added the tree icon in our book to help you find them.

VISIT CHAMPION TREES

ABERDEENSHIRE

Cruickshank Botanic Gardens
Quercus ilex, *Acer griseum* and
a tri-stemmed *Nothofagus obliqua*

ARGYLL & LOCHABER

Ardkinglas Woodland Garden
The mightiest conifer in Europe and others

AYRSHIRE & ARRAN

Glenapp Castle
Abies cilicica, *Cercidiphyllum japonicum* and *Picea likiangensis*

EAST LOTHIAN

The Walled Garden, Tyninghame
Two British and seven Scottish

INVERNESS, ROSS, CROMARTY & SKYE

Dundonnell House
Yew and holly

House of Aigas and Field Centre
Douglas fir, Atlas cedar and *Sequoiadendron giganteum*

Old Allangrange
Yew and sweet chestnut

KIRKCUDBRIGHTSHIRE

Threave Garden
Acer platanoides 'Princeton Gold'; *Carpinus caroliniana*; X *Cuprocyparis leylandii* 'Picturesque' and a further 25 Scottish Champion Trees

PEEBLESSHIRE & TWEEDDALE

Dawyck Botanic Garden
Numerous

Kailzie Gardens
Larch planted 1725

PERTH & KINROSS

Fingask Castle
Pinus wallichiana (Japanese maple)
Megginch Castle
Acer palmatum

WIGTOWNSHIRE

Castle Kennedy and Gardens
Six British, 11 Scottish and 25 for Dumfries and Galloway
Logan Botanic Garden
Polylepis and *Eucalyptus*
Logan House Gardens
Seven UK and 11 Scottish

A mighty Thuja at House of Aigas and Field Centre, Inverness.

NATIONAL PLANT COLLECTIONS

National Plant Collection® (NPC) mission is to conserve, grow, propagate and record cultivated plants in the UK. NPC holders oversee particular genus or group of plants, preserving diversity in the UK for future generations. Some of them are opening their gardens with us this year and you will be able to come and see these plants.

For more information about these collections, please see the Plant Heritage website.

VISIT NATIONAL PLANT COLLECTIONS

ARGYLL & LOCHABER

Benmore Botanic Garden
Abies, South American temperate conifers, *Picea*

PEEBLESSHIRE & TWEEDDALE

Dawyck Botanic Garden
Larix and *Tsuga*

PERTH & KINROSS

Explorers Garden
Meconopsis

Glendoick
Rhododendron sect. *Pogonanthum*, subsect. *Uniflora*, subsect. *Campylogyna* & subsect. *Glauca* and Cox hybrids

Megginch Castle
Scottish cider apples, Scottish Heritage apples and pears

Parkhead House
Lilium (Mylnefield lilies)

WIGTOWNSHIRE

Logan Botanic Garden
Gunnera, *Leptospermum*, *Griselinia*, *Cianthus* and *Sutherlandia*

Catherine Drummond-Herdman, holder of the National Scottish Heritage Apple and Pear and National Scottish Cider Apple collections with a Bloody Ploughman eating apple. This variety was bred at Megginch Castle in the 19th century.

A mass of rhododendron Yakushiman hybrids ideal for smaller gardens. Some of these were bred at Glendoick.

GET GARDENING FOR WILDLIFE

Photo by Philip Gillespie

Simon Milne MBE is the Regius Keeper for Royal Botanic Garden Edinburgh. Here he shares his expertise on how to garden with wildlife in mind, in gardens great or small.

We recently recorded over 1,000 species of wildlife at the Royal Botanic Garden Edinburgh; which should come as no surprise given that all known life depends on plants. From badgers to butterflies and kingfishers to caddis flies, our four Gardens at Edinburgh, Benmore, Logan and Dawyck are havens for wildlife. Whilst the primary draw for our one million visitors is our extraordinary collection of plants from around the world, our visitors are also lured by the wide range of other biodiversity that calls our Gardens home.

As every gardener understands, plants are not 'in' the environment, they are the environment. Plants are an essential resource for our health, wellbeing and the economy. We depend on them for food, oxygen and medicines. They provide the raw materials for the clothes we wear and the shelter that protects us. They mitigate climate change and help to provide clean water. Plants and fungi are our life support system and all gardens, big and small, have a real role to play in sustaining biodiversity – season by season.

A fundamental role of the Botanics is to identify and document diversity. My colleagues in science and conservation horticulture work closely to extract every piece of available information from the plants we collect and grow to add to the ever-growing bank of knowledge that underpins our ability to conserve fragile habitats and provide the natural capital on which humankind relies. Celebrating 350 years of plant research and cultivation in 2020, we are as clear as ever that the basis of our success has been the cultivation skills of those who propagate and nurture plants, along with our ongoing quest for scientific knowledge.

Painted Lady. Photo by Heidi Stone

Photo by Philip Gillespie

Highlands Garden, Shetland

In the face of climate crisis and biodiversity loss, it would be easy to wonder what gardeners could possibly do to help. However, those who tend plots are well placed to make changes for the better and encourage positive mindsets.

What we plant and where need not only be to create a thing of beauty, it can protect the garden from the ravages of weirding weather caused by climate change and sustain wildlife. For example, an experimental Raingarden, at Edinburgh, has proved its worth during heavy rainfall and could influence future site management and planting schemes.

Established on the Garden's Birch Lawn, formerly notorious for flooding, the Raingarden features a range of carefully selected plants in a special mix of soil, compost, sand and gravel. It successfully absorbs excess water and reduces floods on nearby paths. Capturing rainwater benefits the plants that grow within its shallow basin and the area is being used as a living laboratory to learn more about the trees, shrubs and wildflowers that are best able to cope with occasional temporary flooding and also those able to withstand other extreme weather events such as drought.

Replacing hard surfaces and grass areas with a mixed selection of herbaceous perennials and shrubs can not only capture water runoff it can increase the wildlife and habitat value of the area, providing nectar sources for insects and bees in the summer. Leaving the stems of the perennials and grasses standing over winter will

This same passion and hunger for knowledge can be transferred from botanic gardens to private gardens, allotments or the smallest patches of land available to any individual. Those who tend plants can gather the talents necessary not only to create places of beauty but grow food and provide shelter for themselves and countless other species.

These are important skills, bearing in mind the ever-growing list of human-induced activities that are contributing to the demise of our environment. Habitats are in danger around the world. With the demise of plants, we witness the loss of insects, birds, mammals, fish and, ultimately, humans.

Quercus Garden Plants. Photo by Kathy Henry

Winter migrant fieldfares eating cotoneaster berries.
Photo by Helen Rushton

also provide a home for invertebrates and food for seed-eating birds. Striking a balance between areas for people and areas for wildlife will help wildlife that is struggling to survive in our over-developed environment.

> ## As every gardener understands, plants are not 'in' the environment, they are the environment.

Many actions can help nurture nature in the garden. They can be simple and effective without taking a radical approach. By leaving hedge-cutting until late September we can give fledgling birds a chance to leave the nests without being disturbed. And, please don't burn your leaves – turn them into compost.

A log pile in a quiet corner of the garden can also be an effective resource. As the wood rots, leaves and other vegetative material will be harboured within the gaps and this will help retain moisture. It makes an ideal habitat for garden insects and many other life forms. Or, why not consider a meadow edge? It would be an ideal start to a more ecologically friendly garden and create a habitat providing cover where small mammals can run. And, please avoid using peat-based compost in your garden. Doing so is destroying valuable peatland habitats and accelerating climate change. Those with higher ambitions can set up a wormery

to process kitchen waste and the odd pernicious weed. Or, think about converting a shed roof to a green roof. A simple wooden frame contains the substrate mix into which drought-tolerant species can be planted.

Anyone arriving at any of the Royal Botanic Garden Edinburgh's four Gardens will become quickly aware they have entered a world of ultra-high plant diversity. In Edinburgh alone we are surrounded by over 36,000 plants representing nearly 8,000 species from 163 countries. With the smallest plots of land, we can all contribute hugely to biodiversity.

Everyone looking for inspiration for their own dear green spaces can gain tips by logging on to www.rbge.org.uk Even better, why not visit our Gardens for ideas and contemplative inspiration. Finally, be mindful of the biodiversity on the other side of your garden fence, invasive non-native species escaping into the wider environment cause real threats to biodiversity. To find out more you can visit: https://www.rhs.org.uk/science/conservation-biodiversity/invasive-plants

Enjoy your wildlife as well as your borders!

Simon Milne MBE, Royal Botanic Garden Edinburgh

THE GARDEN CURE

Photo by Ben Hutchinson

Jan Cameron has worked in therapeutic and community gardens for 40 years and has seen first-hand in many different contexts how the experience of gardening and gardens directly and deeply benefits our health.
Her forthcoming book
The Garden Cure has many stories of how this works.
Below are just a few.

There is something in the whole metaphor of gardening that helps us to understand the way we ourselves grow and thrive and blossom.
It starts right away in the language we use to describe our well-being. We 'languish' or we 'flourish', we talk of people, especially children, 'blossoming' and pregnant women are 'blooming'. We talk about our work 'bearing fruit' young people 'in the flower of their youth'. When we look at the story of the garden it is the story of ourselves. We are intricately intertwined. Monty Don summed it up beautifully in *Gardeners World Magazine* recently: 'What is true about a healthy mind and body is true in creating a healthy garden.'

MEANINGFUL WORK

First thing in the morning in a busy therapeutic working garden there was the usual bustle of volunteers crowding round the notice board to see what job they had been assigned to that day -

friendly banter, a bit noisy, a bit crowded - looking forward to the day and keen to get started.

That morning John came into the garden and his body language was the picture of dejection. He wore a baseball cap firmly pulled over his face and his shoulders were slumped, his back was rounded and his eyes were downcast. He was carefully trying to avoid catching anyone's eye or engaging with anyone. His body language was saying very clearly 'I am feeling very fragile and afraid, please don't come near me.' When I watched him put his boots on I could see he was trembling.

To create a garden is to search for a better world

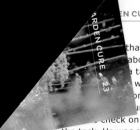
that this was not a good
about why he was feeling
a task in the garden
was to tie back the
on the south facing
unny day. Two hours
check on him he was fully
ged in the task. He was standing with the sun

in a completely different universe, the world of plants, the weather, nature and its many creatures. It's both hard work and restful at the same time. After a day in the garden you feel 'nicely tired' not worn out. Gradually your body becomes fitter and your mind begins to relax.

SEED SOWING

Sowing seeds is the most magical process in gardening. To hold a seed in your hand and know that the whole DNA blueprint for life is contained within it, no matter how tiny it might be. You sow, you tend, and you wait and if you are lucky, magic happens.

on his back which was easing all his muscles, he had his arms outstretched on either side in order to reach the bits of the tree he had to tie up. His back had straightened, his chest had opened, his head had come up, he was breathing deeply and he was talking easily to the person standing next to him so that they could work together to put the ties up. He looked relaxed and confident. It was like he had had a lesson in several alternative therapies:- Alexander technique, yoga, mindfulness, massage and talking therapies all rolled into one – AND, the apple tree got supported and we got apples, so he had achieved something.

It's that subtle combination of things that opens people up and helps them to talk and feel more at ease, and develops a sense of purpose.

The beauty of working with people in a garden is that it is most definitely a place of work with a clear 'firmly rooted' agenda of 'creating growth' for the future. (Just can't stop these metaphors!) We, and others, benefit from it but it is not about us. It's a chance to have a break from our own problems and dilemmas and to get involved, immersed, absorbed

The nature of trying to get seeds to germinate is such that you are constantly involved with problem solving. You always have to ask yourself lots of questions before you sow seed. What kind of soil, how deep, how much water, how warm, how much sun, is it the right season and so on.

This takes you right out of yourself, engages your brain in problem solving and takes it out of unproductive ruminating and helps to open your mind to lots of possibilities.

It is a wondrous thing to put seeds into the ground and watch them grow. People often approach it with scepticism and lack of confidence that a seed sown by them would actually grow. It can seem like a strange fiddly job and they do it without much faith until they see the results. Those first shoots when you point them out fill people with such satisfaction. Often they are so delighted by the crop they have produced they will eat it every day for the whole season – boiled, baked, mashed, fried, raw!

And of course they can collect the seeds at the end of the season and do it all again next year.

COMPOST

I love compost, it's the engine of the garden. It's the perfect metaphor for the recovery process. When people first came to the garden (a mental health training service) I would usually greet them and have a wee chat then take them for a wander round.

On our tour we would pass the compost heaps. It is generally considered good practice to build three compost heaps. The first one is where you put all the fresh garden waste, the second one you leave for a season to cook, and the third is usually about two seasons old and is compost ready to use.

When I showed people the first heap and explained its purpose they often said things like 'That should be me in there, I am rubbish, and people think I am a waste of time'. Such is the persistent stigma of having a mental health problem, often coupled with unemployment that people do genuinely feel like they are society's rubbish and are unwanted and unvalued – of no value.

When we moved on to the third compost bay and took off the cover people were usually amazed at the rich, sweet, fertile compost that was there, transformed from the rubbish.

Hopefully, the metaphor, the story of compost, takes root in their mind and at some much deeper level people gain an understanding that the transformational process, of turning a waste product into a richly valued one, can happen to them too.

Jan's book will be published by Saraband and she plans to launch it at the Melrose Book Festival 11-14 June.

BIODIVERSITY IN OUR GARDENS

Poplar Hawk Moth. Photo by Helen Rushton

Anyone can create and safeguard wild habitats. The way gardens are cared for can benefit the natural world. That said, you don't need to own land to make a difference. You can contribute in many ways, educating yourself on how to protect wildlife is a great place to start. Visit our open gardens, be nosy, ask questions and gather ideas. Here are some tips from our Garden Openers who pride themselves in maintaining wildlife-friendly grounds.

'Start with a tree, even a small one. They are the food-plant for the caterpillars of many kind of moths which in turn are food for many garden birds and bats.'

Helen Rushton, Bruckhills Croft, Aberdeenshire

Pebble the hedgehog keeps slugs and snails at bay in the garden, Helensbank, Fife.

Common Blue Damselflies mating. Bruckhills Croft, Aberdeenshire

'Leave some areas rough to provide shelter for insects and small mammals, this is important over winter.'

Helen Rushton, Bruckhills Croft, Aberdeenshire

Small Copper on greenhouse basil. Dal an Eas, Argyll

'A shallow birdbath with regular clean water will encourage birds into the garden, and you will find bumblebees and other insects coming to visit it.'

Helen Rushton, Bruckhills Croft Garden, Aberdeenshire

'I have seen 18 of our native butterflies on our land. All I can do is encourage and try and do no harm.'

Mary Lindsay, Dal an Eas, Argyll

Wildflower meadow by the pond. Bruckhills Croft, Aberdeenshire

Cream-spot ladybird. Backhouse Rossie Estate, Fife

'There are no introduced species in the main area that we look out on and it has been interesting to see the changes over the years. Cutting late in the season means that the orchid seed gets a chance to ripen.'

Mary Lindsay, Dal an Eas, Argyll

'This cream-spot ladybird (*Calvia quatuordecimguttata*) was seen in the vegetable garden at Backhouse Rossie during the summer. Like other ladybirds it is a ferocious predator of aphids and so is very welcome at Backhouse Rossie Estate, helping us to control pests naturally as we avoid using pesticides in the Walled Garden.'

Tim Viney, Backhouse Rossie Estate, Fife

Greater butterfly-orchids. Dal an Eas, Argyll

TOGETHER FOR CHARITY

Working together, our community of Volunteers and Garden Openers have raised over £1 million for charity in the last 4 years. We are so proud to support more than 250 charities each year, big and small, local and national.

Aberdeen Royal Infirmary Roof Garden ABF The Soldiers' Charity Absolute Classics Acting for Others Action Medical Research Action Porty All Saints Episcopal Church Alzheimer Scotland - Action On Dementia Alzheimer's Research UK Amnesty International UK Section Charitable Trust Appin Community Development Trust Appin Parish Church (Church of Scotland) Argyll Animal Aid Artlink Central Ltd Association Of Local Voluntary Organisations (Rural South Lanarkshire) Ayrshire Cancer Support Ayrshire Hospice Barrmill and District Community Association Beatson Cancer Charity Befriend A Child Ben Walton Trust Bennachie Guides Black Isle Bee Gardens Blebo Craigs Village Hall Comm Blood Bikes Scotland Board Of Trustees Of The Royal Botanic Garden Edinburgh Book Aid International Border Group Of Riding For The Disabled (SCIO) Border Women's Aid Ltd Borders Childrens Charity Borders General Hospital, Margaret Kerr Unit Breast Cancer Care Brechin Cathedral Church of Scotland Brechin Healthcare Group British Diabetic Association British Heart Foundation British Limbless Ex-Service Men's Association Brooke Action for Working Horses & Donkeys Bumblebee Conservation Trust Cambo Heritage Trust Cancer Research UK Canine Partners For Independence Ltd Capability Scotland Carbon Disclosure Project Castle Loch Lochmaben Community Trust Chest Heart & Stroke Scotland Cheviot Churches: Church of Scotland Children 1st Children's Hospice Association Scotland Children's Liver Disease Foundation Christ Church Scottish Episcopal Church Christ Church, Kincardine O'neil CLIC Sargent Cancer Care for Children Coach House Trust Coldstream Gateway Association Colinsburgh Community Trust Ltd Coronation Hall, Muckhart Corsock & Kirkpatrick Durham Church Of Scotland Cowal Elderly Befrienders SCIO Craigentinny Telferton Allotments Crail Community Partnership Crail Preservation Society Creich Crolck & Kincardine District Day Care Association Cromarty Firth Men's Shed Crossroads Care Skye & Lochalsh Dalbeattie Community Initiative Dairymple Community Landscape Project David Sheldrick Wildlife Trust Diocese of Edinburgh Scottish Episcopal Church Dirleton Village Association Dogs for Good Dogs Trust Donation to SGS Dorward House, Montrose Doune Pipe Band Dr. Neils Garden Trust Dunbarney And Forgandenny Parish Church (Church of Scotland) Dundee Chamber Music Club Earl Haig Fund (Scotland) East Lothian Special Needs Playschemes Eddleston Parish Church of Scotland Ellon and District Men's Shed Erskine Hospital Euan Macdonald Centre for Motor Neurone Disease Research Fauna & Flora International Feedback Trust Feis na h'apainne Fighting For Sight Aberdeen Fingask Follies Forgan Arts Centre SCIO Forth Driving Group RDA SCIO Forth Valley Sensory Centre Fortingall Parish Church Freedom from Fistula Foundation Friends of Craigtoun Friends Of Glasgow West Friends of Hilary Storm School Uganda Friends Of Kirkcudbright Swimming Pool Friends Of Loch Lomond & The Trossachs Friends Of The Cruickshank Botanic Garden Gardeners' Royal Benevolent Society Gargunnock Community Trust Ltd Gifford Community Land Company Gifford Horticultural Society Girlguiding Montrose District Glasserton and the Isle Of Whithorn Church of Scotland Glenfarg Riding For The Disabled Association Group Gordon Lennox Trust Great Ormond Street Hospital Children's Charity Guthrie and Rescobie Church of Scotland Helensburgh & District Twinning Association Help for Heroes Hidden Gardens Trust Highland Disability Sport Highland Hospice Hillfoot Harmony Barbershop Singers Home-Start Wigtownshire Hope Kitchen SCIO Horatio's Garden Host Humanist Society Scotland Inch Church Of Scotland Independence from Drugs & Alcohol Scotland Innerleithen Pipe Band James Street Community Garden Jewish Care Scotland Juvenile Diabetes Research Foundation Limited Kilmadock Development Trust Limited Kilninver & Kilmelford Parish Church of Scotland Kincardine Children's Gala Kirkandrews Kirk Trust Kirkcudbright Hospital League Of Friends Kirkmahoe Parish Church of Scotland Kirriemuir Day Care Ltd Laggan and Newtonmore Church of Scotland Laggan Church of Scotland Lamancha And District Community Association Lanark Community Development Trust Lanarkshire Cancer Care Trust Leighton Library Leuchars: St Athernase Church of Scotland Leuchie Lismore Parish Church (Church of Scotland) Now Live Music Scotland Loch Arthur Com

Our Garden Openers can elect for up to 60% raised at their opening to be donated to a charity of their choice. The net remaining raised supports our annual guest charity and our three core beneficiaries: The Queen's Nursing Institute, Maggie's and Perennial. Read more about them in the following pages.

OUR GUEST CHARITY: TRELLIS

Wreath making workshop in Kilmarnock

Scotland's Gardens Scheme offers a bursary of up to £5,000 for projects that will improve the physical, mental and emotional wellbeing of adults and/or children across Scotland using the sustaining help that gardens and gardening can bring. This year we were very pleased to award this bursary to Trellis Scotland to help with their excellent work to support therapeutic gardens across Scotland.

Tending Our Health - Snapshots from across the Therapeutic Gardening Network

Gardens make us feel good: it's no secret to those who visit the wonderful places in this Guidebook, or those who tend them and open the gates each year. Gardens restore us in so many ways, coaxing us into a better mood or getting us moving when we don't feel like it, taking our mind off nagging worries when a beautiful blossom opens. Across Scotland, at 480 therapeutic gardening projects in the Trellis network, skilled practitioners harness these benefits, helping over 12,000 people feel better each week.

For many care home residents, a tabletop bulb-planting session sparks memories of happy days in gardens from times gone by, scents and colours recalling a lifetime of people and places. It's not uncommon for residents to burst into song, or for a normally reticent person to participate with real enthusiasm. Extra care may be needed to bring gardening into palliative care facilities as patients' immune systems may be fragile. But it's worth the effort. One gentleman, after cutting daffodils for a vase and sowing rocket seeds said he'd forgotten the overwhelming pain he'd had before he started the session. The corridors and treatment rooms of a psychiatric care unit can be oppressive, even with homely and welcoming design. Being away from home and your routine can be disorientating,

especially if you're a young person who's waited months for therapy. The chance to be outdoors, to feel the sun or rain on your face and notice how the air smells offers a crucial chance to reconnect with normal life.

Thanks to support from Scotland's Gardens Scheme, we've been able to help more people like those featured in the stories here. The bursary received enabled us to provide inspirational demonstration sessions in care homes, hospitals and other healthcare settings that give staff, volunteers and residents the confidence and ideas to start gardening. Sometimes these are tabletop sessions, specially designed to enable everyone to take part whether they're wheelchair gardeners or affected by the fatigue of cardiovascular disease or neurological conditions. We also used the bursary to make 'how-to' videos, such as our 'Nifty Spring Onions' film that care workers can consult any time the opportunity arises to squeeze in a gardening session. And finally, the grant from SGS funded advisory site visits so that we could go and see people on location to give really tailored advice on how to make a plot accessible, relaxing and fun for the unique group of gardeners who will be using it.

QNIS SUPPORT
NURTURING
EDUCATION
BE THE BEST
EQUIPPING
CARE

CARE
DEVELOPING PRACTICE
BE THE **CONNECTING**
BEST ACHIEVING
CARE POTENTIAL
EDUCATION
EQUIPPING

CARE
SUPPORT **EQUIPPING**
RESEARCH
CONNECTING
CHAMPIONING ACHIEVING POTENTIAL
ACHIEVING **BE THE BEST**
POTENTIAL
COMPASSION CARE ACROSS GENERATIONS
HEALTH COMMUNITY NURSING
QNIS FELLOWSHIP & WELFARE CARE
QNIS QNIS **FACILATATORS** ACHIEVING POTENTIAL
RESEARCH EQUIPPING
CARE **CONNECTING CHAMPIONING**
BE **CARE** PROMOTING EXCELLENCE IN COMMUNITY NURSING
THE SUPPORT **DEVELOPING PRACTICE**
BEST SHAPING
SHAPING POLICY **EQUIPPING SUPPORT**
POLICY COMMUNITY SUPPORT RESEARCH
NURSING **LEADERSHIP AT EVERY LEVEL**
WELFARE SHAPING
OF RETIRED POLICY PROFESSIONAL DEVELOPMENT
SUPPORT CARE
SUPPORT RESEARCH **COMPASSION** NURTURING
FELLOWSHIP SHAPING SUPPORT COMMUNITY
& WELFARE POLICY **CARE** NURSING
SUPPORT COMMUNITY **FELLOWSHIP & WELFARE** EDUCATION
EDUCATION CARE NURSING CARE
CARE PROFESSIONAL **CHAMPIONING** CARE
DEVELOPMENT SHAPING
CHAMPIONING CHERISHING OUR HISTORY POLICY
BE CONFIDENCE & RESILIENCE
CARE COMMUNITY NURSING FACILATATORS
THE QNIS DEVELOPMENT PROGRAMMES FELLOWSHIP & WELFARE
BEST **CHAMPIONING** EDUCATION CARE
SUPPORT **CONNECTING BE THE BEST**
HEALTH
SHAPING RESEARCH **LEADERSHIP AT EVERY LEVEL**
POLICY **SCOTLAND'S COMMUNITIES**
COMMUNITY
NURSING CARE FELLOWSHIP **FELLOWSHIP & WELFARE**
CARE & WELFARE & WELFARE
WELFARE **CARE** CARE PROMOTING EXCELLENCE IN COMMUNITY NURSING
OF RETIRED CARE HEALTH SUPPORT
BE QNIS **LEADERSHIP AT EVERY LEVEL**
THE RESEARCH PROMOTING
BEST EXCELLENCE **EDUCATION**
IN COMMUNITY
NURSING **CONNECTING** CARE
SHAPING
POLICY **BE THE BEST**
SUPPORT COMPASSION COMPASSION
WELFARE OF RETIRED
CARE SUPPORT CARE
RESEARCH
HEALTH
CARE

www.qnis.org.uk   @QNI_Scotland

A Scottish Charitable Incorporated Organisation. Charity Number SC005751

BENEFICIARY MESSAGES

THE QUEEN'S
NURSING
INSTITUTE
SCOTLAND

Last year, the Queen's Nursing Institute Scotland (QNIS) marked its 130th anniversary by holding a series of events and celebrations across the country. As part of this, we launched a new section on our website dedicated to showcasing the history of Queen's Nursing in Scotland. Using photos from our extensive archive and based on historical research, the website charts 130 years from the very beginnings of the concept of district nursing through to the present day. Contained within this fascinating history is a look at the link with Scotland's Gardens Scheme established in 1931 – a connection which we are proud to see thriving to this day.

The Catalysts for Change programme, which has been supported with funding from Scotland's Gardens Scheme, has also been awarded National Lottery funding. Grants are available to help community nurses in Scotland and their local partners explore short-term initiatives that prevent, reduce or overcome health inequalities. New projects have now been supported across Scotland addressing recovery from trauma and a range of other important issues.

The Queen's Nurse development programme continues, and we now have 61 Queen's Nurses working in communities across Scotland. They work in diverse roles – including advanced nurse practitioners in remote areas, community mental health nurses, midwives, district nurses, health visitors, and school nurses, to those working in settings including care homes and hospices.

A number of these Queen's Nurses have been familiar faces at garden openings as they are keen to share their stories of how QNIS has benefited from the generosity of Scotland's Gardens Scheme and to express their thanks to garden openers and visitors for their ongoing support.

2020 has been designated the Year of the Nurse and Midwife by the World Health Organisation, and it also sees the 200th anniversary of the birth of Florence Nightingale. It is an important opportunity to celebrate the strength, excellence and diversity of community nursing in the 21st century and we would invite you all to participate.

We look forward to joining more garden openings throughout the year and to spreading the word about our gratitude for the ongoing support of Scotland's Gardens Scheme to the work of community nurses in Scotland.

Clare Cable
Chief Executive and Nurse Director, QNIS

Find your way through cancer

Come to Maggie's

Maggie's provides free practical, emotional and social support for people with cancer and their family and friends.

Built in the grounds of NHS hospitals, our network of centres across the UK are warm and welcoming places, with professional staff on hand to offer the support you need to find your way through cancer.

Our centres are open Monday to Friday, 9am – 5pm, and no referral is required.

Maggie's centres across Scotland receive vital funds from every garden opening. Our heartfelt thanks go to everyone who supports Scotland's Gardens Scheme by opening their garden, volunteering or visiting a garden.

Scotland's
GARDENS
Scheme
OPEN FOR CHARITY

maggiescentres.org

Maggie Keswick Jencks Cancer Caring Centres Trust
(Maggie's) is a registered charity, no. SC024414

MAGGIE'S
Everyone's home of cancer care

BENEFICIARY MESSAGES

MAGGIE'S

Everyone's home of cancer care

The annual open day of The Garden of Cosmic Speculation in Dumfriesshire is the most popular in the SGS calendar. This year, due to the death of its designer Charles Jencks at the age of 80 in October 2019, the Jencks family has decided not to open to the public while they grieve Charles's passing. Along with his late wife Maggie Keswick, Charles was our co-founder and Maggie's fully supports the family's decision.

Charles will be remembered for his visionary landscape design, and as a renowned architectural historian and cultural theorist. For me personally his greatest legacy lies in the contribution he has made to ensuring that people living with cancer, and those close to them, have the best possible support – and Maggie's would not be the organisation it is today without his tenacity, dedication and charisma.

Maggie and Charles were determined to create a new kind of cancer care – a thoughtfully designed space where people with cancer could find help away from the often stark, clinical environment of the hospital. After Maggie's death in 1995 Charles helped make their vision a reality, working with the architect Richard Murphy to turn an abandoned stable block at Edinburgh's Western General Hospital into a cancer centre; the first "Maggie's".

This blueprint for a model of cancer care has grown into a network of centres across Scotland and beyond, supporting and empowering hundreds of thousands of people with cancer, as well as their families and friends. We couldn't do this without the continued support of Scotland's Gardens Scheme and everyone who opens or visits a garden under the scheme. Thank you.

We are certain you join us in sending our best wishes to Charles's family and look forward to the garden re-opening for Scotland's Gardens Scheme in 2021.

Dame Laura Lee DBE
Chief Executive
Maggie's

Helping people
in horticulture
Perennial

WHATEVER
THE PROBLEM

WE'RE HERE FOR YOU

If you work with plants, trees or grass, or work in the places where they grow, Perennial is your charity. Everyone working in or retired from horticulture, forestry or arboriculture is eligible for our free and confidential help, which includes friendly one-to-one advice, support and financial assistance.

> " The biggest barrier to people approaching Perennial for help is simply not knowing about us. Those living and working remotely are even more difficult to reach. We rely on people like you to help us spread the word by telling a friend or someone you know in the industry about Perennial. "

Dougal Philips
Chairman of Perennial
Owner of New Hopetoun
Gardens in Edinburgh

GEORGE'S STORY

George is one of 119 people and families in Scotland who accessed our services last year when he had to stop working due to ill health.

" I was in and out of hospital and just couldn't see an end to my problems. I was working as much as I could to try to pay off debts, but it was never enough. I just couldn't see a way out, I felt suicidal at times and was just waiting to die.

Perennial came along and everything changed. My caseworker helped with my bankruptcy claim, negotiated with debtors on my behalf and he gave me confidence that we had a plan and there was a way out.

I really can't thank Perennial enough. They have allowed me to focus on getting better, safe in the knowledge that I'm not missing deadlines and that the paperwork has all been filled in correctly. This year has been a journey and I'm just thankful to have had Perennial with me on it. Perennial saved my life - I know I wouldn't be here today without them. "

George - Self-employed gardener

" Perennial is here for people for as long as it takes and thanks to our partnership with Scotland's Gardens Scheme, we are helping more individuals and families each year. "

Carole Baxter
Perennial Trustee
Presenter of BBC Scotland
Beechgrove TV programme

DONATE NOW
0800 093 8792
Perennial.org.uk/donate

Registered Charity Nos 1155156 | Scotland SC040180. Perennial's Debt Advice Service is authorised and regulated by the Financial Conduct Authority (www.fca.org.uk).

SUPPORT OUR SCHEME

From urban allotments to castles in the country; from big, mature gardens to small cottage ones and all-around Scotland, Scotland's Gardens Scheme is a charity that helps Scotland flourish.

Our Scheme is a simple one. We use Scotland's army of gardeners to raise much-needed funds for many worthy causes – local and national. We encourage people to visit Scotland's gardens, learn about gardening, enjoy a cup of tea, a bit of cake and a little social time with others and most-importantly to enjoy the benefits of time in a lovely garden. Every year we offer about 500 gardens to visit and raise about £350 - £400K. We are very proudly 98% volunteer-led with over 175 core Volunteers, as well as our many generous Garden Openers. The money raised through our openings supports about 250 different charities every year.

As well as the funds that are raised for great causes, SGS makes a significant contribution to Scotland's wellbeing in many other ways. There is growing evidence that gardening and volunteering both provide a positive health impact and improve individual wellbeing. Finding a connection with plants and the environment can help people on the natural path to wellbeing and improved quality of life: through reduced stress, increased physical fitness, a sense of achievement, and not to mention the nutritional value of 'growing your own'.

The benefits of volunteering and joining our community of openers supports and develops a foundation of shared interests and the benefits of fellowship.

Scotland's Gardens Scheme, as a charity in its own right, is dedicated to helping our many Garden Openers share their beautiful gardens with the public, offering all the enjoyment, wellbeing and community fellowship this provides. And we also strive to maximise the monies raised to support other charities. Your giving can help us to enable these enjoyable garden days out and maximise the rewards for everyone involved.

If you would like to help support Scotland's Gardens Scheme, with a donation or legacy we would love to hear from you. Please ring the office on 0131 226 3714, email at **giving@scotlandsgardens.org** or visit our website where you'll find a link to donate on our home page.

Enjoyable, inspiring, rewarding

Craigentinny Telferton Allotments, Edinburgh. Photo by B Hutchison

DIANA MACNAB AWARD
FOR OUTSTANDING SERVICE

Janet Glaisher, Druimneil House, Argyll

About 20 miles north of Oban, tucked away along a leafy, winding track lies Druimneil House, Port Appin. Owner, Janet Glaisher, is the winner of the Diana Macnab Award 2020, given to a Volunteer who has shown outstanding service to Scotland's Gardens Scheme.

A more-hard working, warm and witty Highlander you could not meet. She will welcome you into her garden with genuine conviviality, regale you with her enthusiasm and inspire you to be positive. Her energy belies her years - she is 84! She has opened Druimneil House for Scotland's Garden Scheme for a remarkable 37 years.

A farmer's daughter, she grew up at Pennyghael Estate on Mull. Bereaved, tragically, at a young age with two sons, she moved to mainland Argyll where she found Druimneil House. At this time, in the 1970s, the formal Victorian garden had become a jungle – lost in swathes of bracken and brambles. Inspired by her grandmother's garden and undaunted, she began the colossal task of restoring the imposing, seven-acre space.

'The wild vegetation towered above our heads. Once we had cleared areas, little by little, we started to see what should go where.'

Now fully restored, Druimneil garden has a distinctive feel. Vast, mature trees tower behind the house, their scale providing a breathtaking architecture to the garden. A clifftop pathway leads the eye across undulating lawns, herbaceous borders, a pond and stream to a blue streak of Loch Linnhe and Morven Hills beyond. Janet believes gardens hold the power to soothe the soul in our hurried, stressful lifestyles. As her late husband said of antiques and gardens, 'We are simply custodians. Our job is to look after it while we can.'

Still running her dinner, bed and breakfast business from the house, Janet is known for her exceptional rapport with visitors. Whatever time they arrive, be it house guests or garden visitors, whether by arrangement or not, they are welcomed with reviving tea and home baking. Always interested in people, she makes herself available to engage with her visitors. Their stories usually trigger some very entertaining ones of her own. Her generous hospitality complements the sounds and sights of her garden and cannot fail to leave visitors feeling uplifted.

Assisted by Andy, her gardener of over 20 years, Janet continues to work cheerfully and tirelessly towards her vision for the garden and local area. Besides receiving many visitors, Druimneil makes a significant contribution to the Appin economy. The walled garden with feature greenhouse is home to vegetables, shrubs, flowers and a productive fig tree. Beyond this, a host of nursery polytunnels are filled with cuttings and potted plants, propagated and reared by Andy. Janet and Andy supply vegetables and plants to local businesses and events and see Scotland's open gardens as an essential service to local and tourist communities.

'The Highlands need tourists and they need things to do. It's important that we provide places of interest to visit. Visitors arrive with the cares of the world and leave having enjoyed relaxation and peacefulness. They talk about it and come back. That's what we can offer.' This charming, intrepid lady is right about that.

LONG SERVICE AWARDS

In 2020, Scotland's Gardens Scheme is delighted to be celebrating a number of milestones of long service of 50, 25 and 10 years of opening gardens. Janet Gillespie, who has opened Danevale Park for snowdrops since 1951, recalls a rather unusual opening day... 'One year it was Snowdrop Day opening and it snowed and snowed and we thought this year is going to be a complete write-off so we all relaxed and were sitting in the kitchen. Suddenly through the gloom came the headlights of a car, the passenger door opened - just a fraction, just enough to allow a hand holding a £5 note to be held out - saying 'this is a little donation'. The car then with difficulty turned around and drove off. The occupants of the car were residents of Crossmichael, Mrs Milligan and her sister Peggy Geddes. Our takings that day were £5. These ladies supported me at every single opening. They always came no matter what, even in the snow!'

DANEVALE PARK
Kircudbrightshire

Danevale Park will open for Snowdrops and Winter Walks for its 50th year on Sunday 23 February, 1pm - 4pm. Please visit and help celebrate this wonderful achievement where an old-fashioned tea will be served in the house.

Janet Gillespie amongst her snowdrops at Danevale Park, Kircudbrightshire

CORBET TOWER
Roxburghshire

DIPPOOLBANK COTTAGE
Lanarkshire

HAYSTOUN
Peeblesshire & Tweeddale

KEVOCK GARDEN
Edinburgh, Midlothian & West Lothian

Corbet Tower, a charming Victorian garden set in the Cheviot foothills and Haystoun's walled garden with ancient yew tree and stunning views, are both stalwart supporters of Scotland's Gardens Scheme, opening first in 1933 and 1932 respectively. Dippoolbank Cottage, an artist's garden with a variety of lovely features is gardened on organic principles and mainly constructed with recycled materials, opening quite consistently since 1996. Don't miss these georgeous and well-established gardens - see the garden pages for open dates.

Haystoun, Peeblesshire & Tweeddale. Photo by Kathy Henry

Beginning this year we wish to recognise gardens that have opened with our charity for 10 years. This is a brilliant show of support and enthusiasm and true generosity of openers sharing their garden with others. Thank you!

ABERDEENSHIRE

Laundry Cottage

AYRSHIRE & ARRAN

Blair House, Blair Estate

CAITHNESS, SUTHERLAND, ORKNEY & SHETLAND

Cruisdale
Highlands Garden
Lea Gardens
Nonavaar
Norby

DUMFRIESSHIRE

Dunesslin

EDINBURGH, MIDLOTHIAN & WEST LOTHIAN

The Glasshouses at the Royal Botanic Garden

FIFE

Glassmount House

KINCARDINE & DEESIDE

Finzean House

KIRKCUDBRIGHTSHIRE

The Waterhouse Gardens at Stockarton

PERTH & KINROSS

Carig Dhubh
Glenlyon House

STIRLINGSHIRE

Rowberrow

Glenlyon House, Perth & Kinross. Photo by David Hay

Lea Gardens, Shetland. Photo by Andrea Jones

WHO'S WHO IN OUR CHARITY

Scotland's Gardens Scheme is supported by Trustees and Staff in the Head Office, each of whom brings their own expertise to the table. Our Trustees and Staff are devoted to the charity.

We also have many fantastic Volunteer Organisers whose hard work we could not do without. They are listed under our Districts.

Scotland's Gardens Scheme is also delighted to have HRH The Duchess of Rothesay as our President.

In keeping with our theme of Healthy Gardens, we've asked our President, Trustees and Staff to share their favourite tip for attracting wildlife into their garden.

PRESIDENT

© Mario Testino

HRH The Duchess of Rothesay

As a beekeeper myself, I would like to encourage people to choose flowers that attract bees throughout the year: crocus, asters, poppies, cornflowers, sedum and heather, to name but a few...

HEAD OFFICE

Terrill Dobson
Director

I don't cut back my flowers and herbs until early spring so that the birds can feed on the seed heads throughout the winter.

Hazel Reid
Office Manager

Climbing plants are great for encouraging wildlife; creating shelter for birds and insects, nectar for bees and leaves for caterpillars.

Julie Golding
Volunteer Manager

I scatter wildflower seeds and watch how the colours and scents invite butterflies and bees to the garden. I also make sure to top up a bird feeder in the months when nuts, fruits and seeds become scarce.

Daria Piskorz
Marketing Manager

I keep my soil healthy and happy. Organisms living there are the base of many wild food chains. I make my own compost, nettle fertilising tea and I mulch generously.

Lisa Pettersson
Graphic Design

Lavender and salvia are easy to keep in our communal garden, and the bees and butterflies love them. Bird feeders outside the tenement windows help the house sparrows nesting in the stone walls.

TRUSTEES

David Mitchell
Chairman

I fill a dried teasel head with niger seeds and place it in the garden. The goldfinches just love this, and it's a great way to take natural photographs.

Sarah Landale
Deputy Chairman

We have red squirrels in our garden and spend a lot of time keeping them fed with hazelnuts. We now have families of them scampering up the trees where the nut feeders are and they have become so friendly that I found one in the basement of the house.

Peter Yellowlees
Treasurer

We plant as many insect loving plants as possible and are now ripping up a slabbed patio to plant a birch tree, grasses, a wisteria and hydrangea. Hopefully that will attract more wildlife. However, don't ask me about snails and slugs...

Charlotte Hunt
Trustee

Don't feed the garden birds in summer. Best to let them fend for themselves.

Emily Stair
Trustee

Simply to let your grass grow! In our garden we have special designated areas of uncut grass, which we leave long over winter and cut in the spring. The result is a wildlife haven full of fluttering and buzzing insects and many beautiful wildflowers.

Jonathan Cobb
Trustee

Keep plenty of spaces in your flower beds where birds can shade and dust their feathers.

David Buchanan-Cook
Trustee

A couple of years ago we adopted a blind hedgehog who roams about in the safety of our walled garden, often during the day. Not only has she kept the garden snails in check, but now that we have stopped using slug pellets thrushes have returned to the garden.

Stephen McCallum
Trustee

Have an untidy bit where you can pile some logs and twigs to create shelter and habitat for a host of creatures, choose plants with single rather than double flowers for pollinating insects and don't use fungicides or insecticides.

'At the heart of our charity are our Volunteer Organisers without whom there would be no gardens to visit.'

ABERDEENSHIRE

Scotland's Gardens Scheme 2020 Guidebook is sponsored by INVESTEC WEALTH & INVESTMENT

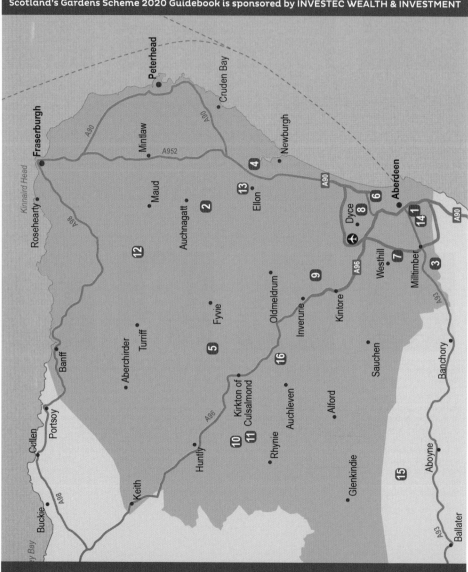

1. 105 Inchgarth Road
2. Airdlin Croft
3. Altries
4. Auchmacoy
5. Bruckhills Croft
6. Cruickshank Botanic Garden
7. Easter Ord Farm
8. Grandhome
9. Heatherwick Farm
10. Laundry Cottage
11. Leith Hall Plant Sale
12. Middle Cairncake
13. Parkvilla
14. Pinetrees Cottage
15. Tarland Community Garden
16. Westhall Castle

Aberdeenshire

OUR VOLUNTEER ORGANISERS

District Organiser:	Verity Walters	Tillychetly, Alford AB33 8HQ E: aberdeenshire@scotlandsgardens.org
Area Organisers:	Linda Colquhoun	Hillview, Rothienorman, Inverurie AB51 8YL
	Gill Cook	
	Anne Fettes	
	Jennie Gibson	6 The Chanonry, Old Aberdeen, Aberdeen AB24 1RP
	Anne Lawson	Asloun, Alford AB33 8NR
	Penny Orpwood	Middle Cairncake, Cuminestown, Turriff AB53 5YS
	Helen Rushton	Bruckhills Croft, Rothienorman, Inverurie AB51 8YB
Treasurer:	To be advised	

GARDENS OPEN ON A SPECIFIC DATE

Auchmacoy, Ellon	Sunday, 12 April
Westhall Castle, Oyne, Inverurie	Sunday, 19 April
Cruickshank Botanic Garden, 23 St Machar Drive, Aberdeen	Saturday, 9 May
Airdlin Croft, Ythanbank, Ellon	Friday/Saturday/Sunday, 22/23/24 May
Airdlin Croft, Ythanbank, Ellon	Friday/Saturday, 5/6 June
Leith Hall Plant Sale, Huntly	Saturday, 6 June
Altries, Maryculter, Aberdeenshire	Saturday, 13 June
Heatherwick Farm, Kintore, Inverurie	Sunday, 21 June
Heatherwick Farm, Kintore, Inverurie	Sunday, 28 June
Tarland Community Garden, Aboyne	Sunday, 23 August

GARDENS OPEN BY ARRANGEMENT

Laundry Cottage, Culdrain, Gartly, Huntly	1 January - 31 December
Grandhome, Danestone, Aberdeen	1 April - 30 September
105 Inchgarth Road, Pitfodels, Cults, Aberdeen	18 May - 14 June
Airdlin Croft, Ythanbank, Ellon	25 May - 30 June
Pinetrees Cottage, Banchory-Devenick	30 May - 5 July
Middle Cairncake, Cuminestown, Turriff	1 June - 31 August
Easter Ord Farm, Easter Ord, Skene, Westhill	15 June - 23 August
Bruckhills Croft, Rothienorman, Inverurie	1 July - 31 August
Parkvilla, 47 Schoolhill, Ellon	12 July - 30 September

Aberdeenshire

105 INCHGARTH ROAD
Pitfodels, Cults, Aberdeen AB15 9NX
Mr and Mrs W McGregor
T: 01224 861090 E: wahmcgregor@me.com

Informal cottage-style garden situated in one-third of an acre featuring azaleas, rhododendrons, orchids, peonies and a selection of alpines.

Open: by arrangement 18 May - 14 June, admission £4.00, children free.

Directions: From North Deeside Road, turn off along Station Road, Pitfodels. Access and parking along back lane.

· *The Archie Foundation*

AIRDLIN CROFT
Ythanbank, Ellon AB41 7TS
Richard and Ellen Firmin
T: 01358 761491 E: rsf@airdlin.com
W: www.airdlin.com

Since 1983 the garden has been developed to be both attractive to wildlife and horticulturally interesting, while also providing fruit and vegetables. One of two polytunnels produces figs, peaches and pumpkins while the other houses a collection of hostas wrestling for space with seed-grown rhododendrons. Native trees form the backbone of the woodland garden, providing shelter for a range of shrubs and herbaceous plants from around the world. In the new windswept garden an embryonic shelterbelt is struggling to protect recent plantings. More details and photos can be found on the Airdlin website.

Open: Friday/Saturday/Sunday, 22/23/24 May, noon - 4pm for the May Weekend Festival. Also open Friday/Saturday, 5/6 June, noon - 4pm. And open by arrangement 25 May - 30 June for groups only please. Admission £5.00, children free.

Directions: From the A948, three miles north of Ellon, take the left turn towards Drumwhindle. After another couple of miles take the second left towards Cairnorrie. Proceed for nearly a mile, ignoring the first Airdlin Croft at Coalmoss, and turn left at the first bend, go down our 300 yard track, parking is in the field at the bottom.

· *Fauna & Flora International*

Aberdeenshire

105 Inchgarth Road

3

ALTRIES
Maryculter, Aberdeenshire AB12 5GD
Mr and Mrs Melfort Campbell

The Altries garden has been redesigned to give a feeling of space and let in the light. The house itself is surrounded by a terraced area, borders and lawns. There is an exceptional view looking west up the River Dee, a woodland walk, a slate sphere sculpture using the original slates of the house following the refurbishment, a striking ten-foot wall making use of the downtakings of the house, a small new greenhouse with rose arbour path and further use of granite, and the original walled garden which has vegetables, fruit, and a picking garden. Each area of the garden has its own feeling of being a separate destination. Beautiful mature beech trees surround the area, giving a great sense of privacy.

Open: Saturday 13 June, 2pm - 5pm, admission £4.00, children free.

Directions: From Bridge of Dee, follow the South Deeside road, B9077. Half a mile after Maryculter House Hotel, turn left at yellow *SGS* sign, and follow signs to car park. For SatNav follow AB12 5GJ.

· *Newton Dee*

Aberdeenshire

Cruickshank Botanic Garden

4 AUCHMACOY
Ellon AB41 8RB
Mr and Mrs Charles Buchan

Auchmacoy House's attractive policies feature spectacular displays of thousands of daffodils.

Open: Sunday 12 April, 1pm - 4pm, admission £3.50, children free. Buchan Pipe Band will play. Please, NO dogs. Easter games. Homemade teas and soup.

Directions: A90 from Aberdeen. Turn right to Auchmacoy/Collieston.

· *The Royal British Legion: Ellon Branch*

5 BRUCKHILLS CROFT
Rothienorman, Inverurie AB51 8YB
Paul and Helen Rushton
T: 01651 821596 E: helenrushton1@aol.com

An informal country-cottage garden extending to three-quarters of an acre with a further acre as wildflower meadow and pond. There are several distinct areas which include a white border, a butterfly alley, kitchen garden with polytunnel, greenhouse and fruit cage, an orchard and a blue and yellow border. Relax on one of the many seats in the garden and soak up the atmosphere.

Open: by arrangement 1 July - 31 August, admission £4.00, children free.

Directions: From Rothienorman take the B9001 north for two-and-a-half miles. On the S bend turn left. Take the second left (*Bruckhills* sign). At the farmyard turn sharp right (opposite farmhouse), and the croft is at the end of the lane.

· *Befriend A Child Ltd*

Aberdeenshire

CRUICKSHANK BOTANIC GARDEN
23 St Machar Drive, Aberdeen AB24 3UU
Cruickshank Botanic Garden Trust, Aberdeen University
W: www.abdn.ac.uk/botanic-garden/
....

A tour is offered by the Curator, Mark Paterson, and Head Gardener, Richard Walker. The garden comprises a sunken garden with alpine lawn, a rock garden built in the 1960s complete with cascading water and pond system, a long double-sided herbaceous border, a formal rose garden with drystone walling, and an arboretum. It has a large collection of flowering bulbs and rhododendrons, and many unusual shrubs and trees. It is sometimes known as 'Aberdeen's best kept secret'.
Champion Trees: *Quercus ilex, Acer griseum* and a tri-stemmed *Nothofagus obliqua*.

Open: Saturday 9 May, 12:30pm - 3pm, admission £5.00, children free. Open for a tour which will start shortly after the annual spring plant sale held by the Friends of Cruickshank Botanic Garden. Plant Sale: 10:30am – noon, next to herbaceous border.

Directions: Come down St Machar Drive over the four-way junction, just before the first set of traffic lights turn left into the Cruickshank Garden car park. The pedestrian garden entrance is off The Chanonry. Limited parking available for this day only in the Cruickshank car park - AB24 3UU.

· *Friends Of The Cruickshank Botanic Garden*

EASTER ORD FARM
Easter Ord, Skene, Westhill AB32 6SQ
Catherine Fowler
T: 01224 742278 E: catherine.a.fowler@gmail.com
....

A one-acre mature cottage garden with year-round interest. The garden has an open aspect with views towards Lochnagar. It is made up of 'rooms'. There is a fruit garden, large herbaceous borders, lawn areas, small wildlife pond, vegetable garden and mini-orchard with wildflowers.

Open: by arrangement 15 June - 23 August, admission £4.00, children free. Teas and home baking available at reasonable cost.

Directions: Two miles from Westhill and can be reached using full postcode on SatNav. From Aberdeen take A944 towards Westhill. At the traffic lights before Westhill take the slip road on to the B9119 then immediately left towards Brotherfield. After one mile turn right at the T junction. After 350 yards turn left into the lane. Garden is first entrance on right.

· *Aberdeen Royal Infirmary Roof Garden*

'Gardening helps to
sharpen the brain'

Aberdeenshire

GRANDHOME
Danestone, Aberdeen AB22 8AR
Mrs D R Paton
T: 01224 722202 E: davidpaton@btconnect.com

Eighteenth-century walled garden incorporating a rose garden (replanted 2010) and policies with daffodils, tulips, rhododendrons, azaleas, mature trees and shrubs.

Open: by arrangement 1 April - 30 September, admission £4.00, children free. Please, no dogs.

Directions: From the north end of North Anderson Drive, continue on the A90 over Persley Bridge, turning left at the Tesco roundabout. After one-and-three-quarter miles, turn left through the pillars on a left-hand bend.

· *Alzheimer Scotland*

HEATHERWICK FARM
Kintore, Inverurie AB51 0UQ
Lucy Narducci

This old farmhouse one-acre garden has been regenerated over the past eight years and continues to evolve and develop. It has an open spacious feel and new landscaping with additional planting has created distinct areas. The garden includes a formal square front lawn with perennial borders, a kitchen garden surrounded by orchard, and a recently added native grass and wildflower meadow.

Open: Sunday 21 June & Sunday 28 June, 1pm - 5pm, admission £4.00, children free.

Directions: From Inverurie centre, take the B9001 southwards. At the corner of St Mary's Place and St James's Place follow signs for *Keithhall*. Then follow signs for *Balbithan*. Heatherwick is signposted and on the left after Hogholm Stables. It is three miles from the centre of Inverurie.

· *Myeloma UK*

LAUNDRY COTTAGE
Culdrain, Gartly, Huntly AB54 4PY
Judith McPhun
T: 01466 720768 E: judithmcphun@icloud.com

An informal cottage-style garden of about one-and-a-half acres by the river Bogie. Two contrasting steep slopes make up the wilder parts. The more intensively gardened area round the cottage includes a wide variety of herbaceous plants, shrubs and trees, an orchard area and fruit and vegetable plots, making a garden of year-round interest.

Open: by arrangement 1 January - 31 December, and for Snowdrops and Winter Walks over February and March, admission £4.00, children free.

Directions: Four miles south of Huntly on the A97.

· *Amnesty International UK Section Charitable Trust*

Aberdeenshire

LEITH HALL PLANT SALE
Huntly AB54 4NQ
The National Trust for Scotland
T: 01464 831148
W: www.nts.org.uk/visit/places/leith-hall/

The west garden was created by Charles and Henrietta Leith-Hay in the Arts and Crafts style during Edwardian times. In summer the magnificent serpentine herbaceous and catmint borders provide a dazzling display. The carefully reconstructed rock garden is currently being replanted.

Open: Saturday 6 June, 10am - 3pm, admission £3.50, children free. The plant sale is a fantastic opportunity to buy a wide selection of potted perennials from the garden's herbaceous borders. Entrance to the garden £3.50, entrance to the plant sale is free.

Directions: On the B9002 one mile west of Kennethmont.

· *The National Trust for Scotland: Leith Hall Garden*

Heatherwick Farm

Aberdeenshire

MIDDLE CAIRNCAKE
Cuminestown, Turriff AB53 5YS
Nick and Penny Orpwood
T: 01888 544432 E: orpwood@hotmail.com

A garden surrounded by farmland and attractive views. Visitors to the garden have described it as - 'beautiful... inspiring ... full of good ideas ... fragrant roses... so much to see... superb vegetables.' New for 2020 is the opportunity to bring a party to visit the garden and enjoy a vintage afternoon tea. Also planned are a few special events which will be advertised nearer the time.

Open: by arrangement 1 June - 31 August, admission £5.00, children free. Homemade tea at additional charge.

Directions: Middle Cairncake is on the A9170 between New Deer and Cuminestown. It is clearly signposted.

· *Scotland's Gardens Scheme & Parkinsons UK*

PARKVILLA
47 Schoolhill, Ellon AB41 9AJ
Andy and Kim Leonard
T: 07786 748296 E: andy.leonard@btinternet.com

A south-facing Victorian walled garden, lovingly developed from a design started in 1990 to give colour and interest all year. Enjoy densely planted herbaceous borders, pause under the pergola clothed in clematis, honeysuckle and rambling roses, continue on to the bottom of the garden where three ponds and a wildflower bed reflect a strong focus on wildlife. This is a hidden gem of a garden that has won awards including *Ellon Best Garden* and with plants rarely seen in north east Scotland.

Open: by arrangement 12 July - 30 September, admission £4.00, children free.

Directions: From centre of Ellon head north towards Auchnagatt. Schoolhill is third left. From Auchnagatt head into Ellon along Golf Road, Schoolhill is first right after the golf course. Limited on-street parking, car parks in Ellon (five minutes walk) and Caroline's Well Wood.

· *St Mary On The Rock Episcopal Church Ellon, Alzheimer Scotland & Ellon Men's Shed*

Pinetrees Cottage   Middle Cairncake

Aberdeenshire

PINETREES COTTAGE

Banchory-Devenick AB12 5XR
Angela and Derek Townsley
T: 01224 869141 E: angela.townsley@me.com

A mature garden, set in three-quarters of an acre, filled with a wide range of hardy plants, including rhododendrons, azaleas, acers, topiary and roses, with two ponds. An alpine house is fronted by stone troughs filled with rock plants. Set in a backdrop of mature pine trees to the north and open fields to the south.

Open: by arrangement 30 May - 5 July, admission £4.00, children free. Teas by arrangement.

Directions: Banchory-Devenick is four miles from Bridge of Dee. Turn off B9077 at Banchory-Devenick church. Follow to T junction, turn right. Next right is Butterywells Steading. Turn into opening and follow track, go around the back of farmhouse (Lochend) and continue on track to Pinetrees.

· *Fighting For Sight Aberdeen*

TARLAND COMMUNITY GARDEN

Aboyne AB34 4ZQ
The Gardeners of Tarland

Tarland Community Garden opened in 2013 and is a Tarland Development Group project. It provides an inclusive and accessible community growing space for local residents. It has indoor (polytunnel) and outdoor raised beds for rent plus communal planting areas including a soft fruit cage, fruit trees and a herb garden. It is a place for members to grow produce, learn, share and have fun.

Open: Sunday 23 August, noon - 4pm, admission £3.00, children free.

Directions: Take the B9094 from Aboyne or the A96 and B9119 from Aberdeen. Arriving at the village square the gardens will be clearly signposted.

· *Tarland Development Group*

WESTHALL CASTLE

Oyne, Inverurie AB52 6RW
Mr Gavin Farquhar
T: 01224 214301 E: enquiries@ecclesgreig.com

Set in an ancient landscape in the foothills of the impressive foreboding hill of Bennachie is a circular walk through glorious daffodils with outstanding views. This interesting garden is in the early stages of restoration, with large groupings of rhododendrons and specimen trees. Westhall Castle is a 16th-century tower house, incorporating a 13th-century building of the bishops of Aberdeen. There were additions in the 17th, 18th and 19th centuries. The castle is semi-derelict, but stabilised from total dereliction. A fascinating house encompassing 600 years of alteration and additions.

Open: Sunday 19 April, 1pm - 4pm, admission £4.00, children free.

Directions: Marked from the A96 at Old Rayne and from Oyne Village.

· *Bennachie Guides*

ANGUS & DUNDEE

Scotland's Gardens Scheme 2020 Guidebook is sponsored by INVESTEC WEALTH & INVESTMENT

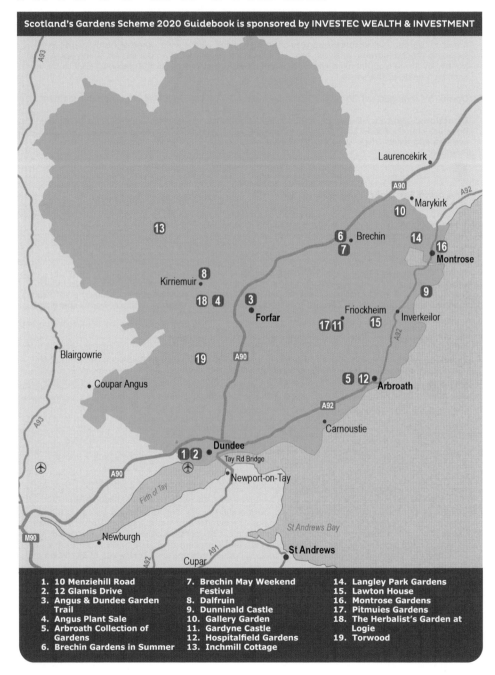

1. 10 Menziehill Road	7. Brechin May Weekend Festival	14. Langley Park Gardens
2. 12 Glamis Drive	8. Dalfruin	15. Lawton House
3. Angus & Dundee Garden Trail	9. Dunninald Castle	16. Montrose Gardens
4. Angus Plant Sale	10. Gallery Garden	17. Pitmuies Gardens
5. Arbroath Collection of Gardens	11. Gardyne Castle	18. The Herbalist's Garden at Logie
6. Brechin Gardens in Summer	12. Hospitalfield Gardens	19. Torwood
	13. Inchmill Cottage	

Angus & Dundee

OUR VOLUNTEER ORGANISERS

District Organisers:	Pippa Clegg	Easter Derry, Kilry, Blairgowrie PH11 8JA
	Terrill Dobson	Logie House, Kirriemuir DD8 5PN
		E: angusdundee@scotlandsgardens.org
Area Organisers:	Debbie Butler	Top Croft, Arniefoul, Angus DD8 1UD
	Moira Coleman	Templeton House, Arbroath DD11 4QP
	Frances and John Dent	12 Glamis Drive, Dundee DD2 1QL
	Jan Oag	Lower Duncraig, 2 Castle Street, Brechin DD9 6JN
	Jeanette Ogilvie	House of Pitmuies, Guthrie DD8 2SN
	Mary Stansfeld	Dunninald Castle, By Montrose DD10 9TD
	Claire Tinsley	Ethie Mains, Ethie DD11 5SN
Treasurer:	James Welsh	Dalfruin, Kirtonhill Road, Kirriemuir DD8 4HU

GARDENS OPEN ON A SPECIFIC DATE

Langley Park Gardens, Montrose	Saturday 29 February/Sunday 1 March
Inchmill Cottage, Glenprosen, near Kirriemuir	Thursday, 16 April
Inchmill Cottage, Glenprosen, near Kirriemuir	Thursday, 7 May
Dalfruin, Kirktonhill Road, Kirriemuir	Sunday, 10 May
Gardyne Castle, by Forfar	Saturday/Sunday, 16/17 May
Inchmill Cottage, Glenprosen, near Kirriemuir	Thursday, 21 May
Brechin May Weekend Festival, Locations across Brechin	Saturday/Sunday/Monday, 23/24/25 May
10 Menzieshill Road, Dundee	Saturday/Sunday/Monday, 23/24/25 May
Torwood, Milton of Ogilvie, Glenogilvy, Glamis by Forfar	Saturday/Sunday, 23/24 May
The Herbalist's Garden at Logie, Logie House, Kirriemuir	Sunday/Monday, 24/25 May
Inchmill Cottage, Glenprosen, near Kirriemuir	Sunday, 24 May
Angus & Dundee Garden Trail, Locations across Angus & Dundee	Thursday/Friday/Saturday, 4/5/6 June
Inchmill Cottage, Glenprosen, near Kirriemuir	Thursday, 4 June
Angus & Dundee Garden Trail, Locations across Angus & Dundee	Thursday/Friday/Saturday, 11/12/13 June
Angus & Dundee Garden Trail, Locations across Angus & Dundee	Thursday/Friday/Saturday, 18/19/20 June
Inchmill Cottage, Glenprosen, near Kirriemuir	Thursday, 18 June
Angus Plant Sale, Logie Walled Garden, Kirriemuir	Sunday, 21 June
Angus & Dundee Garden Trail, Locations across Angus & Dundee	Thursday/Friday/Saturday, 25/26/27 June
Arbroath Collection of Gardens, Locations across Arbroath	Saturday, 4 July
Inchmill Cottage, Glenprosen, near Kirriemuir	Thursday, 16 July
Brechin Gardens in Summer, Locations across Brechin	Sunday, 26 July
Montrose Gardens, Various locations across Montrose	Sunday, 2 August
Inchmill Cottage, Glenprosen, near Kirriemuir	Thursday, 13 August
Inchmill Cottage, Glenprosen, near Kirriemuir	Thursday, 17 September
Hospitalfield Gardens, Hospitalfield House, Westway	Saturday, 3 October
12 Glamis Drive, Dundee	Saturday/Sunday, 17/18 October

Angus & Dundee

GARDENS OPEN REGULARLY

Dunninald Castle, Montrose	1 February - 29 February
Lawton House, Inverkeilor, by Arbroath	1 March - 15 March
Pitmuies Gardens, House of Pitmuies, Guthrie	1 April - 30 September
Langley Park Gardens, Montrose	1 May - 30 August (Frids, Sats & Suns)
Dunninald Castle, Montrose	10 May - 31 August
Gallery Garden, Gallery, by Montrose	1 June - 31 August (Tuesdays only)

GARDENS OPEN BY ARRANGEMENT

Torwood, Milton of Ogilvie, Glenogilvy, Glamis by Forfar	1 January - 31 December
Inchmill Cottage, Glenprosen, near Kirriemuir	1 April - 30 September
10 Menzieshill Road, Dundee	1 May - 31 May
The Herbalist's Garden at Logie, Logie House, Kirriemuir	1 June - 31 August
Gallery Garden, Gallery, by Montrose	1 June - 31 August

Angus & Dundee

10 MENZIESHILL ROAD
Dundee DD2 1PW
Frances Tait
T: 01382 665719

On a sloping site facing the river, No 10 is home to one of the nine wells in this part of the west end of Dundee. At one time the well provided drinking water for a nearby farmhouse and two cottages. It was also the first and last water available to carriers' horses on their way to/from Dundee. Now it feeds rhododendrons and camellias, many of which came from the Rothschilds' garden at Exbury, Hampshire. Of particular interest are magnolia 'Manchu Fan' and rhododendrons 'Loderic King George' and 'Lady Chamberlain'. More recently an area near the well has been given over to bulbs and small herbaceous plants, various irises and primulas.

Open: Saturday/Sunday/Monday, 23/24/25 May, 2pm - 5pm for the May Weekend Festival. Also open by arrangement 1 May - 31 May. Admission £3.00, children free.

Directions: Turn off A85/Riverside Avenue at the roundabout towards the Dundee Botanic Garden. Pass the Botanics and the road bears left and becomes Perth Road. Take a right on to Invergowrie Drive and then first left on Menzieshill Road. Buses 5 and 9 to the foot of Glamis Road and walk west to Invergowrie Drive.

· *Plant Heritage*

Menzieshill Road, one of the Dundee's nine wells.

Angus & Dundee

12 GLAMIS DRIVE
Dundee DD2 1QL
John and Frances Dent

A half-acre, south-facing garden overlooking the River Tay and Fife hills. Wander among shady trees and shrubs and discover water features and hidden areas in a variety of garden styles, all enhanced by vibrant autumn colours.

Open: Saturday 17 October 6pm - 8pm and Sunday 18 October 2pm - 5pm, admission £4.00, children free. Come in the afternoon and have tea and cake. Or come in the evening to see the garden transformed by coloured floodlighting and to enjoy musical performances, hot drinks and nibbles in the marquee.

Directions: Buses 5, 22 or 73 from Dundee city centre. Please note there is no roadside parking on Glamis Drive. Limited disabled parking available at the house.

· *UK Committee Dr Graham's Homes, Kalimpong, India*

12 Glamis Drive

Angus & Dundee

3

ANGUS & DUNDEE GARDEN TRAIL
Various locations across Angus & Dundee DD postcodes
Gardeners of Angus & Dundee
E: angusdundee@scotlandsgardens.org

The Angus & Dundee Garden Trail offers a flexible way to keep up your weekly dose of beautiful gardens, and is excellent value for money. These 16 gardens are all new to SGS and run from the Dundee city centre to the coast around Arbroath, over through Forfar to Edzell and down to Meigle. Visit a community garden, productive walled garden, as well as 12 other private gardens of varying sizes and styles. The Dundee Botanic Garden will promote the trail with entry for trail ticket holders over the first weekend and Maggie's Dundee garden will also be available to visit throughout the trail.

2 Whitewalls Farm Cottage off Emmock Road, by Tealing, Dundee DD3 0QE (Tracey Williams)
Open Fridays and Saturdays in June 2pm - 5pm
5 Glamis Place Il Gardino de Giovanni, Dundee DD2 1NB (John Egan)
Open Saturdays in June 11am - 4pm
6 Glamis Place Dundee DD2 1NB (Jim and Janet Paterson)
Open Thursdays, Fridays and Saturdays in June 9am - 6pm
8 Leemount Lane Broughty Ferry DD5 1LA (Hannah Anthony)
Open Thursdays in June 10am - 4pm
Balhary Walled Garden Balhary, Alyth, Blairgowrie PH11 8LT (Teri and Paul Hodge-Neale)
Open Thursdays, Fridays and Saturdays in June 3pm - 8pm
Damside Cottage Leysmill, Arbroath DD11 4RR (Arthur Blair)
Open Thursdays in June 10am - 2pm
Dundee Botanic Garden Riverside Drive, Dundee DD2 1QH (University of Dundee)
Open for trail Thursday 4, Friday 5, Saturday 6 June only, 10am - 7pm
Forfar Open Garden 36 Lochside Road, Forfar DD8 3JD (Forfar Open Gardeners)
Open Saturdays in June 10am - 2:30pm
Lawton House Inverkeilor, by Arbroath DD11 4RU (Katie and Simon Dessain)
Open Thursdays in June 10am - 2pm
Maggie's Dundee Ninewells Hospital, Tom McDonald Ave, Dundee DD2 1NH (Maggie's)
Available to visit at any time
Mains of Balgavies Forfar DD8 2TH (Georgie and Tom Sampson)
Open Thursdays in June 2pm - 5pm
Millden of Stracathro Brechin DD9 7QF (Alison and Hugh Campbell Adamson)
Open Fridays in June 10am - 2pm
North Lodge 36 Church Street, Edzell DD9 7TQ (Robin and Paul McIntosh)
Open Fridays in June noon - 4pm
Reswallie House Forfar DD8 2SA (Caroline and Hugh Graham Watson)
Open Thursdays in June 2pm - 5pm
St Bride's Cottage South Kingennie, Broughty Ferry DD5 3PA (Alison and Donald Gordon)
Open Fridays and Saturdays in June 1pm - 5pm
Templeton House Garden Arbroath DD11 4QP (Moira Coleman)
Open Thursdays in June 10am - 2pm
The Doocot Kinloch, Meigle, Blairgowrie PH12 8QX (Liz and George McLaren)
Open Saturdays in June 2pm - 5pm

Open: The Angus & Dundee Garden Trail offers various gardens and times over the Thursdays, Fridays and Saturdays of June. Admission £25.00 (early bird £20.00 before 1 May) children free. Tickets available from Eventbrite (browse 'SGS Angus & Dundee Trail 2020') or at the gardens on the day. Gardens can be visited individually, and tickets purchased at each garden for £5.00. See pages 16-17 for further details.

Directions: Directions to each garden will be provided with the tickets.

· *Maggie Keswick Jencks Cancer Caring Centres Trust (Dundee)*

Angus & Dundee

ANGUS PLANT SALE
Logie Walled Garden, Kirriemuir DD8 5PN
SGS Angus & Dundee Organisers
E: herbalistsgarden@gmail.com

Our annual plant sale is now becoming an Angus 'regular' event, so please join us. We will offer a good, interesting selection, sourced from private gardens and with some donations from our local nurseries. It's advisable to come promptly and bring boxes and trays. Donations of plants either before or during sales will always be welcome.

Open: Sunday 21 June, 2pm - 5pm, admission £3.00, children free. Light refreshments will be available. The Herbalist's Garden will also be open.

Directions: From the A90, take A926 towards Kirriemuir. Just after the *Welcome to Kirriemuir* sign take a sharp left on to a single track road, or from Kirriemuir take A926 towards Forfar and fork right at Beechwood Place onto the single track road. Take the first left and follow signs to *The Walled Garden*.

· *All proceeds to SGS Beneficiaries*

Inverbrothick School Sensory Garden and Forest Garden, Arbroath Collection of Gardens

Angus & Dundee

5

ARBROATH COLLECTION OF GARDENS
Locations across Arbroath DD11 4AH
Gardeners of Arbroath
W: www.ashbrook.co.uk

....

10 George Street Arbroath DD11 3BU (Wilma Simpson): A delightful small walled garden in the Lochlands area well worth a visit with a collection of 70 varieties of clematis and interesting perennials: a gem of a garden.
37 Duncan Avenue NEW Arbroath DD11 2DA (Alison Connelly): The front garden has a small terrace with wonderful evergreen grasses planted into gravel with a group of trees, an unusual weeping malus, liquid amber and unusual beech. The rear garden is a feast of interesting planting, including acers, hostas, hellebores, ferns and many more. There are many secret gardens to discover with all their nooks and crannies.
Ashbrook Nursery and Garden Centre Forfar Road, Arbroath DD11 3RB (Anne Webster): This family-run garden centre grows the majority of its plants, including over 2,000 varieties of bedding and patio plants, alpines, herbaceous perennials, ferns and grasses. There are also comprehensive A-Z displays of trees, conifers, shrubs, alpines and perennials.
Brechin Road Allotments Brechin Road, Arbroath DD11 4AH (Arbroath Allotments Association): The Brechin Road site is open this year and as always has loads of interest including plants, vegetables, fruit and creative sheds and shelters. A team of helpers will be on had to answer any questions.
HOPE Organic Garden The Plot next to Hospitalfield House, The Westway, Arbroath DD11 2NH (The HOPE Trustees): An organic fruit and vegetable garden, which provides training and work experience for adults with learning and/or physical disabilities. Note, this garden closes at 4pm.
Inverbrothick School Sensory Garden and Forest Garden NEW East Kirkton Road, Arbroath DD11 4GR (Inverbrothrick Pupils and Staff): These two gardens have been designed and created by the pupils, staff and parents. The Sensory Garden is a great asset to all children and staff, especially children who need additional support. There are areas of raised beds for growing vegetables, a dry river bed with interesting grasses and plants, large stone features to climb on, and different shelters and corners to play in. A polytunnel is used for outdoor classes and seed sowing. The Forest Garden includes interesting mounds and trees, an area to build dens and play amongst trees. Gardens created by and for young minds.
Springfield Rose Garden Springfield Park, Arbroath DD11 1AH (Friends of the Rose Garden): Springfield Rose Garden is a small, traditional, walled garden set in Springfield Park, close to the centre of Arbroath. The day to day upkeep and maintenance is managed by the volunteers, 'Friends of the Rose Garden', who work in co-operation with, and under the direction of, the local authority, to improve and regenerate the rose garden. It is a work in progress.

Open: Saturday 4 July, 1pm - 5pm, admission £5.00, children free. Ashbrook Nursery will run tours of the nursery at 2pm, 3pm and 4pm. Teas will be available at the Brechin Road Allotments.

Directions: Tickets and maps will be available from the various gardens and Ashbrook Nursery on the day. Look for the SGS yellow arrows around town to help you locate the gardens.

· *The Arbroath Garden Allotment Association SCIO*

Angus & Dundee

BRECHIN GARDENS IN SUMMER
Locations across Brechin DD9 6LE
The Gardeners of Brechin

Come and visit this lovely selection of gardens spread across the town of Brechin.
24 North Latch Road DD9 6LE (Alistair and Mary Gray): Learn how the owners grow and show vegetables and create spectacular displays of colourful bedding.
9 Pearse Street DD9 6JR (Irene and James Mackie): A recently redesigned garden with trees, colourful herbaceous border and unique ferns.
Andover Primary School Garden NEW 50A Drumachlie Park DD9 7BU (Staff and Pupils): A magical colourful garden and play space where classes grow and harvest their own produce.
Bishops Walk 11A Argyll St DD9 6JL (Steff and Mike Eyres): Winding paths lead through an eclectic mix of perennials, shrubs, conifers.
Brechin Cathedral Allotments Chanory Wynd DD9 6EU (Brechin Cathedral Allotments Gardeners): Eleven varied plots reflect the interests and personalities of each plot-holder.
Brechin in Bloom Community Garden Montrose Street DD9 7EF (Brechin Community Garden Volunteers): Sharing experience and learning skills involved in gardening for their own use and for local people.
Latchlea NEW 17A North Latch Road DD9 6LE (Pamela Stevens): NEW! A new garden featuring 100 newly planted trees, some fine stonework, shrubs, herbaceous plants and bulbs and also a courtyard garden.
Liscara Castle Street DD9 6JW (June and Mike Hudson): A 'secret' south-facing small garden with raised beds, circular lawn and fountain, espaliered pear tree and pretty summerhouse.
Rosehill West NEW 15C North Latch Road DD9 6LF (Dr Robert and Mrs Jenny Martin): NEW! A newly planted garden featuring mature original trees, herbaceous areas, fruit trees, and a path.

Open: Sunday 26 July, noon - 5pm, admission £5.00, children free.

Directions: Most gardens are located around the town of Brechin. Look for the SGS yellow arrows.

· *Brechin Healthcare Group*

BRECHIN MAY WEEKEND FESTIVAL
Locations across Brechin DD9 6JR
The Gardeners of Brechin

Several of the Brechin gardens open this summer will also be available to visit over the May Weekend Festival. Descriptions for these gardens are listed under the Brechin Summer listing.
9 Pearse Street DD9 6JR (Irene and James Mackie): 23, 24 and 25 May, 2pm - 4pm
Bishops Walk 11A Argyll St DD9 6JL (Steff and Mike Eyres): 23, 24 and 25 May, noon - 5pm
Brechin Cathedral Allotments Chanory Wynd DD9 6EU: 23 and 24 May, 1pm - 5pm
Kirkside of Lochty Menmuir by Brechin DD9 6RY (Ed and Fi Troughton): 23 May 1pm - 5pm. Renovated by a well-known local plantswoman 20 years ago, the current owners are nurturing the existing garden whilst opening up vistas to embrace nearby hills and the Angus Glens. A well-stocked courtyard garden and large island beds extend the garden towards the wildlife meadow.
Latchlea 17A North Latch Road DD9 6LE (Pamela Stevens): 23 May 1pm - 5pm
Rosehill West 15C North Latch Road DD9 6LF (Dr Robert and Mrs Jenny Martin): 24 May 1pm - 5pm

Open: Saturday/Sunday/Monday, 23/24/25 May, 1pm - 5pm for the May Weekend Festival, admission £5.00, children free. Note that individual gardens are open at different times, see each garden for specific days and times. Tickets, providing access to all gardens over the long weekend, will be available from each of the gardens.

Angus & Dundee

Directions: Most gardens are located around the town of Brechin. Kirkside of Lochty is outside town, off the A90 and along the road to Careston/Fern/Menmuir. Look for the SGS yellow arrows.

· *Brechin Cathedral*

8 DALFRUIN

Kirktonhill Road, Kirriemuir DD8 4HU
Mr and Mrs James A Welsh

A well-stocked connoisseur's garden of about a third of an acre situated at the end of a short cul-de-sac. There are many less common plants like varieties of trilliums, meconopsis (blue poppies), tree peonies (descendants of ones collected by George Sherriff and grown at Ascreavie), dactylorhiza and codonopsis. There is a scree garden and collection of ferns. The vigorous climbing rose, Paul's Himalayan Musk, grows over a pergola. Interconnected ponds encourage wildlife.

Open: Sunday 10 May, 2pm - 5pm, admission £4.00, children free. Good plant stall with many unusual plants including trilliums, meconopsis and tree peonies.

Directions: From the centre of Kirriemuir turn left up Roods. Kirktonhill Road is on the left near top of the hill. Park on Roods or at St Mary's Episcopal Church. Disabled parking only in Kirktonhill Road. Bus 20 (from Dundee) getting off at either stop on the Roods.

· *Kirriemuir Day Care Ltd*

9 DUNNINALD CASTLE

Montrose DD10 9TD
The Stansfeld family
T: 01674 672031 E: estateoffice@dunninald.com
W: www.dunninald.com

We welcome our visitors to explore our 100 acres of woods, wild garden, policies and a walled garden. From January to May the main interest is the wild garden and policies where snowdrops in January are followed by daffodils and finally bluebells in May. In June the emphasis turns to the walled garden, rich in interest and colour throughout the summer. Situated at the bottom of the beech avenue, the walled garden is planted with rose borders, traditional mixed borders, vegetables, herbs, soft fruits and fruit trees and there is a greenhouse.

Open: 1 February - 29 February, 10am - 4pm for Snowdrops and Winter Walks. Also open 10 May - 31 August, 1pm - 5pm. Admission £5.00, children free. Castle tours: 4 July - 2 August (closed Mondays) 1pm - 5pm (last entry 4:30pm).

Directions: Three miles south of Montrose, ten miles north of Arbroath, signposted from the A92.

· *Donation to SGS Beneficiaries*

Angus & Dundee

10

GALLERY GARDEN
Gallery, by Montrose DD10 9LA
Mr John Simson
T: 07903 977395 E: galleryhf@googlemail.com

The redesign and replanting of this historic garden have preserved and extended its traditional framework of holly, privet and box. A grassed central alley, embellished with circles, links themed gardens, including the recently replanted Gold Garden and Hot Border, with the fine collection of old roses and the fountain and pond of the formal White Garden. A walk through the woodland garden, home to rare breed sheep, with its extensive border of mixed heathers, leads to the River North Esk. From there rough paths lead both ways along the bank. This very special garden has been featured in *Homes & Gardens* in 2015, *English Garden* in 2017, *Country Life* in 2018 and *Scottish Field* in January 2019.

Open: 1 June - 31 August (Tuesdays only), 1pm - 5pm. Also open by arrangement 1 June - 31 August. Admission £5.00, children free.

Directions: Please DO NOT use SatNav - see the SGS website map for location. From the A90 south of Northwater Bridge take the exit to Hillside and next left to Gallery and Marykirk, or from the A937 west of rail underpass follow signs to *Gallery and Northwater Bridge*.

· *All proceeds to SGS Beneficiaries*

11

GARDYNE CASTLE
by Forfar DD8 2SQ
William and Camilla Gray Muir

Gardyne Castle, dating from the 16th century, is one of the most attractive small castles in Angus. After a turbulent history of battles with the neighbouring Guthries, it is now surrounded by an enchanting garden created by its current owners over the past 16 years. To the east, the walled garden runs down to the Denton Burn. The castle's extraordinary stone-capped turrets overlook a long romantic double border, bursting with tulips and alliums in May. The castle's southern front was extended in the 17th and 18th centuries and is complemented by a large enclosed knot garden of box and yew mixed with white roses and lavender. Beyond is an immaculate formal lawn surrounded by yew topiaries and specimen trees, with a gentle path leading down through an orchard. To the north, a new upper garden, centred on an extraordinary pepper pot doocot, provides an area for quiet contemplation with white planting, a fishpond and the family's collection of chickens. Beyond the formal gardens the grounds merge into mature woods and parkland with a spectacular display of bluebells and romantic walks along the Denton Burn.

Open: Saturday/Sunday, 16/17 May, 2pm - 5pm, admission £5.00, children free.

Directions: Turn off A932 at signpost to *Pitmuies Garden*. Go over two stone bridges and follow road uphill past small hamlet. Take first road on left. At sharp right-hand bend take private drive straight ahead (beside cream lodge).

· *Guthrie and Rescobie Parish Church*

Angus & Dundee

HOSPITALFIELD GARDENS
Hospitalfield House, Westway, Arbroath DD11 2NH
Hospitalfield Trust
E: info@hospitalfield.org.uk
W: www.hospitalfield.org.uk

Visit the Gardens at Hospitalfield in Arbroath for this event to be among the first to experience the new garden design by Nigel Dunnett. In the 19th century, the artist Patrick Allan-Fraser (1813-1890) remodelled a 13th-century hospital to create his 19th-century home in the Arts and Crafts style. The walled gardens have been cultivated from the early medieval period, from the medicinal garden and the orchard to the Victorian passion for collecting ferns. This beautiful space, set against the red sandstone neo-Gothic architecture, has been comprehensively developed to a design by celebrated designer Nigel Dunnett to tell the horticultural story of this extraordinary site. The planting of this garden is very new and this is a chance to see the design at its very earliest state. Also discover the fascinating new space that is The Fernery at Hospitalfield, complete with exotic collections of tree ferns.

Open: Saturday 3 October, 11am - 3pm, admission £4.00, children free. Enjoy lunch in the new Hospitalfield café.

Directions: See website for directions and more details about Hospitalfield and its international cultural programme rooted in contemporary visual arts.

· Donation to SGS Beneficiaries

Gardyne Castle

Angus & Dundee

13 **INCHMILL COTTAGE**
Glenprosen, near Kirriemuir   DD8 4SA
Iain Nelson
T: 01575 540452

This is a long, sloping and terraced garden at over 800 feet in the Braes of Angus, developed to be a garden for all seasons. Half is dominated by bulbs, rhododendrons, azaleas, primulas, meconopsis and clematis. The other half is mainly later summer bulbs, herbaceous plants and roses. There is also a rockery/scree and fernery.

Open: Sunday 24 May, 2pm - 5pm for the May Weekend Festival. Also open Thursdays 16 April, 7, 21 May, 4, 18 June, 16 July, 13 August and 17 September, 2pm - 5pm. And open by arrangement 1 April - 30 September. Admission £3.00, children free. Car parking beside the church (50 yards away) and by the village hall opposite.

Directions: Please DO NOT use SatNav. From Kirriemuir take the B955 (signposted to *The Glens*) to Dykehead (about five miles). From there follow the *Prosen* sign for about five miles. Inchmill is the white-fronted cottage beside the phone box.

· *The Archie Foundation*

14 **LANGLEY PARK GARDENS**
Montrose   DD10 9LG
Marianne and Philip Santer
T: 01674 810735 E: philipsanter1@gmail.com
W: www.langleyparkgardens.co.uk

Set overlooking Montrose Basin, Langley Park Gardens include four walled gardens, three filled with herbaceous borders, fruit trees and vegetable plots, the fourth is a small arboretum. The 27 acres of policies contain woodland walks among both ancient and recently planted trees. Walk down through the 20-acre wildflower meadow along the banks of the wildlife pond, enjoy the views over Montrose, The Basin and the hills beyond. In winter enjoy long woodland walks among our stunning snowdrops.

Open: Saturday 29 February & Sunday 1 March, noon - 4pm for Snowdrops and Winter Walks. Also open 1 May - 30 August (Fridays, Saturdays & Sundays), 10am - 4pm. Admission £5.00, children free.

Directions: Just off the A935 Montrose to Brechin Road, one-and-a-half miles from Montrose.

· *Donation to SGS Beneficiaries*

15 **LAWTON HOUSE**
Inverkeilor, by Arbroath   DD11 4RU
Katie and Simon Dessain

Woodland garden of beech trees, carpeted with snowdrops, aconites and crocuses in spring, set around a 1755 house. There is also a walled garden planted with fruit trees and vegetables. The property was owned for many years by Elizabeth and Patrick Allan Fraser who built Hospitalfield House in Arbroath.

Open: 1 March - 15 March, 10am - 4pm for Snowdrops and Winter Walks, admission £3.00, children free.

Angus & Dundee

Directions: Take B965 between Inverkeilor and Friockheim, turn right at sign for *Angus Chain Saws*. Drive approximately 200 yards, then take first right.

· **The Julia Thomson Memorial Trust**

Arwin House, Montrose Gardens

MONTROSE GARDENS
Various locations across Montrose DD10 8SB
The Montrose Gardeners
....

A variety of beautiful gardens in the charming seaside town of Montrose, including the stunning garden at Arwin House (17 Renny Crescent DD10 9BW) featured on *The Beechgrove Gardens* in 2019, the therapeutic garden at Dorward House. and some new gardens as well. More information will be available nearer the date.

Open: Sunday 2 August, 1pm - 5pm, admission £5.00, children free. Homemade teas, and tickets on the day, will be available at Dorward House, 24 Dorward Road DD10 8SB. Advance tickets will be available from Rossie Braes Garden Centre, A92, DD10 9TA.

Directions: Approach Montrose on A92 or A90 via Brechin. Parking available around town. Gardens will be identified with SGS yellow arrows.

· **Dorward House, Montrose**

Angus & Dundee

PITMUIES GARDENS
House of Pitmuies, Guthrie, by Forfar DD8 2SN
Jeanette and Ruaraidh Ogilvie
T: 01241 828245 E: ogilvie@pitmuies.com
W: www.pitmuies.com

Two renowned semi-formal walled gardens adjoin an 18th-century house and steading and shelter long borders of herbaceous perennials, superb old-fashioned delphiniums and roses, together with pavings rich with violas and dianthus. An extensive and diverse collection of plants, interesting kitchen garden, spacious lawns, river and lochside walks beneath fine trees. A wide variety of shrubs with good autumn colour and a picturesque turreted doo'cot and a 'Gothick' wash house. Myriad spring bulbs include carpets of crocus following massed snowdrops and daffodils.

Open: 1 April - 30 September, 10am - 5pm, admission £5.00, children free.

Directions: From Forfar take A932 east for seven miles and gardens are signposted on the right. From Brechin take A933 south to Friockheim and turn right onto A932; then gardens are signposted on the left after one-and-a-half miles.

· *Donation to SGS Beneficiaries*

Torwood

Angus & Dundee

THE HERBALIST'S GARDEN AT LOGIE
Logie House, Kirriemuir DD8 5PN
Terrill and Gavin Dobson
E: herbalistsgarden@gmail.com
....

This garden, featured on *The Beechgrove Garden* in 2014, is set amid an 18th-century walled garden and large Victorian-style greenhouse within Logie's organic farm. Featuring more than 150 herbs, the physic garden is divided into eight rectangles including medicinal herbs for different body systems. All the herbs are labelled with a brief description of actions to help novices learn more about this ancient art. The garden also features a herbaceous border and productive fruit and vegetable garden.

Open: Sunday/Monday, 24/25 May, 2pm - 5pm for the May Weekend Festival. Also open by arrangement 1 June - 31 August. Admission £5.00, children free.

Directions: From the A90, take A926 towards Kirriemuir. Just after the *Welcome to Kirriemuir* sign take a sharp left on to a single track road, or from Kirriemuir take A926 towards Forfar and fork right at Beechwood Place onto the single track road. Take the first left and follow signs to *The Walled Garden*.

· *The Glens and Kirriemuir United Parish Church of Scotland: Thrums Tots & Messy Church*

TORWOOD
Milton of Ogilvie, Glenogilvy, Glamis by Forfar DD8 1UN
John Gordon
T: 07988 010418 E: j.gordon.82@btinternet.com
W: www.gardendisplays.co.uk
....

A small attractively laid-out country garden striving towards year-round interest, enjoyment and relaxation through association and succession planting of trees, shrubs, herbaceous, perennials and bulbs. The garden is separated into rooms focusing on different colour schemes and styles including a small woodland area, mixed borders and prairie-style planting.

Open: Saturday/Sunday, 23/24 May, 2pm - 5pm for the May Weekend Festival. Also open by arrangement 1 January - 31 December. Admission £4.00, children free.

Directions: Take A928 between Kirriemuir turnoff on A90 or Glamis turnoff on A94. Follow road signposted *Glenogilvie, Handwick, Dryburn*. Torwood is second house from the end on the left.

· *Alzheimer Scotland*

ARGYLL & LOCHABER

Scotland's Gardens Scheme 2020 Guidebook is sponsored by INVESTEC WEALTH & INVESTMENT

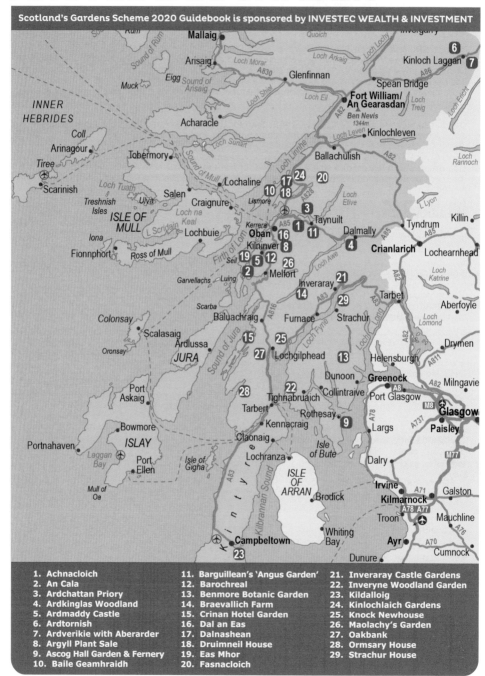

1. Achnacloich	11. Barguillean's 'Angus Garden'	21. Inveraray Castle Gardens
2. An Cala	12. Barochreal	22. Inveryne Woodland Garden
3. Ardchattan Priory	13. Benmore Botanic Garden	23. Kildalloig
4. Ardkinglas Woodland	14. Braevallich Farm	24. Kinlochlaich Gardens
5. Ardmaddy Castle	15. Crinan Hotel Garden	25. Knock Newhouse
6. Ardtornish	16. Dal an Eas	26. Maolachy's Garden
7. Ardverikie with Aberarder	17. Dalnashean	27. Oakbank
8. Argyll Plant Sale	18. Druimneil House	28. Ormsary House
9. Ascog Hall Garden & Fernery	19. Eas Mhor	29. Strachur House
10. Baile Geamhraidh	20. Fasnacloich	

Argyll & Lochaber

OUR VOLUNTEER ORGANISERS

District Organisers:	Minette Struthers	Camasmaddy, Ardmaddy, by Oban PA34 4QY E: argyll@scotlandsgardens.org
Area Organisers:	Yvonne Anderson	Melfort House, Kilmelford, by Oban PA34 4XD
	Grace Bergius	Craignish House, Ardfern, by Lochgilphead PA31 8QN
	Shian Carlow	Balliemore, Loch Striven, Dunoon PA23 8RH
	Mary Lindsay	Dal an Eas, Kilmore, Oban PA34 4XU
District Photographers:	Maurice Wilkins	Oban
Treasurer:	Minette Struthers	Camasmaddy, Ardmaddy, by Oban PA34 4QY

GARDENS OPEN ON A SPECIFIC DATE

Benmore Botanic Garden, Benmore, Dunoon	Sunday, 19 April
Knock Newhouse, Lochgair	Saturday/Sunday, 25/26 April
Maolachy's Garden, Lochavich, by Kilmelford	Saturday/Sunday, 25/26 April
Knock Newhouse, Lochgair	Saturday/Sunday, 16/17 May
Dalnashean, Port Appin, Appin	Saturday/Sunday, 16/17 May
Inveryne Woodland Garden, Kilfinan, Tighnabruaich	Saturday/Sunday, 23/24 May
Strachur House Flower & Woodland Gardens, Strachur	Saturday/Sunday, 23/24 May
Maolachy's Garden, Lochavich, by Kilmelford	Saturday/Sunday, 23/24 May
Braevallich Farm, by Dalmally	Sunday, 24 May
Fasnacloich, Appin	Sunday, 31 May
Ardverikie with Aberarder, Kinloch Laggan, Newtonmore	Sunday, 31 May
Argyll Plant Sale, Kilmore Village Hall, near Oban	Saturday, 13 June
Maolachy's Garden, Lochavich, by Kilmelford	Saturday/Sunday, 27/28 June

GARDENS OPEN REGULARLY

Ardkinglas Woodland Garden, Cairndow	1 January - 31 December
Ardmaddy Castle, by Oban	1 January - 31 December
Barguillean's 'Angus Garden', Taynuilt	1 January - 31 December
Achnacloich, Connel, Oban	1 January - 31 December (Saturdays only)
Ardtornish, by Lochaline, Morvern	1 January - 31 December
Kinlochlaich Gardens, Appin	3 March - 15 October
Druimneil House, Port Appin	30 March - 31 October
Ardchattan Priory, North Connel	1 April - 31 October
An Cala, Ellenabeich, Isle of Seil	1 April - 31 October
Ascog Hall Garden and Fernery, Ascog, Isle of Bute	1 April - 31 October
Inveraray Castle Gardens, Inveraray	1 April - 31 October
Crinan Hotel Garden, Crinan	1 May - 31 August
Baile Geamhraidh, Isle of Lismore, Oban	1 May - 1 October (Wednesdays & Saturdays)
Oakbank, Ardrishaig	1 July - 31 July

Argyll & Lochaber

GARDENS OPEN BY ARRANGEMENT

Braevallich Farm, by Dalmally	1 January - 31 December
Maolachy's Garden, Lochavich, by Kilmelford	1 January - 31 December
Ormsary House, Ormsary, Lochgilphead	1 January - 31 December
Dal an Eas, Kilmore, Oban	1 April - 30 September
Knock Newhouse, Lochgair	13 April - 13 September
Baile Geamhraidh, Isle of Lismore, Oban	1 May - 1 October
Barochreal, Kilninver, Oban	1 May - 30 September
Eas Mhor, Cnoc-a-Challtuinn, Clachan Seil, Oban	1 May - 30 September
Kildalloig, Campbeltown	1 May - 31 October

Argyll & Lochaber

ACHNACLOICH
Connel, Oban PA37 1PR
Mr T E Nelson
T: 01631 710223 E: charlie_milne@msn.com

The 20-acre woodland garden, overlooking Loch Etive, has been planted over the last century with a wide range of trees and shrubs from Asia, China, Japan, North America, Chile and New Zealand. Many have grown to considerable size. The light woodland canopy consists of native oaks and a number of magnificent 150-year-old Scots pines and European larch. Amongst these are open glades, carpeted with bluebells and numerous other bulbs. Two ponds and streams are planted with primulas, iris species, lysichitum, and astilbes. The woodland contains innumerable species of rhododendron and azalea, of which the triflorums and yunnanense are outstanding. Amongst these are species of acer, betula, camellia, cercidiphyllum, cornus, crinodendron, drimys, embothrium, enkianthus, eucryphia, hoheria, magnolia, malus, nothofagus, pieris, sorbus, stewartia, telopea and viburnum. Beside the house is a giant Douglas fir from Douglas' original introduction. One of the first Dawyck beeches stands beside the drive. The autumn colour is very fine.

Open: 1 January - 31 December (Saturdays only), 10am - 4pm, admission £5.00, children free.

Directions: On the A85 two miles east of Connel. Car park at bottom of drive.

· **Macmillan Cancer Support**

AN CALA
Ellenabeich, Isle of Seil PA34 4RF
Mrs Sheila Downie
W: www.gardens-of-argyll.co.uk/view-details.php?id=447

A wonderful example of a 1930s designed garden, An Cala sits snugly in its horseshoe shelter of surrounding cliffs. A spectacular and very pretty garden with streams, waterfall, ponds, many herbaceous plants as well as azaleas, rhododendrons and cherry trees in spring. Archive material of Thomas Mawson's design was found recently and is available to visitors.

Open: 1 April - 31 October, 10am - 6pm, admission £5.00, children free.

Directions: Proceed south from Oban on Campbeltown Road for eight miles, turn right at *Easdale* sign, a further eight miles on the B844; garden is between the school and village. Bus Oban - Easdale.

· **Donation to SGS Beneficiaries**

'Thinking of opening your
garden – we're here to help'

Argyll & Lochaber

3

ARDCHATTAN PRIORY
North Connel PA37 1RQ
Mrs Sarah Troughton
T: 01796 481355 E: admin@ardchattan.co.uk
W: www.ardchattan.co.uk

Overlooking Loch Etive, Ardchattan Priory Garden has a mature rockery, extensive herbaceous and rose borders to the front of the house. On either side of the drive shrub borders, numerous roses and ornamental trees, together with bulbs give colour throughout the season. The Priory, founded in 1230, is now a private house. The ruins of the chapel and graveyard are in the care of *Historic Environment Scotland* and open with the garden.

Open: 1 April - 31 October, 9:30am - 5:30pm, admission £5.00, children free. There will be a fête on Sunday 26 July from noon - 4pm.

Directions: Oban 10 miles. From north, turn left off the A828 at Barcaldine onto the B845 for six miles. From east or from Oban on the A85, cross Connel Bridge and turn first right, proceed east on Bonawe Road.

· *Donation to SGS Beneficiaries*

4

ARDKINGLAS WOODLAND GARDEN
Cairndow PA26 8BG
Ardkinglas Estate
T: 01499 600261
W: www.ardkinglas.com

In a peaceful setting overlooking Loch Fyne, the garden contains one of the finest collections of rhododendrons and conifers in Britain. This includes the mightiest conifer in Europe — a silver fir, as well as many other Champion Trees. There is a gazebo with a unique scriptorium based around a collection of literary quotes. The garden has a Fairy Trail and a Gruffalo Trail; come and find him! It is a *VisitScotland* 3-star garden.
Champion Trees: The mightiest conifer in Europe and others.

Open: 1 January - 31 December, dawn - dusk, admission £5.00, children £2.00 (4-16 yrs), 3 yrs and under free.

Directions: Entrance through Cairndow village off the A83 Loch Lomond/Inveraray road.

· *Donation to SGS Beneficiaries*

5

ARDMADDY CASTLE
by Oban PA34 4QY
Mr and Mrs Archie Struthers
T: 01852 300353 E: minette@ardmaddy.com
W: ardmaddy.com/places-visit/

The gardens lie in a most spectacular setting in the centre of a horseshoe valley sheltered by mixed mature woodlands and the elevated castle standing on a volcanic mound to seaward. The walled garden is full of magnificent rhododendrons, a collection of rare and unusual shrubs and plants, the Clock Garden with its cutting flowers, the Crevice Garden, fruit and vegetables grown with labour saving formality, all within dwarf box hedging. Beyond, a woodland walk, with its 60-foot *Hydrangea petiolaris*, leads to the Water Garden which in spring has a mantle of bluebells and daffodils and in early summer a riot of *Primula candelabra*, irises, rodgersias and other damp-loving plants and grasses. There is also lovely autumn colour. This is a plantsman's garden for all seasons.

Argyll & Lochaber

Open: 1 January - 31 December, 9am - dusk including for Snowdrops and Winter Walks, admission £5.00, children free. Seasonal vegetables, summer fruit and plant stall. Toilet suitable for the disabled – see garden website for further details.

Directions: Take the A816 south of Oban for eight miles. Turn right onto the B844 to Seil Island/ Easdale. Four miles on, turn left on to Ardmaddy Road (signposted) for a further two miles.

· *Donation to SGS Beneficiaries*

Ardmaddy Castle

6

ARDTORNISH
by Lochaline, Morvern PA80 5UZ
Mrs John Raven
W: www.ardtornishgardens.co.uk

Ardtornish Estate spreads out around Loch Aline, a huge, wooded, U-shaped bay, a natural haven. Wonderful gardens of interesting mature conifers, rhododendrons, deciduous trees, shrubs and herbaceous, set amid magnificent scenery. Much of the garden is covered by native birch, alongside extensive planting of exotic species, under mature groups of larch, firs and pine, whose strong form and colour complement the pink sandstone towers and gables of Ardtornish House.

Open: 1 January - 31 December, 10am - 6pm, admission £4.00, children free.

Directions: Three miles from Lochaline along the A884.

· *Donation to SGS Beneficiaries*

Argyll & Lochaber

ARDVERIKIE WITH ABERARDER
Kinloch Laggan, Newtonmore PH20 1BX
The Feilden family, Mrs P Laing and Mrs E T Smyth-Osbourne
T: 01528 544300

Aberarder Kinloch Laggan, Newtonmore PH20 1BX (The Feilden family): The garden has been laid out over the last 20 years to create a mixture of spring and autumn plants and trees, including rhododendrons, azaleas and acers. The elevated view down Loch Laggan from the garden is exceptional.
Ardverikie Kinloch Laggan, Newtonmore PH20 1BX (Mrs P Laing and Mrs E T Smyth-Osbourne): Lovely setting on Loch Laggan with magnificent trees. Walled garden with large collection of acers, shrubs and herbaceous plants. Architecturally interesting house (not open) featured in *Monarch of the Glen* and *The Crown*.

Open: Sunday 31 May, 2pm - 5:30pm, admission £5.50, children free.

Directions: On the A86 between Newtonmore and Spean Bridge. The entrance to Aberarder Lodge is 200 yards west of the Ardverikie entrance next to the small cottage. The entrance to Ardverikie House is at the east end of Loch Laggan via the bridge by Gatelodge.

· *Laggan Parish Church & Highland Hospice*

ARGYLL PLANT SALE
Kilmore Village Hall, near Oban PA34 4XT
The Argyll Gardeners and SGS Organisers
E: dalaneas@live.com

Charity plant sale of locally grown and donated perennials, shrubs and more. A great chance to buy plants suited to the Argyll climate. Bring your own box.

Open: Saturday 13 June, 2pm - 5:30pm, admission by donation.

Directions: Ten minutes south of Oban. In Kilmore on the A816, turn off on the Musdale Road, then immediately left for the hall.

· *Mary's Meals & Hope*

ASCOG HALL GARDEN AND FERNERY
Ascog, Isle of Bute PA20 9EU
Karin Burke
T: 01700 503461 E: info@ascogfernery.com
W: www.ascogfernery.com

The outstanding feature of this three-acre garden is the Victorian Fernery, a magnificent gilded structure fed by natural spring waters and housing many fern species, including Britain's oldest exotic fern, a 1,000-year-old *Todea babara* or king fern. Rare and unusual species await the visitor wandering through the original garden 'rooms' while the stables and coach house ruins feed the imagination with memories of long-lost times. The garden is generally well-labelled and contains a plant-hunters' trail. A climate change BioTape was introduced in 2018.

Open: 1 April - 31 October, 10am - 5pm, admission £5.00, children free. Restricted mobility parking at the top of the drive (close to the house). Personal assistance available for disabled access to the Fernery.

Argyll & Lochaber

Directions: Three miles south of Rothesay on the A844. Close to the picturesque Ascog Bay. Bus every half hour Rothesay - Kilchattan.

· **Donation to SGS Beneficiaries**

10

BAILE GEAMHRAIDH
Isle of Lismore, Oban, Argyll PA34 5UL
Eva Tombs
T: 01631 760128 E: eva.tombs@gmail.com

This unique garden forms part of a biodynamic farm on the Island of Lismore in the Inner Hebrides. Created quite recently from a field, the garden has a strong geometric layout that reflects the ecclesiastical history of the island. It has a vegetable garden, a tree nursery, a physic garden and an orchard. Wildflowers, birds, bees and butterflies abound. Standing stones, meadows, new woodlands, mountains and the sea encompass the whole. Some weeds and long grass benefit the Lismore herd of rare breed Shetland horned cattle that roam the fields round about.

Open: 1 May - 1 October (Wednesdays & Saturdays), 10am - 5pm. Also open by arrangement 1 May - 1 October. Admission £4.00, children free. Plants, seeds, vegetables, flowers and meat for sale. No dogs please, there are lots of animals around.

Directions: From the Oban to Lismore ferry travel west then north for seven miles till you see the *SGS* yellow sign. Travel up the track over two cattle grids and follow the arrows. From Port Appin to Lismore ferry (foot and cycles) travel one-and-a-half miles till you see the *SGS* yellow sign and as above.

· **Lismore Parish Church (Church of Scotland): St Moluag's Cathedral on Lismore**

Baile Geamhraidh, photo by Mairi Fleck

Argyll & Lochaber

BARGUILLEAN'S 'ANGUS GARDEN'
Taynuilt PA35 1HY
The Josephine Marshall Trust
T: 01866 822333 E: info@barguillean.co.uk
W: www.barguillean.co.uk

Nine-acre woodland garden around an 11-acre loch set in the Glen Lonan Hills. Spring-flowering shrubs and bulbs, extensive collection of rhododendron hybrids, deciduous azaleas, conifers and unusual trees. The garden contains a large collection of North American rhododendron hybrids from famous contemporary plant breeders. Some paths can be steep. Three marked walks from 30 minutes to one-and-a-half hours.

Open: 1 January - 31 December, 9am - dusk, admission £4.00, children free. Coach tours by appointment.

Directions: Three miles south off the A85 Glasgow/Oban road at Taynuilt, road marked *Glen Lonan*, three miles up a single track road, turn right at the sign.

· *Donation to SGS Beneficiaries*

BAROCHREAL
Kilninver, Oban, Argyll PA34 4UT
Nigel and Antoinette Mitchell
T: 01852 316151 E: toni@themitchells.co.uk
W: www.barochreal.co.uk

The garden was started in 2006. Fencing and stone walling define it from the rest of Barochreal land, every year an area has been added, resulting in the gardens you will see today. There are rhododendron banks, a water feature, waterfalls and burns, a pond, a walled rose garden, active beehives, tiered areas, a greenhouse and wild garden across the burn. Maintained walking tracks in the fields lead to viewpoints. Biodiversity studies revealed that rare butterflies inhabit the small glen by the waterfall, there are forty different species of moths including rare micro moths and over seventy species of wildflowers in the fields, including three types of wild orchids. There is an abundance of wildlife including red squirrels, pine martins and a wide range of birds can be seen. This garden is a haven of tranquillity.

Open: by arrangement 1 May - 30 September, admission £4.00, children free.

Directions: Fifteen minutes south of Oban. Please disregard SatNav. On the main A816 Oban to Lochgilphead road just to the south of the village of Kilninver on the left-hand side of the road. Bus Oban - Lochgilpead stops at Kilninver School, short walk after.

· *Argyll Animal Aid*

BENMORE BOTANIC GARDEN
Benmore, Dunoon PA23 8QU
A Regional Garden of the Royal Botanic Garden Edinburgh
T: 01369 706261 E: benmore@rbge.org.uk
W: www.rbge.org.uk

Benmore is a regional garden of the Royal Botanic Garden Edinburgh which celebrates its 350th anniversary in 2020. For more information, visit www.rbge.org.uk/350
Benmore's magnificent mountainside setting is a joy to behold. Its 120 acres boast a world-famous collection of plants from the Orient and Himalayas to North and South America, as well as an impressive avenue of giant redwoods, one of the finest entrances to any botanic garden. Established in 1863, these majestic giants stand over 150 foot high. Seven miles of trails

Argyll & Lochaber

throughout lead to a restored Victorian Fernery and a dramatic viewpoint at 420 feet looking out to surrounding mountains and Holy Loch. There are also traditional Bhutanese and Chilean pavilions and the magnificent Golden Gates. Keep an eye out for red squirrels and other wildlife as you explore the garden.
National Plant Collection: Abies, South American Temperate Conifers, Picea.

Open: Sunday 19 April, 10am - 6pm, admission details can be found on the garden's website. See website for details of regular opening times.

Directions: Seven miles north of Dunoon or 22 miles south from Glen Kinglass below Rest and Be Thankful pass. On the A815. Bus service is limited.

· *Donation to SGS Beneficiaries*

14

BRAEVALLICH FARM
by Dalmally PA33 1BU
Mr Philip Bowden-Smith
T: 01866 844246 E: philip@brae.co.uk

Discover two gardens, one at the farm and the upper garden 120 feet above the house. The former is approximately one-and-a-half acres and developed over the last 40 years. Its principal features include dwarf rhododendron, azaleas (evergreen and deciduous), large drifts of various primula and meconopsis and bluebells, and mixed herbaceous perennials/shrubs; there is also quite a serious kitchen garden. The second garden has been developed over the last 30 years out of a birch and sessile oak wood and is a traditional West Coast glen garden intersected by two pretty burns with waterfalls. The garden has been extended over the last few years and now covers nearly ten acres with extensive new paths, and a suspension bridge over the ravine. Whilst the plants are important, many say that it is the topography with its differing vistas which make this garden such a peaceful and special place.

Open: Sunday 24 May, 2pm - 5pm for the May Weekend Festival. Also open by arrangement 1 January - 31 December. Admission £5.00, children free.

Directions: South east of Loch Awe on the B840, 15 miles from Cladich, seven miles from Ford.

· *Mary's Meals*

15

CRINAN HOTEL GARDEN
Crinan PA31 8SR
Mrs N Ryan
T: 01546 830261 E: nryan@crinanhotel.com
W: www.crinanhotel.com

Small rock garden with azaleas and rhododendrons created in a steep hillside over a century ago; with steps leading to a sheltered, secluded garden with sloping lawns, herbaceous beds and spectacular views of the canal and Crinan Loch.

Open: 1 May - 31 August, dawn - dusk, admission by donation. Raffle of signed limited-edition fine art print by Frances Macdonald. Tickets available at the coffee shop, art gallery and hotel.

Directions: Take the A83 to Lochgilphead, then the A816 to Oban, then the A841 Cairnbaan to Crinan. Daily bus.

· *Feedback Madagascar*

Argyll & Lochaber

DAL AN EAS
Kilmore, Oban PA34 4XU
Mary Lindsay
T: 01631 770246 E: dalaneas@live.com

An informal country garden with the aim of increasing the biodiversity of native plants and insects while adding interest and colour with introduced trees, shrubs and naturalised perennials. There is a structured garden round the house and beyond there are extensive flower-filled 'meadows' with five different species of native orchid. Grass paths lead to waterfalls, vegetable plot, woodland garden, views and ancient archaeological sites.

Open: by arrangement 1 April - 30 September, admission by donation. Teas on request.

Directions: From Oban take the A816 to Kilmore three-and-a-half miles south of Oban. Turn left on road to Barran and Musdale. Keep left at junction for Connel. Dal an Eas is approximately one mile on the left before the big hedges.

· *Hope: Oban*

Dal an Eas, photo by Nick Edgington

Argyll & Lochaber

17 DALNASHEAN
Port Appin, Appin PA38 4DE
Allister and Kathleen Ferguson

Established garden sheltered by a beechwood hill giving views over Loch Linnhe and Lismore. There are camellias, rhododendrons and magnolias as well as many unusual shrubs and trees and more recent planting in adjoining field with ponds surrounded by rhododendrons and azaleas and tree and shrub borders.

Open: Saturday/Sunday, 16/17 May, 2pm - 6pm, admission £4.50, children free. Woodcrafts for sale.

Directions: Take the A828 to Appin then the road signposted to *Port Appin* and *Lismore Ferry*. After two miles, turn into the drive opposite the large mirror on roadside.

· Appin Parish Church (Church of Scotland) & Appin Community Development Trust

18 DRUIMNEIL HOUSE
Port Appin PA38 4DQ
Mrs J Glaisher (Gardener: Mr Andrew Ritchie)
T: 01631 730228 E: druimneilhouse@btinternet.com

Large garden overlooking Loch Linnhe with many fine varieties of mature trees and rhododendrons and other woodland shrubs. Nearer the house, an impressive bank of deciduous azaleas is underplanted with a block of camassia and a range of other bulbs. A small Victorian walled garden is currently being restored. Owner, Janet Glaisher, is the winner of the Diana Macnab Award 2020. She has opened Druimneil House for Scotland's Garden Scheme for a remarkable 37 years.

Open: 30 March - 31 October, dawn - dusk, admission by donation. Teas normally available. Lunch by prior arrangement.

Directions: Turn in for Appin off the A828 (Connel/Fort William Road). After two miles, sharp left at Airds Hotel, second house on right.

· Appin Parish Church (Church of Scotland)

**'Observe butterflies and bees in
the garden – why not create
a wildflower area?'**

Argyll & Lochaber

EAS MHOR

Cnoc-a-Challtuinn, Clachan Seil, Oban PA34 4TR
Mrs Kimbra Lesley Barrett
T: 01852 300469 E: kimbra1745@gmail.com

All the usual joys of a west coast garden plus some delightful surprises! A small contemporary garden on a sloping site - the emphasis being on scent and exotic plant material. Unusual and rare blue Borinda bamboos (only recently discovered in China) and bananas. The garden is at its best in mid to late summer when shrub roses and sweet peas fill the air with scent. The delightful sunny deck overlooks stylish white walled ponds with cascading water blades. Recent additions include a 20-foot citrus house, Chinese pergola walk and peony border.

Open: by arrangement 1 May - 30 September, admission £4.00, children free.

Directions: Turn off the A816 from Oban onto the B844 signposted *Easdale*. Over the bridge onto Seil Island, pass Tigh an Truish pub and turn right after a quarter mile up Cnoc-a-Challtuin road. Public car park is on the left at the bottom; please park there and walk up the road. Eas Mhor on right after second speed bump. Please do not block driveway. Bus Oban - Clachan Seil, two/three per day.

· *MS Centre (Therapy Centre): Oban*

FASNACLOICH

Appin PA38 4BJ
Mr and Mrs David Stewart

South-facing 15-acre woodland garden sloping down to Loch Baile Mhic Cailein in Glen Creran. Partly laid out in the mid-19th century with extensive structural water features added in the early 20th century. The garden mainly consists of hybrid and species rhododendrons, azaleas and magnolias with, over the last 25 years, a more recent addition of trees from Eastern Europe, Central Asia and the Northern United States (including a small pinetum).

Open: Sunday 31 May, noon - 5pm, admission £5.00, children free.

Directions: On the A828 at the roundabout on the north side of Creagan Bridge take the road for Invercreran. At the head of the loch go straight ahead for about one-and-a-half miles. The house is on the right side.

· *Mary's Meals*

INVERARAY CASTLE GARDENS

Inveraray PA32 8XF
The Duke and Duchess of Argyll
T: 01499 302203 E: enquiries@inveraray-castle.com
W: www.inveraray-castle.com

Rhododendrons and azaleas abound and flower from April to June. Very fine specimens of *Cedrus deodars*, *Sequoiadendron giganteum* (wellingtonia), *Cryptomeria japonica*, *Taxus baccata* and others thrive in the damp climate. The Flag-Borders on each side of the main drive with paths in the shape of Scotland's national flag, the St Andrew's Cross, are outstanding in spring with *Prunus* 'Ukon' and *P. subhirtella* and are underplanted with rhododendrons, eucryphias, shrubs and herbaceous plants giving interest all year. Bluebell Festival during flowering period in May.

Open: 1 April - 31 October, 10am - 5:45pm, admission £5.00, children free (under five years).

Argyll & Lochaber

Wheelchair users please note that there are gravel paths. Assistance dogs allowed within the garden. Last admission to garden is 5pm.

Directions: Inveraray is 60 miles north of Glasgow on the banks of Loch Fyne on the A83 and 15 miles from Dalmally on the A819. Regular bus service from Glasgow - Lochgilphead.

· *Donation to SGS Beneficiaries*

INVERYNE WOODLAND GARDEN
Kilfinan, Tighnabruaich PA21 2ER
Mrs Jane Ferguson

In ten acres of a 100-year-old amenity wood at Inveryne Farm, on a sloping site, somewhat sheltered from the loch, the garden was begun in 1994. Scrub birches were gradually cleared, bridges installed and amongst rocky outcrops were planted rhododendrons, azaleas, dogwoods, Japanese maples, sorbuses, eucryphias, hydrangeas and more. Gunnera, skunk cabbage, primulas and rodgersias cling to the banks of the burn and ferns provide the backdrop for our growing shrubs. Storms have varied its character and created features, and it is still a work in progress. Spring and autumn colour and an interest in varied vistas and textures of bark and leaf inspire us.

Open: Saturday/Sunday, 23/24 May, 1pm - 5pm for the May Weekend Festival, admission £5.00, children free. Parking is opposite the disused tennis court. Wellies are essential. Dog owners please note that there are sheep in the fields.

Directions: Approximately six miles north of Tighnabruaich towards Kilfinan on the B8000. After turning right at the crossroads at Millhouse, follow the road past the turning to Ardmarnock, over the little bridge at the bottom. The next track on the left is unpaved and leads to Inveryne.

· *Cowal Elderly Befrienders SCIO*

KILDALLOIG
Campbeltown PA28 6RE
Mr and Mrs Joe Turner
T: 07979 855930 E: kildalloig@gmail.com

Coastal garden with some interesting and unusual shrubs including Australasian shrubs and trees, climbing roses, and herbaceous perennials. There is a woodland walk and a pond garden with aquatic and bog plants.

Open: by arrangement 1 May - 31 October, admission £4.00, children free.

Directions: Take the A83 to Campbeltown, then three miles south east of town past Davaar Island.

· *Marie Curie & Macmillan Cancer Support*

Argyll & Lochaber

KINLOCHLAICH GARDENS
Appin PA38 4BD
Miss F M M Hutchison
T: 07881 525754 E: fiona@kinlochlaich.plus.com
W: www.kinlochlaichgardencentre.co.uk

....

Octagonal walled garden incorporating a large Nursery Garden Centre with a huge variety of plants growing and for sale. Bluebell woodland walk and spring garden. Many rhododendrons, azaleas, trees, shrubs and herbaceous plants, including many unusual ones such as embothrium, davidia, stewartia, magnolia, eucryphia and tropaeolum. A quarter of the interior of the walled garden is borders packed with many unusual and interesting plants, espaliered fruit trees, and with an ancient yew in the centre, and another quarter is vegetable growing.

Open: 3 March - 15 October, 11am - 4pm, admission £3.00, children free. Mid-October through March, generally open 10am - 4pm. Best to check.

Directions: On the A828 in Appin between Oban, 18 miles to the south, and Fort William, 27 miles to the north. The entrance is next to the police station. Bus Oban to Fort William.

· The Appin Village Hall & Feis na h'apainne

Kilnochlaich Gardens

Argyll & Lochaber

25

KNOCK NEWHOUSE
Lochgair PA31 8RZ
Mr and Mrs Hew Service
T: 01546 886628 E: corranmorhouse@aol.com

The six-acre woodland garden is centred on a small waterfall, a 250-foot lochan and lily pond. Since the 1960s there has been constant planting including major plantings in 1989 and the 90s. The storms of 2011/12 caused great damage to trees and bushes, but created space for additional azaleas, rhododendrons, camellias, hoheria, eucryphia and other flowering shrubs. There are over 100 species of rhododendron, as well as hybrids. Among the mature and young trees are cut leaf oak and alder, specimen conifers, redwoods, eucalyptus, acers and a wollemi pine, which was thought to be extinct until found in Australia in 1994.

Open: Saturday/Sunday, 25/26 April & Saturday/Sunday, 16/17 May, 1:30pm - 5pm. Also open by arrangement 13 April - 13 September. Admission £4.00, children free. Waterproof footwear is highly recommended other than in very dry weather.

Directions: On the A83. The house is not visible from the road. From Lochgilphead, half a mile south of Lochgair Hotel and on the left-hand side of the road, and from Inveraray on the right side of the road half a mile after the Lochgair Hotel; the drive opening is marked and enters the woods.

· *MND Scotland & Christ Church Scottish Episcopal Church*

Knock Newhouse

Argyll & Lochaber

26 MAOLACHY'S GARDEN
Lochavich, by Kilmelford PA35 1HJ
Georgina Dalton
T: 01866 844212

Three acres of woodland garden with a tumbling burn — created in a small glen over 40 years. At an altitude of 450 feet and two weeks behind the coastal changes, the growing season is shorter. By not struggling to grow tender or late species, the owner can enjoy those that are happy to grow well here and give everyone much pleasure. Snowdrops, followed by early rhododendrons, masses of daffodils in many varieties, bluebells, wildflowers and azaleas, primulas and irises. A productive vegetable patch and tunnel feed the gardener and family.

Open: Saturday/Sunday, 23/24 May, 2pm - 5pm for the May Weekend Festival. Also open Saturday/Sunday, 25/26 April, 2pm - 5pm. And open Saturday/Sunday, 27/28 June, 2pm - 5pm. And open by arrangement 1 January - 31 December. Admission £4.00, children free.

Directions: Ignore SatNav. A816 to Kilmelford. Turn uphill between shop and church, signposted *Lochavich 6*, steep and twisty road with hairpin bend shortly after leaving village, check for passing places. Maolachy Drive is four miles from village. Cross three county cattle grids; after the third ignore the forestry tracks to left and right. Continue downhill towards Loch Avich, and Maolachy is up on the left, first house after Kilmelford.

 · *Kilninver & Kilmelford Parish Church Of Scotland: Kilmelford Church Project & Hope: Oban*

27 OAKBANK
Ardrishaig PA30 8EP
Helga Macfarlane
T: 01546 603405 E: helga@macfarlane.one
W: www.gardenatoakbank.blogspot.com

This unusual and delightful garden will appeal to adults and children alike with lots for each to explore, including a secret garden. It extends to some three acres of hillside with a series of paths winding among a varied collection of trees, shrubs, bulbs and wildflowers. There are several small ponds, many wonderful wood carvings, an active population of red squirrels and a viewpoint overlooking Loch Fyne to the Isle of Arran.

Open: 1 July - 31 July, 1pm - 6pm, admission £4.00, children free.

Directions: On the Tarbert (south) side of Ardrishaig - entry to the garden is at the junction of Tarbert Road (A83) and Oakfield Road opposite the more southerly *Scottish Water* lay-by.

 · *Diabetes UK*

28 ORMSARY HOUSE
Ormsary, Lochgilphead, Argyll PA31 8PE
Lady Lithgow
T: 01880 770738 E: mclithgow@ormsary.co.uk

Ormsary is on the shore of Loch Caolisport looking across to Islay and Jura. The house policies are resplendent in spring with bluebells and daffodils under fine oak trees. There are woodland gardens with azaleas, rhododendrons and a collection of trees and shrubs. The walled garden, which has evolved over a couple of centuries, is on two levels. The top half is a kitchen garden producing plants, fruit and vegetables for the house; a winter garden and 'Muscat of Alexandria' vinery have been heated by hydroelectric power for 100 years. A magnificent *Polylepis australis* beckons to the lower Secret Garden with its lawn, roses, magnolias and long mixed border. It opens onto the banks of Ormsary Water. There are also woodland walks accessed via the upper woodland garden.

Argyll & Lochaber

Open: by arrangement 1 January - 31 December, admission £5.00, children free.

Directions: Take the A82 road from Lochgilphead towards Campbeltown for four miles, then take the B8024 signposted to *Kilberry* and travel ten miles and follow signs to the *Estate office* for directions to the garden.

· *All proceeds to SGS Beneficiaries*

STRACHUR HOUSE FLOWER & WOODLAND GARDENS
Strachur PA27 8BX
Sir Charles and Lady Maclean

The flower garden is sheltered by magnificent beeches, limes, ancient yews and Japanese maples. There are herbaceous borders, a burnside rhododendron and azalea walk, rockery, tulips and spring bulbs. Enjoy the old woodland of Strachur Park, laid out in 1782, and the wildlife rich lochan.

Open: Saturday/Sunday, 23/24 May, 1pm - 5pm for the May Weekend Festival, admission £4.00, children free.

Directions: Turn off the A815 at Strachur House Farm entrance. Park in farm square. Bus Dunoon - Inveraray. From Edinburgh/Glasgow take ferry from Gourock to Dunoon.

· *British Red Cross*

Strachur House Flower and Woodland Gardens

AYRSHIRE & ARRAN

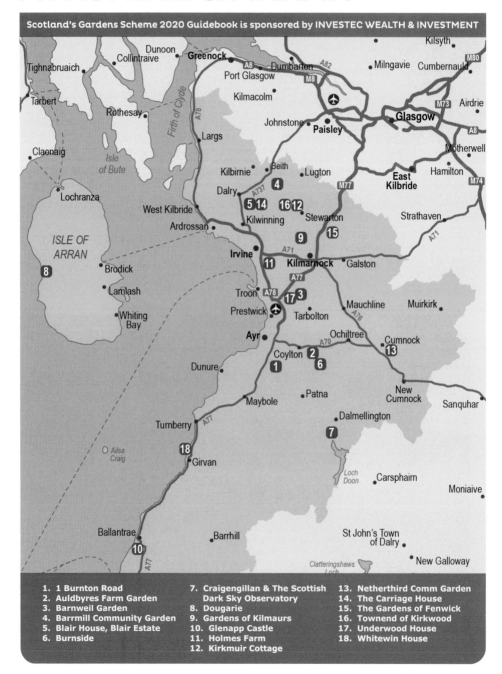

Scotland's Gardens Scheme 2020 Guidebook is sponsored by INVESTEC WEALTH & INVESTMENT

1. 1 Burnton Road
2. Auldbyres Farm Garden
3. Barnweil Garden
4. Barrmill Community Garden
5. Blair House, Blair Estate
6. Burnside
7. Craigengillan & The Scottish Dark Sky Observatory
8. Dougarie
9. Gardens of Kilmaurs
10. Glenapp Castle
11. Holmes Farm
12. Kirkmuir Cottage
13. Netherthird Comm Garden
14. The Carriage House
15. The Gardens of Fenwick
16. Townend of Kirkwood
17. Underwood House
18. Whitewin House

Ayrshire & Arran

OUR VOLUNTEER ORGANISERS

District Organisers:	Rose-Ann Cuninghame	45 Towerhill Avenue, Kilmaurs, Kilmarnock KA3 2TS
	Lavinia Gibbs	Dougarie, Isle of Arran KA27 8EB
		E: ayrshire@scotlandsgardens.org
Area Organisers:	Kim Donald MBE	19 Waterslap, Fenwick, Kilmarnock KA3 6AJ
	Pattie Kewney	Failford House, Mauchline, Ayrshire KA5 5TA
	Fiona McLean	100 Main Road, Fenwick KA3 6DY
	Rosie Pensom	Kilmarnock
	Wendy Sandiford	Harrowhill Cottage, Kilmarnock KA3 6HX
	Jane Tait	The Wildings, Bankwood, Galston KA4 8LH
	Sue Veitch	Auldbyres Farm Garden, Coylton, Ayr KA6 6LE
	Linda Vosseler	39 Langmuir Quadrant, Kilmaurs KA3 2UA
District Photographers:	David Blatchford	1 Burnton Rd, Dalrymple, Ayr KA6 6DY
	Rob Davis	24 Bellevue Crescent, Ayr KA7 2DR
Treasurers:	Lizzie Adam (Arran)	Bayview, Pirnmill, Isle of Arran KA27 8HP
	Carol Freireich (Ayrshire)	Sundrum, Colyton, Ayr KA6 5JX

GARDENS OPEN ON A SPECIFIC DATE

Blair House, Blair Estate, Dalry, Ayrshire	Saturday, 15 February
Craigengillan Estate and The Scottish Dark Sky Observatory	Saturday, 16 May
Barnweil Garden, Craigie, near Kilmarnock	Sunday, 17 May
Glenapp Castle, Ballantrae, Girvan	Saturday/Sunday/Monday, 23/24/25 May
Townend of Kirkwood, Stewarton	Saturday/Sunday/Monday, 23/24/25 May
Kirkmuir Cottage, Stewarton	Sunday/Monday, 24/25 May
Gardens of Kilmaurs, Kilmaurs	Sunday, 24 May
Netherthird Community Garden, Craigens Road, Netherthird	Saturday, 30 May
Holmes Farm, Drybridge, by Irvine	Saturday/Sunday, 6/7 June
Barrmill Community Garden, Barrmill Park and Gardens	Sunday, 21 June
Dougarie, Isle of Arran	Tuesday, 30 June
The Gardens of Fenwick, Fenwick	Saturday, 4 July
Whitewin House, Golf Course Road, Girvan	Saturday/Sunday, 18/19 July
Whitewin House, Golf Course Road, Girvan	Saturday/Sunday, 25/26 July
Whitewin House, Golf Course Road, Girvan	Saturday/Sunday, 1/2 August
Whitewin House, Golf Course Road, Girvan	Saturday/Sunday, 8/9 August
Underwood House, Craigie, Ayrshire	Sunday, 23 August

GARDENS OPEN BY ARRANGEMENT

Glenapp Castle, Ballantrae, Girvan	17 March - 22 December
Burnside, Littlemill Road, Drongan	1 April - 31 August
Auldbyres Farm Garden, Coylton	1 April - 30 September
The Carriage House, Blair Estate, Dalry	1 May - 31 July
Barnweil Garden, Craigie, near Kilmarnock	18 May - 15 July
1 Burnton Road, Dalrymple	13 June - 31 July
Whitewin House, Golf Course Road, Girvan	30 June - 31 August
Townend of Kirkwood, Stewarton	1 September - 15 October

Ayrshire & Arran

1 BURNTON ROAD
Dalrymple KA6 6DY
David and Margaret Blatchford
T: 01292 561988 E: d.blatchford273@btinternet.com

A tiny slice of jungle nestled within a small triangular plot. To the front of the house are two beds planted with nectar-secreting plants and in a larger bed a sea of *Stipa tenuissima* studded with perennials. To the rear a small patio is home to some bonsai and a collection of potted terrestrial ferns including rare blechnum species and succulents. A serpentine path meanders through dense planting of palms, bamboos and tree ferns. Of particular note are hardy and tender bromeliads and aroids such as arisaema and colocasia. Flower highlights are provided by lilies (species and cultivars), cannas and gingers.

Open: by arrangement 13 June - 31 July, admission £5.00, children free.

Directions: From the north take A77 Ayr to Stranraer. At junction with A713 take left, follow road past hospital to junction with B742, turn right. Into village, park in White Horse car park at T junction. Garden on corner of Burnton and Barbieston Roads. From the south off A77 take B7034, turn right. Follow into village, at Kirkton Inn junction turn left. Follow Barbieston Road. Bus 52 from Ayr.

· *Dalrymple Community Landscape Project*

1 Burnton Road, photo by David Blatchford

Ayrshire & Arran

2

AULDBYRES FARM GARDEN
Coylton KA6 6HG
Marshall and Sue Veitch
E: su.pavet@btinternet.com

Surrounded by a working farm, this compact garden has mature shrubs, wildlife pond, bog garden and stream. The exposed location has been challenging, but compensated for by stunning views towards Ayr and Arran. Shelter is provided by an unobtrusive boundary fence, 'borrowing' the panoramic landscape. The crisp freshness of the well-behaved spring borders, with woodland gems, gives way to a riot of summer perennial favourites. In addition, an extensive 'pot theatre' of containers brightens the farmyard with seasonal displays. There are small vegetable beds and a five-bay polytunnel (grapevine, tomatoes, basil, cucumber and oleanders). Dogs on leads for family farm walks through bluebell woods.

Open: by arrangement 1 April - 30 September, admission £5.00, children free.

Directions: In Coylton take road signposted *B742*, past Coylton Arms Pub in Low Coylton, *Auldbyres* signposted on left after half a mile.

· **Beatson Cancer Charity**

3

BARNWEIL GARDEN
Craigie, near Kilmarnock KA1 5NE
Mr and Mrs Ronald W Alexander
E: ronaldwalexander@btinternet.com

Rhododendrons and azaleas thrive in the woodlands set on heavy clay soil with a dense underplanting of candelabra primulas and other woodlanders. Oscar's Ditch, dug three years ago, is now fully planted with gunnera, bamboo, rheum, grasses, iris, ferns and hostas. A path leads from the lawn on the south side of the house through heavy shade, bursting into the Golden Glade with golden-leaved and -flowered trees, shrubs designed to give a blink of sunshine on dreich days, including golden acer, elderflower, philadelphus, ornamental bramble, grasses, hostas, etc. Nearby are drifts of 'Postford White' candelabra primula self-seeding every year, interplanted with meconopsis and black iris. Early variety roses and herbaceous planting should be flowering in the more open borders around the house lawns.

Open: Sunday 17 May, 2pm - 5pm. Also open by arrangement 18 May - 15 July. Admission £5.00, children free.

Directions: Two miles from Craigie. Right off B730, two miles south of A77 heading to Tarbolton.

· **Tarbolton Parish Church of Scotland & CLDF**

'Bees and other insects
pollinate most of our fruit and
vegetables'

Ayrshire & Arran

BARRMILL COMMUNITY GARDEN
Barrmill Park and Gardens KA15 1HW
The Barrmill Conservation Group
T: 07920 098171

This large woodland garden is carved from a 19th-century whinstone quarry and situated within an 1890s parkland, once known for the quoiting green provided for the village thread mill and ironstone pit workers of that time. Enhancement of the gardens began in 2010 by volunteers with assistance from *The Beechgrove Garden*. Features include enchanted woodland walks, the Vale Burn, views of the Dusk Water, a restored 19th-century cholera pit aka 'the Deid Man's Plantin', wish trees, wishing wells, doors to the Elfhame, guided walks, nature trail and traditional Ayrshire quoits game. The woodland backdrop is complemented by an understory of natural planting throughout.

Open: Sunday 21 June, 2pm - 5pm, admission £4.00, children free.

Directions: From Stewarton take A735 to Dunlop, left down Main Street B706 to Burnhouse, over at crossroads to Barrmill B706. From Lugton south on A736, right at Burnhouse, B706 to Barrmill. From Glasgow on M8 take J28a signposted *Irvine*, on Beith bypass take left B706 to Barrmill.

· *Barrmill and District Community Association*

BLAIR HOUSE, BLAIR ESTATE
Dalry, Ayrshire KA24 4ER
Charles and Sallie Hendry
T: 01294 833100 E: enquiries@blairestate.com
W: www.blairestate.com

Blair has beautiful landscaped gardens, with a collection of trees dating back to the 19th century. Over the past few years, the gardens have been undergoing restoration, with new beds created including a collection of rhododendrons, magnolias and azaleas. Walks on the estate will include beautiful displays of snowdrops and access to the private gardens.

Open: Saturday 15 February, noon - 4pm for Snowdrops and Winter Walks, admission £5.00, children free.

Directions: Exit the A737, at the Highfield roundabout, towards Stewarton. Immediately, continue straight ahead and follow the road for three-quarters of a mile. Turn right at the T junction towards Dalry. Access via North Lodge gates on the left. A one-way system will be in place. Public transport to Dalry.

· *Marie Curie*

BURNSIDE
Littlemill Road, Drongan KA6 7EN
Sue Simpson and George Watt
T: 01292 592445 E: suesimpson33@btinternet.com

This maturing and constantly changing six-and-a-half acre garden began in 2006. There is a wide range of plants from trees to alpines, giving colour and variability all year. Next to the road flows the Drumbowie Burn parallel to which is a woodland border with snowdrops, erythroniums, hellebores, trilliums and more, rhododendrons and acers. Near the house is a raised bed and large collection of troughs with an interesting range of alpines. The garden boasts herbaceous beds, ericaceous garden, screes, three alpine glass houses with award-winning plants, polytunnel, pond and arboretum - underplanted with daffodils, camassia, fritillaries and crocus. With a view towards matrimonial harmony there are two sheds which may be of interest.

Ayrshire & Arran

Open: by arrangement 1 April - 31 August, admission £5.00, children free.

Directions: From A77 Ayr bypass take A70 Cumnock for five-and-a-quarter miles, at Coalhall, turn onto B730 Drongan (south) for two-and-a-half miles. Burnside entrance immediately adjacent before black/white parapeted bridge. Ordnance survey grid ref: NS455162.

· *Beatson Cancer Charity*

Burnside, photo by David Blatchford

CRAIGENGILLAN ESTATE AND THE SCOTTISH DARK SKY OBSERVATORY
Dalmellington KA6 7PZ
Mark Gibson and Fi McClelland
T: 01292 551118 E: fi@craigengillan.com
W: www.scottishdarkskyobservatory.co.uk
....

Peacefully set in rugged 'Highland' landscape recognised by Historic Environment Scotland's Inventory of Gardens and Designed Landscapes. Beautiful gardens, with 'rock and water garden' by James Pulham & Sons. Extensive displays of native bluebells with great swathes of vibrant blue under the fresh greens of newly forming leaf canopies. At night there are some of the darkest skies most people will ever see with stars, planets, comets and constellations all visible.

Open: Saturday 16 May, 2pm - 5pm, admission £4.00, children free. Immersive Planatarium and Stellarium presentations available at the Dark Sky Observatory, tickets for this are ADDITIONAL cost to garden opening tickets - prices and times listed on Observatory website.

Directions: A713 from Ayr, at the round red *30mph* sign on entering Dalmellington turn right (signposted *Craigengillan Stables*) - drive for about two-and-a-quarter miles to Craigengillan House. From Carsphairn, stay on the main road through Dalmellington then take first turning on left after the Jet petrol station.

· *The Scottish Dark Sky Observatory*

Ayrshire & Arran

 DOUGARIE
Isle of Arran KA27 8EB
Mrs S C Gibbs
E: office@dougarie.com

Most interesting terraced garden in castellated folly built in 1905 to celebrate the marriage of the 12th Duke of Hamilton's only child to the Duke of Montrose. Good selection of tender and rare shrubs and herbaceous border. Small woodland area with trees including azara, abutilon, eucryphia, hoheria and nothofagus.

Open: Tuesday 30 June, 2pm - 5pm, admission £4.00, children free. Homemade cream teas in the 19th-century boathouse.

Directions: Five miles from Blackwaterfoot. Regular ferry sailing from Ardrossan and Claonaig (Argyll). Information from Caledonian MacBrayne, Gourock, T: 01475 650100. Parking is free.

· *Pirnmill Village Association*

 GARDENS OF KILMAURS
Kilmaurs KA3 2TD
Mr & Mrs R Mair and Mr F Murray
E: raymair27@aol.com, frankmm@btinternet.com

27 Crosshouse Road Kilmaurs KA3 2SA (Mr and Mrs R Mair): The garden to the rear of the house is in a sheltered position allowing growth of a wide range of plants which offer both spring and summer interest. Each of the two back garden areas contain both a pond and patio. The lower garden has about a third of its area devoted to a productive kitchen garden, soft fruit area and a cold greenhouse. The upper garden is entirely given over to flowering shrubs, perennials, climbers and annuals. The garden has been developed over 40 years.
5 Kirkton Road Kilmaurs KA3 2NW (Mr F Murray): A small burn runs through this one-acre garden. Informal planting lies to the south, fairly steeply banked with bulbs, bluebells, specimen trees and a short woodland walk. The north side is laid out in formal lawns, edged by beech hedging and shrub plantations, divided by dry-stone dykes. Visitors will find a 17th-century doocot which once served Tour House as a larder. To the back of the house lies the working garden, with polytunnels for roses, dahlias and chrysanthemums.

Open: Sunday 24 May, 2pm - 5pm for the May Weekend Festival, admission £7.00, children free.

Directions: Kilmaurs Village is to the north west of Kilmarnock and south of Stewarton. From Glasgow or Ayr on M77 follow signs to *Kilmaurs* (J7 heading south) and (J8 heading north). B751 goes from Fenwick to Kilmaurs.

· *Ayrshire Hospice*

 GLENAPP CASTLE
Ballantrae, Girvan KA26 0NZ
Mr Paul Szkiler
T: 01465 831212 E: info@glenappcastle.com
W: www.glenappcastle.com

The 36-acre grounds at Glenapp Castle are secluded and private. Many rare and unusual plants and shrubs can be found, including magnificent specimen rhododendrons. Paths wander round the azalea pond, through established woodland leading to the wonderful walled garden with a 150-foot Victorian glasshouse. Fresh herbs and fruit from the garden are used every day in the castle kitchen. Much of the gardens were designed by Gertrude Jekyll (1843-1932), the world-famous garden architect, applying the principles of the Arts and Crafts Movement, who worked

Ayrshire & Arran

in collaboration with Edwin Lutyens. A new walk has been created opening up the Glen, where Glenapp's Champion Trees will be found.
Champion Trees: *Abies cilicica*, *Cercidiphyllum japonicum* and *Picea likiangensis*.

Open: Saturday/Sunday/Monday, 23/24/25 May, 10am - 5pm for the May Weekend Festival. Also open by arrangement 17 March - 22 December. Admission £5.00, children free.

Directions: From north take A77 South. Pass through Ballantrae, crossing the River Stinchar as you leave. Take first turning on right, 100 yards beyond the river (not signposted). From the south take A77 north, turn left 100 yards before bridge over Stinchar at Ballantrae. Castle gates are one mile along this road.

· *Donation to SGS Beneficiaries*

27 Crosshouse Road, Gardens of Kilmaurs

HOLMES FARM
Drybridge, by Irvine KA11 5BS
Mr Brian A Young
T: 01294 311210 E: hfplants@live.co.uk
W: www.holmesfarmplants.com

A plantsman's garden created by a confirmed plantaholic. Meandering paths guide the eye through predominantly herbaceous plantings, with small trees and shrubs. The garden in front of the house is having a complete replant. No doubt chaos will ensue as time is short but happy to show work in progress. The plant nursery, Holmes Farm Plants, is located at the garden, where a wide selection of plants from the garden can be purchased.

Open: Saturday/Sunday, 6/7 June, 1pm - 5pm, admission £5.00, children free.

Directions: Holmes is the only farm between Drybridge and Dreghorn on B730. *SGS* garden open signs will be positioned and visitors should follow these.

· *The National Trust for Scotland: Threave Gardens*

Ayrshire & Arran

12 KIRKMUIR COTTAGE

Stewarton KA3 3DZ
Mr and Mrs Brian Macpherson
T: 01560 483816 E: dhmmacp@gmail.com

A one-and-a-half-acre mature garden with paths weaving through many different areas including woodland, formal borders, laburnum arch, herbaceous borders, rhododendrons and azaleas. Large lawn area and wildlife pond. Garden also features many interesting and unusual artefacts and sculptures.

Open: Sunday/Monday, 24/25 May, 11am - 5pm for the May Weekend Festival, admission £5.00, children free.

Directions: From M77 take B778 to Stewarton. At traffic lights turn left, and continue to mini-roundabout. Turn right at mini-roundabout signposted *B778 Kilwinning*. Continue for 100 yards under the railway bridge, take immediate left at war memorial. Parking for Kirkmuir Cottage will be well signposted.

· *Capability Scotland*

13 NETHERTHIRD COMMUNITY GARDEN

Craigens Road, Netherthird, Cumnock KA18 3AR
Netherthird Community Development Group
E: jamielor@aol.com
W: Facebook (Netherthird Community Development Group)

Netherthird Community Garden will be opening with a 'Wildlife for Families Theme' to suit all ages. Follow our nature trail wild orchids, new bog garden, beehives to aid pollination, and meet our hens . See our long cottage border bursting with shrubs, perennials and annuals, vegetable beds, polytunnels where we grow tomatoes and plants. The striking wooden gazebos were funded by the Prince's Trust for outdoor lessons. Teas at the vintage beach hut cafe. Visit the swing park, the vast sandpit, bouncy castle, a treasure hunt and fancy dress class for young dog owners. All run by and for volunteers and the local community.

Open: Saturday 30 May, noon - 3pm, admission £3.00, children free.

Directions: Driving south on the A76 Cumnock bypass look for the roundabout signposted *B7083*, take this exit which heads to Cumnock, after few hundred yards take right turn into Craigens Road, Netherthird Primary School is on the right. Parking available here, Community Garden nearby. Disabled parking at garden.

· *Netherthird Community Development Group*

14 THE CARRIAGE HOUSE

Blair Estate, Dalry KA24 4ER
Mr and Mrs Luke Borwick
T: 01294 832816 E: lina@blairtrust.co.uk

The Stables were built (c1800) on rocky outcrop with little soil depth. In 2001, The Carriage House was created from old stables, cowshed and dairy. The Garden has evolved over the past fifteen years, and has been designed by the owners to provide colour and interest all year round, many plants provided by friends and family. Divided into many different 'rooms', some contain sculptures by artists including Lucy Poett, Lucy Fisher and Mary Stormonth Darling. Ironwork by Kev Paxton. Small copses have been formed in the adjoining ten-acre field, containing many interesting trees and shrubs. Paths are designed to take you round the field to discover items of interest, such as the mermaids rescuing a girl, some unusual trees such as a variegated tulip tree, a golden dawn redwood, and a wellingtonia grown from seed here at Blair.

Ayrshire & Arran

Open: by arrangement 1 May - 31 July, for groups. Admission £5.00, children free.

Directions: A737 from Beith. At roundabout before Dalry take first left signposted *Stewarton*. Then go straight on, signposted *Bike Route Irvine*. Keep going for approximately two miles and keep estate wall on right till you come to South Lodge (white building) Turn right down drive for Blair Estate Carriage House on right. Public transport to Dalry.

· *Friends of Hilary Storm School Uganda*

15

THE GARDENS OF FENWICK
Fenwick KA3 6AJ
Fenwick Gardeners
T: 07836 583546 E: kd581@aol.com

10 Raith Road Fenwick KA3 6DQ (Mrs Sandra Macpherson): Front garden landscaped with gravel and shrubs and east-facing back garden with terraces, grass and beds with perennials and shrubs; masses of pots and containers. Terrace at the top provides tranquil seating. and quirky ornaments lurk in the shrubbery. A new wildlife pond, lined with marginal planting.
2 Fulton's Crescent NEW Fenwick KA3 6GJ (Janek Sawczyn and Marco Surraka): A cottage garden with peonies, delphiniums, foxgloves, lavender. Walled back garden with wisteria, Virginia creeper, honeysuckle, clematis, acer, laburnum, Norwegian maple, lilac, magnolia, hellebores, fritillaria, calendula, echinacea, rudbeckia, echinops and a summer house. Tiered terrace with hawthorn, bamboo and box.
25 Kirkton Road NEW Fenwick, Ayrshire KA3 6DJ (Mr and Mrs Paul Whitton): Hilly garden with mature hedges, trees, fruit, vegetables and compost area. Side borders are filled with heathers perennials, succulents, shrubs, climbers and roses. Masses of pots, greenhouse and a path lined with dahlias and summer bedding leads to sloping lawn with well-planted border.
5 Fowld's View NEW Fenwick KA3 6GF (Linda Creanor): This garden, established in 2016, complements a modern house. Based on a circular design with lawn and patio, mixed planting in borders with small trees, shrubs and varied herbaceous perennials. A north east aspect presents challenges with shady areas, and the planting allows for interest throughout the year.
7 Raith Road NEW Fenwick KA3 6DQ: An informal natural garden, large lawn bordered with shrubs, perennials and mature trees. An area has been left wild for nature's sake with nesting boxes and small pond. A gateway in the beech hedge leads to a vegetable plot and steps lead to a seating area by the burn.
9a Maunsheugh Road NEW Fenwick KA3 6AN (John Logan): Immaculate south-facing lawn edged with flamboyant begonias and a mass of containers. To the rear are patio areas, raised beds with begonias, dahlias, annuals, heathers and shrubs, summer house, vegetable beds and greenhouse. A lawn runs to a seating area set off by roses.

Open: Saturday 4 July, noon - 5pm, admission £6.00, children free. Tickets, refreshments, and loos at church hall.

Directions: From the north, take J7 off M77 Fenwick, turn left into village, right at roundabout and Kirkton Road is on left. From the south, take slip road off A77 Kilmarnock/Fenwick turn right for Fenwick (B7038) after two roundabouts enter village on to Main Road, turn right into Kirkton Road for church hall.

· *Ayrshire Hospice & Ayrshire Cancer Support*

Ayrshire & Arran

TOWNEND OF KIRKWOOD
Stewarton KA3 3EW
Mrs Katrina Clow
T: 01560 483926 / 07914 316119 E: katrina.clow@btinternet.com

Townend of Kirkwood is a new garden created on three acres of wet field, started in 2013. On the left towards the house there is extensive planting around a wildlife pond, and on the right some interesting wind-breaking planting which is maturing well. There is an excellent range of interesting shrubs and young trees throughout. Beyond the courtyard is a lawn, surrounded by well-established mixed borders enclosed on the north side by a beech hedge. To the rear of the house is a delightful sheltered garden with lawn and herbaceous beds full of plants and a path leading to a small young orchard with productive trees. Good all-year-round colour.

Open: Saturday/Sunday/Monday, 23/24/25 May, 2pm - 5pm for the May Weekend Festival. Also open by arrangement 1 September - 15 October. Admission £5.00, children free.

Directions: In Stewarton take B778, heading towards the Glasgow / Irvine road. Parking - bear right half way up road in and park at the side of the byre.

· *The Younger (Benmore) Trust*

UNDERWOOD HOUSE
Craigie, Ayrshire KA1 5NG
Baroness Ford of Cunninghame OBE
T: 01563 830719 E: margaretford@hotmail.co.uk

The garden was laid out in 1780 in the landscape style, fashionable at the time. The original features of the garden remain unchanged, with sweeping lawns, large specimen trees, with a natural pond and burn which runs through the whole garden. The woodland is being restored and replanted with specimen rhododendrons and hydrangeas and woodland carpeters. A formal pleasure garden is being created in sympathetic style. Underwood House provides activity, training and employment for young people with neurological conditions. in 2019 a beautiful sensory area was created by partner schools working with young volunteers from the Prince's Trust.

Open: Sunday 23 August, noon - 5pm, admission £5.00, children free.

Directions: South bound on A77 pass Hansel Village, take next left signposted *Underwood/ Ladykirk*. At stone bridge take left, continue to Underwood Lodge. Pass the Lodge, go for 150 yards. Take left to Underwood House. From Ayr on A77 take exit to Symington, take first right, signposted *Underwood/Ladykirk*. Cross over A77 on to south carriageway.

· *Underwood House SCIO*

WHITEWIN HOUSE
Golf Course Road, Girvan KA26 9HW
Linda Finnie and Graeme Finnie
T: 01465 712358 M: 07855 269247 E: lafinnie@hotmail.com

Whitewin House has an interesting history. It was the first house to be built on Golf Course Road by the Tate & Lyle sugar-refining family in the late 1800s. It has a prime location with stunning views over the Firth of Clyde and to Ailsa Craig and the Kintyre Peninsula. Set in an acre of ground there are four separate gardens: the Ailsa Craig Garden at the front; the Gable Garden; the Central Rear Garden and the Rear Golf Course Garden. The layout is formal with lawns, borders, shrubs, rockeries and statuary complementing the Victorian architecture of Whitewin. Changes for 2020 include a Gable Garden water feature.

Ayrshire & Arran

Open: 18/19 July, 25/26 July, 1/2 August and 8/9 August, 1pm - 5pm. Also open by arrangement 30 June - 31 August. Admission £5.00, children free.

Directions: Approaching Girvan from the north on A77 the turning to Golf Course Road is on right hand side of the road before the town centre (follow signs for the *Golf Course*). From the south on the A77 come through Girvan, turn left at the lights, then first left and follow signs for the *Golf Course*. Entrance to the property will be signposted.

· *All proceeds to SGS Beneficiaries*

Underwood House

'Many of our gardens run
children's activities for
younger visitors'

BERWICKSHIRE

Scotland's Gardens Scheme 2020 Guidebook is sponsored by INVESTEC WEALTH & INVESTMENT

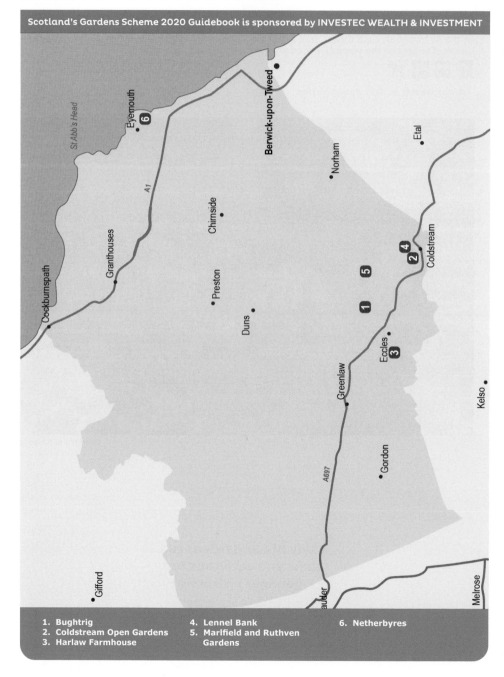

1. **Bughtrig**
2. **Coldstream Open Gardens**
3. **Harlaw Farmhouse**
4. **Lennel Bank**
5. **Marlfield and Ruthven Gardens**
6. **Netherbyres**

Berwickshire

OUR VOLUNTEER ORGANISERS

District Organiser:	Christine McLennan	Marlfield, Coldstream TD12 4JT
District Photographers:	Kenneth Patterson	3 Yarrow Close, East Ord TD15 2YE
	Malcolm Ross	2 Dall Hollow, North Berwick EH39 5FN
Treasurer:	Forbes McLennan	Marlfield, Coldstream TD12 4JT

GARDENS OPEN ON A SPECIFIC DATE

Harlaw Farmhouse, Eccles near Kelso, Roxburghshire	Sunday, 19 April
Netherbyres, Eyemouth	Sunday, 28 June
Lennel Bank, Coldstream	Sunday, 5 July
Coldstream Open Gardens, Coldstream Community Centre, High Street, Coldstream	Sunday, 12 July
Marlfield and Ruthven Gardens, Coldstream	Sunday, 19 July

GARDENS OPEN REGULARLY

Bughtrig, Near Leitholm, Coldstream	1 June - 1 September

GARDENS OPEN BY ARRANGEMENT

Lennel Bank, Coldstream	1 January - 31 December
Marlfield and Ruthven Gardens, Coldstream	1 January - 31 December

Berwickshire

BUGHTRIG
near Leitholm, Coldstream TD12 4JP
Mr and Mrs William Ramsay
T: 01890 840777 E: ramsay@bughtrig.co.uk

A traditional hedged Scottish family garden with an interesting combination of sculpture, herbaceous plants, shrubs, annuals and fruit. It is surrounded by fine specimen trees, which provide remarkable shelter.

Open: 1 June - 1 September, 11am - 5pm, admission £5.00, children free.

Directions: Quarter of a mile east of Leitholm on the B6461.

· *Donation to SGS Beneficiaries*

Bughtrig, photo by Kenneth Patterson

Berwickshire

COLDSTREAM OPEN GARDENS
Coldstream Community Centre, High Street, Coldstream TD12 4AP
The Gardeners of Coldstream

Historic Coldstream, Scotland's 'First True Border Town' is the home of Coldstream's Guards, the country's second oldest infantry regiment. Cross the bridge over the River Tweed, which forms a natural boundary between England and Scotland and pause to admire the wonderful views along the river to the Cheviots and beyond. Coldstream, as a previous winner of the *Borders Floral Gateway Awards,* will have a great variety of gardens open for the garden enthusiast to explore. Wander around and chat to an exponent of permaculture, a giant vegetable grower and numerous other gardeners; several of whom are opening for the first time this year. All garden owners will be delighted to share their garden triumphs and interests with you.

Open: Sunday 12 July, 1pm - 5pm, admission £5.00, children free. Tickets, teas, route maps, plant sales and facilities at the Community Centre on the High Street

Directions: Coldstream is on the A697 equidistant between Kelso and Berwick-upon-Tweed. The Community Centre (an old church building) is in the west end of town. There is ample parking on the street and in nearby car parks.

· ***Coldstream Gateway Association***

HARLAW FARMHOUSE
Eccles near Kelso, Roxburghshire TD5 7RA
Jean Wood
T: 07479 357999

Harlaw is set in a one-acre garden surrounding a typical Berwickshire farmhouse, in a truly rural setting with lovely Border views. The owner has spent many years building up a collection of over 65 varieties of named daffodils and narcissus, naturalised throughout the garden. It has a mature nuttery with several highly productive walnut, hazel and gingko biloba trees and an orchard with apple, pear and plum trees. In the summer there is a large cutting garden and vegetable patch. There are two greenhouses with a large cactus collection. The gardener is a keen plantswoman, propagating most of her own stock.

Open: Sunday 19 April, 1pm - 4pm, admission £4.00, children free. A large flock of poultry including geese, ducks, guinea fowl, turkeys and fancy hens wander the garden free range; please wear wellington boots or stout footwear.

Directions: From the east drive through Eccles village then take the first turning right signposted *Loan Knowe.* Continue to the *cycle route* sign, turn left and the house is one mile on the left. From Ednam, go through the village, take left turn to Hume, go to T junction, turn right and continue to the white cottage, take right fork *cycle route*, Harlaw is half mile on right.

· ***Border Womens Aid***

Berwickshire

LENNEL BANK
Coldstream TD12 4EX
Mrs Honor Brown
T: 01890 882297

. . . .

Lennel Bank is a terraced garden overlooking the River Tweed, consisting of wide borders packed with shrubs and perennial planting, some unusual. The water garden, built in 2008, is surrounded by a rockery and utilises the slope, ending in a pond. There is a small kitchen garden with raised beds in unusual shapes. Different growing conditions throughout the garden from dry, wet, shady and sunny, lend themselves to a variety of plants and enhance interest in the garden.

Open: Sunday 5 July, 10:30am - 5pm. Also open by arrangement 1 January - 31 December. Admission £5.00, children free.

Directions: On A6112 Coldstream to Duns road, one mile from Coldstream.

· *British Heart Foundation*

Lennel Bank, photo by Jannie Bos

MARLFIELD AND RUTHVEN GARDENS
Coldstream TD12 4JT
Christine & Forbes McLennan and Keith & Karen Fountain
T: 01890 840700 E: forbes.mclennan@gmail.com

. . . .

Marlfield TD12 4JT (Christine and Forbes McLennan): Marlfield is a two-and-a-half-acre garden with extensive lawns, specimen trees, shrubberies, flower beds, a half-acre woodland wind break, half-acre paddock with a large allotment-type raised vegetable garden, fruit cage and small orchard. The present owners have worked extensively over the past five years to create the allotment and fruit beds from a vacant field. The main garden is still a work in progress, restoring

Berwickshire

or creating order from what was a very neglected garden. The rockery and fish pond are almost complete. Marlfield is a lovely tranquil garden where one can hear little birds singing and our bees buzzing.

Ruthven House TD12 4JU (Keith and Karen Fountain): Ruthven has lovely views toward the Cheviots and is accessed via a sweeping driveway. There are three acres divided into various interconnected areas; including a traditional knot garden, gravel gardens, an orchard set in meadow planting, a newly established rose garden and informal herbaceous borders which lead to the garden's main feature, two ponds connected by a winding stream. The owners have over the last few years expanded the garden extensively from the original small beds around the house, adding different areas as inspiration struck. The most recent additions are a substantial kitchen garden and (perhaps optimistically) a small lavender field.

Open: Sunday 19 July, 1pm - 5pm. Also open by arrangement 1 January - 31 December. Admission £5.00, children free.

Directions: Four miles north of Coldstream on the old Duns road. Half a mile off the main road.

· *Macmillan Cancer Support*

Marlfield, photo by Malcolm Ross

NETHERBYRES
Eyemouth TD14 5SE
Col S J Furness
T: 01890 750337

A traditional Scottish walled garden, with a mixture of fruit, flowers and vegetables. It is thought to be the only elliptical walled garden in the world, dating from 1740. A pear tree planted at that time still survives, next to the largest rose in Berwickshire (*Rosa filipes* 'Kiftsgate').

Open: Sunday 28 June, 2pm - 5pm, admission £5.00, children free.

Directions: Half a mile south of Eyemouth on the A1107 to Berwick.

· *St Ebba Episcopal Church Eyemouth*

CAITHNESS & SUTHERLAND

Scotland's Gardens Scheme 2020 Guidebook is sponsored by INVESTEC WEALTH & INVESTMENT

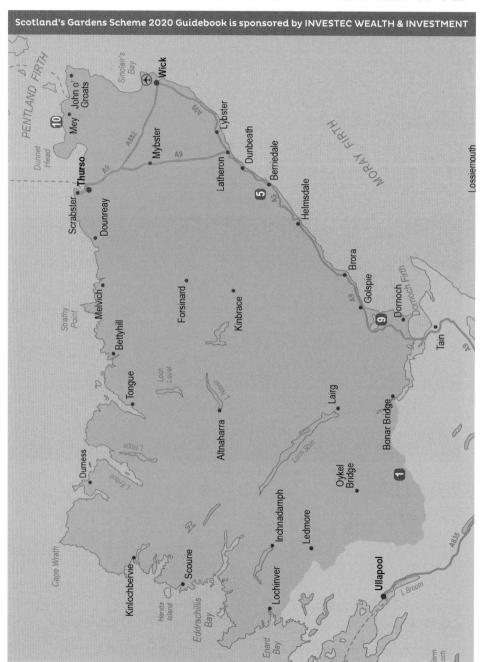

SHETLAND

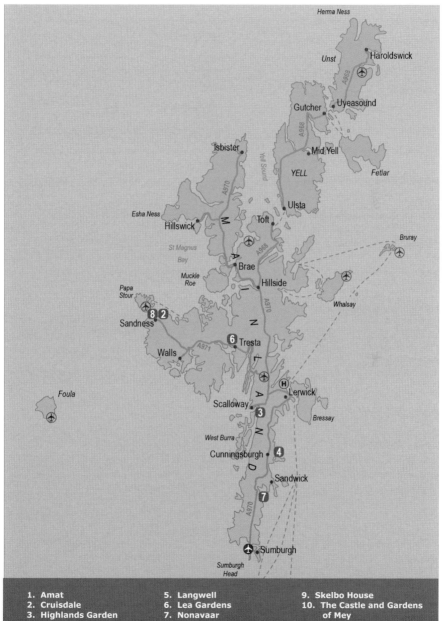

Herma Ness

Unst

Haroldswick

A968

Uyeasound

Gutcher

Mid Yell

Isbister

YELL

Fetlar

Yell Sound

Ulsta

A970

Esha Ness

Toft

Bruray

Hillswick

M

St Magnus
Bay

A968

Brae

Muckle
Roe

Hillside

Papa
Stour

A970

Whalsay

8 **2**

N

Sandness

6 Tresta

Walls

A971

H Lerwick

Foula

I

Scalloway

A

3

Bressay

West Burra

N

Cunningsburgh

4

D

Sandwick

A970

7

Sumburgh

Sumburgh
Head

1. Amat	5. Langwell	9. Skelbo House
2. Cruisdale	6. Lea Gardens	10. The Castle and Gardens
3. Highlands Garden	7. Nonavaar	of Mey
4. Keldaberg	8. Norby	

Caithness, Sutherland, Orkney & Shetland

OUR VOLUNTEER ORGANISERS

District Organiser:	Sara Shaw	Amat, Ardgay, Sutherland IV24 3BS E: caithness@scotlandsgardens.org
Area Organisers:	Caroline Critchlow Mary Leask Steve Mathieson	The Quoy of Houton, Orphir, Orkney KW17 2RD VisitScotland, Market Cross, Lerwick ZE1 0LU VisitScotland, Market Cross, Lerwick ZE1 0LU
District Photographer:	Colin Gregory	Iona, Reay, Caithness, KW14 7RG
Treasurer:	Nicola Vestey	The Old School House, Bunloit IV63 6XG

GARDENS OPEN ON A SPECIFIC DATE

Amat, Ardgay	Saturday/Sunday, 30/31 May
The Castle and Gardens of Mey, Mey	Friday, 3 July
The Castle and Gardens of Mey, Mey	Friday, 17 July
Skelbo House, Skelbo, Dornoch	Saturday, 18 July
Langwell, Berriedale	Sunday, 2 August
The Castle and Gardens of Mey, Mey	Friday, 14 August

GARDENS OPEN REGULARLY

Norby, Burnside, Sandness, SHETLAND	1 January - 31 December
Lea Gardens, Tresta, SHETLAND	1 March - 30 October (not Thursdays)
The Castle and Gardens of Mey, Mey	1 May - 30 September
Nonavaar, Levenwick, SHETLAND	1 May - 31 August (Sundays only)

GARDENS OPEN BY ARRANGEMENT

Cruisdale, Sandness, SHETLAND	1 January - 31 December
Langwell, Berriedale	1 January - 31 December
Highlands Garden, East Voe, Scalloway, SHETLAND	1 May - 31 October
Nonavaar, Levenwick, SHETLAND	1 May - 31 August
Amat, Ardgay	1 May - 31 August
Keldaberg, Cunningsburgh, SHETLAND	1 June - 30 September

Caithness, Sutherland, Orkney & Shetland

AMAT
Ardgay IV24 3BS
Jonny and Sara Shaw
E: sara.amat@aol.co.uk

Riverside garden surrounded by the old Caledonian Amat Forest. Herbaceous borders and rockery set in a large lawn looking onto a salmon pool. Old and new rhododendrons grow along the woodland and river walk, plus large specimen trees in policies. Red squirrels were reintroduced six years ago and are often seen in and around the garden.

Open: Saturday/Sunday, 30/31 May, 2pm - 5pm. Also open by arrangement 1 May - 31 August. Admission £5.00, children free.

Directions: Take the road from Ardgay to Croick, nine miles. Turn left at the red phone box and the garden is 500 yards on the left.

· *Creich Croick & Kincardine District Day Care Association & Canine Partners*

CRUISDALE
Sandness, SHETLAND ZE2 9PL
Alfred Kern
T: 01595 870739

The garden is in a natural state with many willows, several ponds and a variety of colourful hardy plants that grow well in the Shetland climate. Work started in 2003 and the garden has continued to expand over the years, with more work planned.

Open: by arrangement 1 January - 31 December, admission £3.00, children free. Delighted to receive visitors, please don't hesitate to call.

Directions: From Lerwick head north on the A970, then at Tingwall take the A971 to Sandness, on the west side of Shetland. Cruisdale is opposite the school, on the right-hand side with a wind generator in the field.

· *Royal Voluntary Service*

'Donate your plants to a local
plant stall and help us to raise
money for charity'

Caithness, Sutherland, Orkney & Shetland

HIGHLANDS GARDEN
East Voe, Scalloway, SHETLAND ZE1 0UR
Sarah Kay
T: 01595 880526/ 07818 845385 E: info@easterhoull.co.uk
W: www.selfcatering-shetland.co.uk/the-garden/ and www.sarahkayarts.com

The garden is in two parts. The upper garden is mostly a rockery, with a large selection of plants, shallow pond, seating area and newly built polycrub and greenhouse with fruit and vegetables. The lower garden is on a steep slope with a spectacular sea view over the village of Scalloway. There is a path to lead visitors around and the garden features a large collection of plants, vegetable patch, deep pond and pergola. It was awarded a *Shetland Environmental Award* in 2014 for its strong theme of recycling. The owner also has an art studio which you are most welcome to visit when you view the garden.

Open: by arrangement 1 May - 31 October, 9am - 9pm, admission £3.50, children free.

Directions: Follow the A970 main road towards the village of Scalloway. Near the top of the hill heading towards Scalloway take a sharp turn to the left, signposted *Easterhoull Chalets*. Follow the road to chalets (painted blue with red roofs) and you will see the yellow *SGS* sign for the garden. Bus 4 from Lerwick/Scalloway.

· *Macmillan Cancer Support*

Highlands Garden

Caithness, Sutherland, Orkney & Shetland

4

KELDABERG
Cunningsburgh, SHETLAND ZE2 9HG
Mrs L Johnston
T: 01950 477331 E: linda.keldaberg@btinternet.com

A 'secret garden' divided into four areas. A beach garden of grasses, flowers and driftwood. The main area is a sloping perennial border leading down to a greenhouse, vegetable plot, up to a decked area with containers and exotic plants including agaves, pineapple lilies, cannas and gunneras. The new area has trees, raised vegetable beds, a rockery, retaining walls and an arbour in which to rest. There is a pond with goldfish and aquatic plants and now a polycrub to grow vegetables, fruit trees and a grapevine.

Open: by arrangement 1 June - 30 September, admission £3.50, children free.

Directions: On the A970 south of Lerwick is Cunningsburgh, take the Gord junction on the left after passing the village hall. Continue along the road to the second house past the *Kenwood* sign.

· *Chest Heart & Stroke Scotland*

5

LANGWELL
Berriedale KW7 6HD
Welbeck Estates
T: 01593 751278 / 751237 E: caithness@welbeck.co.uk

A beautiful and spectacular old walled garden with outstanding borders situated in the secluded Langwell Strath. Charming wooded access drive with a chance to see deer.

Open: Sunday 2 August, noon - 4pm. Also open by arrangement 1 January - 31 December. Admission £4.00, children free.

Directions: Turn off the A9 at Berriedale Braes, up the private (tarred) drive signposted *Private - Langwell House*. It is about one-and-a-quarter miles from the A9.

· *RNLI*

6

LEA GARDENS
Tresta, SHETLAND ZE2 9LT
Rosa Steppanova
T: 01595 810454

Lea Gardens, started in the early 1980s, now covers almost two acres. The plant collection, the largest north of Inverewe Gardens, consists of 1,500 different species and cultivars from all over the world, including phyto-geographic elements of collections of plants from New Zealand, South Africa and South America. Planted to provide all-year-round interest, it has been divided into a variety of habitats: woodland and shade, borders, wetland, raised beds and acid and lime lovers. A winner of the 2011 *Shetland Environmental Award*.

Open: 1 March - 30 October (not Thursdays), 2pm - 5pm, admission £4.00, children free.

Directions: From Lerwick take the A970 north, turn left at Tingwall onto the A971 past Weisdale along Weisdale Voe and up Weisdale hill. Coming down, Lea Gardens is on your right surrounded by trees.

· *Donation to SGS Beneficiaries*

Caithness, Sutherland, Orkney & Shetland

 NONAVAAR
Levenwick, SHETLAND ZE2 9HX
James B Thomason
T: 01950 422447

This is a delightful country garden, sloping within drystone walls and overlooking magnificent coastal views. It contains ponds, terraces, trees, bushes, varied perennials, annuals, vegetable garden and greenhouse.

Open: 1 May - 31 August (Sundays only), noon - 6pm. Also open by arrangement 1 May - 31 August. Admission £4.00, children free.

Directions: Head south from Lerwick. Turn left at the *Levenwick* sign soon after Bigton turnoff. Follow the road to the third house on the left after the Midway stores. Park where there is a *Garden Open* sign. Bus 6 from Lerwick - Sumburgh.

· *Cancer Research UK*

 NORBY
Burnside, Sandness, SHETLAND ZE2 9PL
Mrs Gundel Grolimund
T: 01595 870246 E: gislinde@tiscali.co.uk

A small but perfectly formed garden and a prime example of what can be achieved in a very exposed situation. Blue painted wooden pallets provide internal wind breaks and form a background for shrubs, climbers and herbaceous plants, while willows provide a perfect wildlife habitat. There are treasured plants such as *Chionochloa rubra*, pieris, Chinese tree peonies, a selection of old-fashioned shrub roses, lilies, hellebores and grasses from New Zealand. There is also a lovely selection of interesting art and textiles in the house.

Open: 1 January - 31 December, dawn - dusk, admission £3.00, children free.

Directions: Head north on the A970 from Lerwick then west on the A971 at Tingwall. At Sandness, follow the road to Norby, turn right at the Methodist Church, Burnside is at the end of the road. Bus 10 Sandness - Walls.

· *Survival International Charitable Trust*

 SKELBO HOUSE
Skelbo, Dornoch IV25 3QG
Alison Bartlett

Extensive woodland garden with spectacular views over Loch Fleet. Mixed herbaceous borders, rose garden and shrubberies surround the house. Lawns slope down to a small lochan and river walkway. Mature trees throughout. Large kitchen garden.

Open: Saturday 18 July, 10am - 4pm, admission £5.00, children free.

Directions: From the south: On A9 take the small turning opposite Trentham Hotel (just past the Dornoch turn offs). At the side of Loch Fleet turn left, at the ruined castle take the second farm road which is fairly rough, and follow round to your right. If coming from the north take the Loch Fleet road signposted to *Embo* from the A9.

· *Mary's Meals*

Caithness, Sutherland, Orkney & Shetland

10

THE CASTLE AND GARDENS OF MEY
Mey KW14 8XH
The Queen Elizabeth Castle of Mey Trust
T: 01847 851473 E: enquiries@castleofmey.org.uk
W: www.castleofmey.org.uk

Her Majesty Queen Elizabeth the Queen Mother, bought what was then Barrogill Castle in 1952 before renovating and restoring the z-plan castle and creating the beautiful gardens you see today; renaming it The Castle and Gardens of Mey. This romantic and unique garden is a reminder that, however daunting the weather, it is often possible with a little vision and energy to create and maintain a garden in the most unlikely of locations. The castle now includes an animal centre, gift shop and tearoom serving delicious locally sourced food and drinks, often using produce from the castle's very own gardens.

Open: Friday 3 and 17 July and Friday 14 August, 10am - 5pm. Also open daily from 1st May to 30th September, 10am - 5pm, except end of July to the start of August, dates to be confirmed. These openings are subject to change, so please keep up to date on our website.

Directions: On the A836 between Thurso and John O'Groats.

· *Donation to SGS Beneficiaries*

The Castle and Gardens of Mey, photo by Colin Gregory

DUMFRIESSHIRE

Scotland's Gardens Scheme 2020 Guidebook is sponsored by INVESTEC WEALTH & INVESTMENT

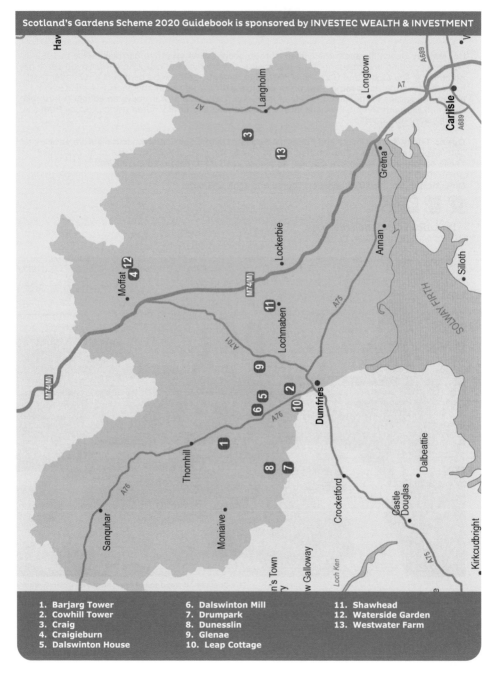

1. Barjarg Tower	6. Dalswinton Mill	11. Shawhead
2. Cowhill Tower	7. Drumpark	12. Waterside Garden
3. Craig	8. Dunesslin	13. Westwater Farm
4. Craigieburn	9. Glenae	
5. Dalswinton House	10. Leap Cottage	

Dumfriesshire

OUR VOLUNTEER ORGANISERS

District Organisers:	Sarah Landale	Dalswinton House, Dalswinton, Dumfries DG2 0XZ
		E: dumfriesshire@scotlandsgardens.org
Area Organisers:	Fiona Bell-Irving	Bankside, Kettleholm, Lockerbie DG11 1BY
	Guy Galbraith	Stanemuir Parkgate, Dumfries DG1 3NE
	Liz Mitchell	Drumpark, Irongray DG2 9TX
Treasurer:	Harold Jack	The Clachan, Newtonairds, Dumfries DG2 0JL

GARDENS OPEN ON A SPECIFIC DATE

Barjarg Tower, Auldgirth	Friday/Saturday/Sunday, 7/8/9 February
Craig, Langholm	Sunday, 16 February
Dunesslin, Dunscore	Sunday, 3 May
Dalswinton House, Dalswinton	Sunday, 10 May
Cowhill Tower, Holywood	Sunday, 31 May
Craigieburn, Craigieburn House, by Moffat	Sunday, 7 June
Glenae, Amisfield	Sunday, 7 June
Leap Cottage, West Cluden, Dumfries	Sunday, 14 June
Westwater Farm, Langholm	Sunday, 19 July
Craigieburn, Craigieburn House, by Moffat	Sunday, 26 July
Shawhead, 7 Vendace Drive, Lochmaben	Sunday, 9 August
Dalswinton Mill, Dalswinton, Dumfries	Sunday, 9 August
Dalswinton Mill, Dalswinton, Dumfries	Fridays, 14, 21 & 28 August

GARDENS OPEN BY ARRANGEMENT

Craig, Langholm	9 February - 8 March
Waterside Garden, Waterside, Moffat, Dumfriesshire	1 April - 30 September
Drumpark, Irongray	1 May - 30 September

Please note: Portrack, The Garden of Cosmic Speculation will not open in 2020, but will open again in 2021. Please see the Beneficiary statement for Maggie's on page 33.

Dumfriesshire

Cowhill Tower

BARJARG TOWER
Auldgirth DG2 0TN
Mary and Archie Donaldson
T: 01848 331545

....

Barjarg Tower lies on a gentle slope enjoying the lovely views of the surrounding Lowther Hills. The original tower house dates back to the late 16th century but has had various cleverly designed additions over the years. The gardens have undergone considerable development over the last years, though the carpets of snowdrops in the surrounding woods remain a tribute to the care of earlier generations. While the gardens will be largely dormant at the chosen date, the spring bulbs should be poking through and the surrounding woods are sure to be thick with the annual display of these snowdrops.

Open: Friday/Saturday/Sunday, 7/8/9 February, 10am - 4pm for Snowdrops and Winter Walks, admission by donation. Teas are available in either Penpont, Auldgirth or Thornhill, all located within a ten-minute drive.

Directions: Situated on the C125 halfway between Auldgirth and Penpont. Driving from Auldgirth, the stone, arched entrance is on the left-hand side with *Barjarg Tower* engraved on sandstone.

· *Alzheimer's Research UK*

Dumfriesshire

COWHILL TOWER
Holywood DG2 0RL
Mr and Mrs P Weatherall
T: 01387 720304 E: cmw@cowhill.co.uk

This is an interesting walled garden. There are topiary animals, birds and figures and a beautiful woodland walk. Splendid views can be seen from the lawn right down the Nith Valley. There are also a variety of statues from the Far East.

Open: Sunday 31 May, 2pm - 5pm, admission £5.00, children free.

Directions: Holywood is one-and-a-half miles off the A76, five miles north of Dumfries.

· *Maggie's*

CRAIG
Langholm DG13 0NZ
Mr and Mrs Neil Ewart
T: 013873 70230 E: nmlewart@googlemail.com

Craig snowdrops have evolved over the last 30 or so years. Round the house and policies, a large variety have been planted with a varied flowering season stretching from the start of January until April and peaking mid-February. Large drifts of *Leucojum vernum* (winter snowflake) have started to naturalise here, and along the riverbank a variety of snowdrops swept down by the river have naturalised in the adjacent woodland, known as the Snowdrop Walk.

Open: Sunday 16 February, noon - 4pm and also open by arrangement 9 February - 8 March for Snowdrops and Winter Walks. Admission £5.00, children free. The village hall serving teas on Sunday 16 February is at Bentpath - see below. For those wanting to visit in groups by arrangement, to see the earlier or later flowering snowdrops, there is access for minibuses or buses through the raceyard.

Directions: Craig is three miles from Langholm on the B709 towards Eskdalemuir. The village hall is at Bentpath, one mile further towards Eskdalemuir.

· *Kirkandrews Kirk Trust*

'Are you snap-happy? Help us
to photograph our gardens'

Dumfriesshire

4

CRAIGIEBURN
Craigieburn House, by Moffat DG10 9LF
Janet and Peter McGowan
T: 07557 928648 E: bideshi@aol.com

A beautiful and varied five-acre plant lovers' garden in a natural location in scenic Moffatdale. Meconopsis, trilliums, rhododendrons, magnolias, arisaemas, bamboos, hoherias and many more types of plants flourish in the shelter of mature woodland. Garden Manager, Datenji Sherpa has recreated a Himalayan gorge with native plants where the Craigie Burn tumbles down through a series of waterfalls. Candelabra primulas, rodgersias, cardiocrimum, ferns and other rare plants thrive in the bog garden and woodland glades. Double herbaceous borders come into their own later in the summer and keep the display going throughout the season. Other garden areas include a Rose Garden, formal pond and Autumn Garden. A nursery sells hardy plants propagated onsite, many of them rare or unusual. The garden has been created over the past 25-30 years, building on its old setting. Its links to Robert Burns – including his song 'Craigieburn Wood' – provide another layer of history.

Open: Sunday 7 June, 10am - 7pm. Also open Sunday 26 July, 10am - 7pm. Admission £3.50, children free. Car parking space is limited so please time your visit early or late if possible to spread the load.

Directions: Three miles from the motorway (junction 15), two miles east of Moffat on the A708 Selkirk Road. Coming from Moffat, there are traffic lights straight ahead at the end of the bend. You can't miss the lodge and prayer flags.

· *Sands: Dumfries and Galloway (Sunday 7 June) & Diabetes UK (Sunday 26 July)*

Craigieburn

Dumfriesshire

Dalswinton House, photo by Jade White

DALSWINTON HOUSE
Dalswinton DG2 0XZ
Mr and Mrs Peter Landale
T: 01387 740220 E: sarahlandale@gmail.com
....

Late 18th-century house sits on top of a hill surrounded by herbaceous beds and well-established shrubs, including rhododendrons and azaleas, overlooking the loch. Attractive walks through woods and around the loch. It was here that the first steamboat in Britain made its maiden voyage in 1788 and there is a life-size model beside the water to commemorate this. Over the past years, there has been much clearing and development work around the loch, which has opened up the views considerably.

Open: Sunday 10 May, 2pm - 5pm, admission £5.00, children free.

Directions: Take the A76 north from Dumfries to Thornhill. After seven miles, turn right to Dalswinton. Drive through Dalswinton village, past the orange church on the right and follow estate wall on the right. Entrance is by either the single lodge or double lodge entrance set in the wall.

· *Kirkmahoe Parish Church of Scotland*

Dumfriesshire

DALSWINTON MILL
Dalswinton, Dumfries DG2 0XY
Colin and Pamela Crosbie
T: 01387 740070 E: colincrosbiehort@btinternet.com

A newly created plantsman's garden set around an 18th-century watermill with the Pennyland Burn running through it. The garden contains a wide range of perennials, trees and shrubs that favour the local climate and have been planted during the last few years. A variety of statuary can be found throughout the garden which sits in a hollow and can be only accessed by steps and there are slopes throughout the garden. Unfortunately, this makes the garden unsuitable for anyone with mobility requirements.

Open: Sunday 9 August, 2pm - 6pm. Also open Friday 14 August, Friday 21 August & Friday 28 August, 2pm - 5pm. Admission £4.00, children free.

Directions: Garden lies in Dalswinton, halfway between the A76 and the A701 on the Auldgirth to Kirkton Road. From Auldgirth take the first left after the Dalswinton Village Hall. The Mill is on the corner before the bridge. We are unable to offer disabled parking.

· IFDAS

Dalswinton Mill

Dumfriesshire

7 **DRUMPARK**
Irongray DG2 9TX
Mr and Mrs Iain Mitchell
T: 01387 820323 E: iain.liz.mitchell@googlemail.com

Well-contoured woodland garden and extensive policies nurture mature azaleas, rhododendrons and rare shrubs among impressive specimen trees. Water garden with primulas and meconopsis. Victorian walled garden with fruit trees and garden produce. There is also a beautiful herbaceous border. All planting is set in a natural bowl providing attractive vistas.

Open: by arrangement 1 May - 30 September, admission £5.00, children free.

Directions: Dumfries bypass, head north on the A76 for a half mile, turn left at the signpost to *Lochside Industrial Estates* and immediately right onto Irongray Road; continue for five miles; gates in sandstone wall on left (half mile after Routin' Brig).

· *Loch Arthur*

8 **DUNESSLIN**
Dunscore DG2 0UR
Iain and Zara Milligan
E: zaramilligan@gmail.com

Set in the hills with wonderful views and borrowed landscapes, the principal garden consists of a series of connecting rooms filled with a great and interesting variety of herbaceous plants, beautifully designed and maintained. There is a substantial rock garden with alpines and unusual plants and a very pretty pond. There is a short walk to three cairns by Andy Goldsworthy, through an evolving woodland garden.

Open: Sunday 3 May, 2pm - 5pm, admission £5.00, children free.

Directions: From Dunscore, follow the road to Corsock. About one-and-a-half miles further on, turn right at the post box, still on the road to Corsock and at small crossroads half a mile on, turn left.

· *Alzheimer Scotland*

9 **GLENAE**
Amisfield DG1 3NZ
Victoria and Charlie Rotheroe
E: tottsrotheroe@gmail.com

A beautiful, well-established walled garden, well-stocked with interesting plants. There are four small lawns surrounded by colourful herbaceous borders, a woodland garden and a lovely new sunken garden with a water feature.

Open: Sunday 7 June, 2pm - 5pm, admission £5.00, children free.

Directions: One and-a-half miles north of Amisfield on the A701. Turn left to Duncow and Auldgirth and one mile on right.

· *The Sally Grant Care Trust*

Dumfriesshire

LEAP COTTAGE
West Cluden, Dumfries DG2 9UW
Mr Raymond Nelson
T: 07906 022 632 E: nelson_nomad@yahoo.com.au

Leap Cottage sits on the site of a former mill dating back to the 1600s. It is situated in the most amazing setting, right down on the banks of the Cluden Water, a tributary of the the River Nith with wonderful views of the river's twists and turns. The tiny and enchanting garden is filled to the brim with a variety of plants and colour. There is a lovely walk through the trees right down to the river's edge, just beside the cottage.

Open: Sunday 14 June, 2pm - 5pm, admission £5.00, children free.

Directions: Take the A76 Dumfries/Thornhill Road. Turn left to Irongray Industrial Estate/Park on the outskirts of Dumfries. Follow Irongray Road, past all the houses until barn on the right. Turn in here and park - access and parking to the cottage is difficult and limited so parking is at the farm. From there, following the yellow signs, walk to the T-junction, turn right and keep going to the end of the road. About 150 yards walk.

· *All proceeds to SGS Beneficiaries*

SHAWHEAD
7 Vendace Drive, Lochmaben DG11 1QN
Mr and Mrs Ian Rankine
T: 01387 811273 E: srankine298@btinternet.com

A young garden situated on the edge of Lochmaben with delightful views overlooking Mill Loch. It has many immaculately maintained and well-furnished borders bursting with colour and a great variety of plants. There are well over 200 *RHS Award of Garden Merit* cultivars and a collection of 150 *Phlox paniculata* cultivars.

Open: Sunday 9 August, 1pm - 5pm, admission £5.00, children free. The walk around Mill Loch takes about 30-40 minutes from the house. Wear suitable walking shoes. For keen walkers, the nearby Castle Loch also has a lovely walk of about three-and-a-half miles.

Directions: From Dumfries, turn left opposite The Crown Hotel, turn left at give way and then sharp left. From Lockerbie, take the right fork beside the Town Hall and after half a mile, take left turn.

· *Castle Loch Lochmaben Community Trust*

WATERSIDE GARDEN
Waterside, Moffat, Dumfriesshire DG10 9LF
Ronnie Cann
T: 01683 221583 E: rtdcann@gmail.com
W: www.holestone.net

Set in beautiful Moffat Dale and bounded on one side by the Moffat Water, Waterside Garden is home to woods, riverside walks and three acres of cultivated garden. There are many mature trees including oaks, birches, beeches and much more. Collections of species and hybrid rhododendrons and azaleas, bamboos, and other flowering shrubs give year-round interest. There are herbaceous beds, giving colour in spring and summer, alpines, mixed plantings, spring bulbs, especially daffodils, and wildflower meadows.

Dumfriesshire

Open: by arrangement 1 April - 30 September every day, other than Fridays, between 10am and 5pm, admission £4.50, children free.

Directions: Three miles north of Moffat on the A708 opposite Craigieburn Forest Car Park. From Selkirk the garden is about 14.5 miles south of St Mary's Loch.

· *Moffat Water Hall & Moffat & District Men's Shed*

13

WESTWATER FARM
Langholm DG13 0LU
Mr and Mrs Charlie Clapperton
T: 01387 381004 E: charlieclapperton@hotmail.com

....

In a wonderful, remote and romantic setting, the interesting walled garden adjacent to the house has both herbaceous plants and shrubs. There is also a woodland garden with a variety of bamboos and interesting trees. Dotted around the house and steadings are some fabulous pots.

Open: Sunday 19 July, 2pm - 5pm, admission £5.00, children free. Strawberry teas will be included in the entry price.

Directions: Thirteen miles from Lockerbie on the B7068 Lockerbie to Langholm road (five miles from Langholm). Entrance is signposted *Westwater* on the left coming from Lockerbie. Keep to left fork for the house.

· *All proceeds to SGS Beneficiaries*

Waterside Garden

DUNBARTONSHIRE

Scotland's Gardens Scheme 2020 Guidebook is sponsored by INVESTEC WEALTH & INVESTMENT

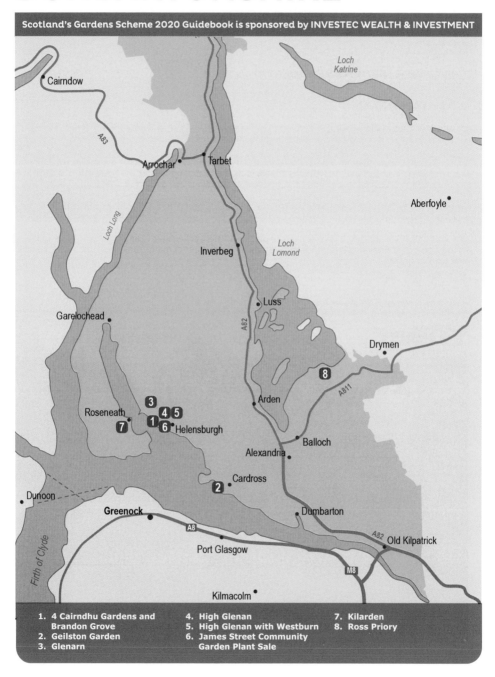

1. **4 Cairndhu Gardens and Brandon Grove**
2. **Geilston Garden**
3. **Glenarn**
4. **High Glenan**
5. **High Glenan with Westburn**
6. **James Street Community Garden Plant Sale**
7. **Kilarden**
8. **Ross Priory**

Dunbartonshire

OUR VOLUNTEER ORGANISERS

District Organisers:	Tricia Stewart	High Glenan, 24a Queen Street, Helensburgh G84 9LG
		E: dunbartonshire@scotlandsgardens.org
Area Organisers:	Graham Greenwell	Avalon, Shore Road, Mambeg Garelochhead G84 0EN
	Kathleen Murray	4 Cairndhu Gardens, Helensburgh G84 8PG
Treasurers:	Claire Travis	54 Union Street, Alexandria G83 9AH

GARDENS OPEN ON A SPECIFIC DATE

Kilarden, Rosneath	Sunday, 19 April
High Glenan with Westburn, Helensburgh	Sunday, 10 May
Glenarn, Glenarn Road, Rhu, Helensburgh	Sunday, 10 May
Ross Priory, Gartocharn	Sunday, 17 May
Geilston Garden, Main Road, Cardross	Sunday, 7 June
High Glenan, Helensburgh	Sunday, 14 June
4 Cairndhu Gardens and Brandon Grove, Helensburgh	Sunday, 28 June
James Street Community Garden Plant Sale, Helensburgh	Sunday, 6 September

GARDENS OPEN REGULARLY

Glenarn, Glenarn Road, Rhu, Helensburgh	21 March - 21 September

Dunbartonshire

4 CAIRNDHU GARDENS AND BRANDON GROVE
Helensburgh G84 8PG
Kathleen Murray and Margery Osborne

4 Cairndhu Gardens NEW Helensburgh G84 8PG (Mrs Kathleen Murray): Kathleen took over this garden last year when she moved from Shandon to Helensburgh. The borders were already well-stocked with interesting perennials and shrubs although growing beyond their space. Kathleen has installed a greenhouse and is currently redesigning the borders and introducing her favourite plants. Come to see the work in progress. There will be a large plant sale, including locally grown plants.

Brandon Grove 119 West Princes Street, Helensburgh G84 8EX (Margery Osborne): Started its life as 'Shore Farm' back in 1750s. This farm preceded the town of Helensburgh. The walled garden is intertwined with hidden paths and stepping stones through areas of mature shrubs. There is a mature *Cornus kousa*, a flowering cherry and a magnolia alongside a varied selection of acers, azaleas and much more. This garden is a hidden gem.

Open: Sunday 28 June, 2pm - 5pm, admission £4.00, children free.

Directions: 4 Cairndhu Gardens One-third of a mile west from the Commodore Hotel on the A814. Please follow signs. Please park in Cairndhu Avenue. **Brandon Grove** At Commodore Hotel on the A814, turn into Glasgow Street and first left onto West Princes Street. Garden is opposite Helensburgh Tennis Club. Please park on West Princes Street.

· *Macular Society*

GEILSTON GARDEN
Main Road, Cardross G82 5HD
The National Trust for Scotland
T: 01389 849187 E: geilstongarden@nts.org.uk
W: www.nts.org.uk/visit/places/Geilston-Garden/

Geilston Garden has many attractive features including the walled garden with herbaceous border providing summer colour, tranquil woodland walks and a large working kitchen garden. This is the ideal season for viewing the Siberian iris in flower along the Geilston Burn and the Japanese azaleas.

Open: Sunday 7 June, 1pm - 5pm, admission details can be found on the garden's website.

Directions: On the A814, one mile from Cardross towards Helensburgh.

· *The National Trust for Scotland: Geilston Garden*

GLENARN
Glenarn Road, Rhu, Helensburgh G84 8LL
Michael and Sue Thornley
T: 01436 820493 E: masthome@btinternet.com
W: www.gardens-of-argyll.co.uk

Glenarn survives as a complete example of a ten-acre garden which spans from 1850 to the present day. There are winding paths through miniature glens under a canopy of oaks and limes, sunlit open spaces, a vegetable garden with beehives, and a rock garden full of surprise and season-long colour, with views over the Gareloch. The famous collections of rare and tender rhododendrons and magnolias give way in midsummer to roses rambling through the trees and climbing hydrangeas, followed by the starry white flowers of hoherias and eucryphias to the end of the season.

Dunbartonshire

Open: Sunday 10 May, 2:30pm - 5pm for *Plant Hunting in Scotland: How the Plant Collections Came to Glenarn* - a guided walk with tea and home baking, admission £10.00 pp, max 30, please phone or email to book. Also open 21 March - 21 September, dawn - dusk, admission £5.00, children free.

Directions: On the A814, two miles north of Helensburgh, up Pier Road. Cars to be left at the gate unless passengers are infirm.

· **Donation to SGS Beneficiaries**

HIGH GLENAN
Helensburgh G84 9LG
Tom and Tricia Stewart

A secluded garden with burn and waterside plants, gravel garden, herb and herbaceous borders, kitchen garden with selection of fruit and vegetables. Extensive programme of hard landscaping has been undertaken over the last ten years.

Open: Sunday 14 June, 2pm - 5pm, admission £4.00, children free. There will be an opportunity to play petanque and watch Highland dancers.

Directions: The garden is situated in west Helensburgh, approximately half a mile along Queen Street from its junction with Sinclair Street on the right-hand side.

· **Helensburgh & District Twinning Association**

Geilston Garden, copyright NTS

Dunbartonshire

HIGH GLENAN WITH WESTBURN
Helensburgh G84 9NH
Tom & Tricia Stewart and Professor & Mrs Baker

High Glenan Helensburgh G84 9LG (Tom and Tricia Stewart): A secluded garden with burn and waterside plants, gravel garden, herb and herbaceous borders and kitchen garden with selection of fruit and vegetables. Extensive programme of hard landscaping has been undertaken over the last ten years.

Westburn 50 Campbell Street G84 9NH (Professor and Mrs Baker): A woodland garden of just over two acres. The Glenan Burn runs through a woodland of oak and beech trees with bluebells in the springtime. Some of the paths are steep, but there are bridges over the burn and handrails in places. There is also an air raid shelter, and the remains of a kiln where James Ballantyne Hannay manufactured artificial diamonds in the 1800s. A lawn is surrounded by rhododendrons and azaleas, and there is a vegetable garden. Over the years the garden has been enjoyed by children, with lots of room to play and fish in the burn.

Open: Sunday 10 May, 2pm - 5pm, admission £4.00, children free. Homemade teas and plant stall.

Directions: High Glenan The garden is situated in west Helensburgh, approximately half a mile along Queen Street from its junction with Sinclair Street on the right-hand side. **Westburn** Proceed along West Montrose Street from Sinclair Street and take the fourth turn on the right. The entrance of Westburn is 100 yards up Campbell Street on the right-hand side.

· Rhu and Shandon Parish Church of Scotland & St Michael & All Angels Church

High Glenan

Dunbartonshire

6 JAMES STREET COMMUNITY GARDEN PLANT SALE
Helensburgh G84 8EY
The Gardeners of James Street
E: j.macaulay1955@gmail.com

....

Developed from a derelict children's playground, the Community Garden is a relaxed area for contemplation with mixed herbaceous beds, maze and young trees. The plant sale will include a wide selection of nursery-grown perennials and locally grown trees, shrubs, herbaceous, alpine and house plants.

Open: Sunday 6 September, noon - 4pm, admission by donation.

Directions: Travel west along Princes Street from Sinclair Street through Colquhoun Square, turn right up James Street and the Community Garden is on the left. Park on the street.

· *James Street Community Garden*

7 KILARDEN
Rosneath G84 0PU
Carol Rowe

....

Sheltered hilly ten-acre woodland part of a 20-acre property with a notable collection of species and hybrid rhododendrons, gathered over a period of 50 years by the late Neil and Joyce Rutherford, as seen on *The Beechgrove Garden*. The collection has been augmented in the last 18 years by the current owner. During this time hurricane- and severe storm-damaged trees and mature specimens of conifers have been cleared as have commercial conifers and *Rhododendron ponticum*. Fruit trees and bushes have been established, of which apples and blueberries are particularly successful, despite a far from favourable north-facing shady site.

Open: Sunday 19 April, 2pm - 5pm, admission £3.00, children free.

Directions: A quarter of a mile from Rosneath off the B833.

· *Rosneath St Modans Church of Scotland*

8 ROSS PRIORY
Gartocharn G83 8NL
University of Strathclyde

....

Mansion house with glorious views over Loch Lomond with adjoining garden. Wonderful rhododendrons and azaleas are the principal plants in the garden, with a varied selection of trees and shrubs throughout. Spectacular spring bulbs, border plantings of herbaceous perennials, shrubs and trees. Extensive walled garden with glasshouses, pergola and ornamental plantings. Children's play area and putting green beside the house.

Open: Sunday 17 May, 2pm - 5pm, admission £5.00, children free.

Directions: Gartocharn one-and-a-half miles off the A811. Bus from Balloch to Gartocharn.

· *Friends Of Loch Lomond & The Trossachs & Children's Hospice Association Scotland*

EAST LOTHIAN

Scotland's Gardens Scheme 2020 Guidebook is sponsored by INVESTEC WEALTH & INVESTMENT

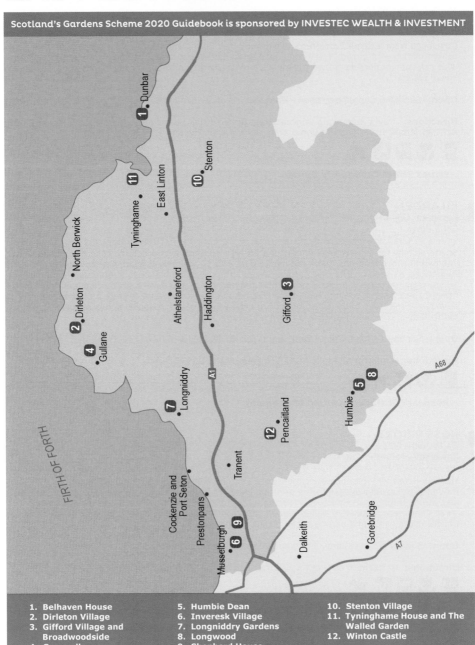

1. **Belhaven House**
2. **Dirleton Village**
3. **Gifford Village and Broadwoodside**
4. **Greywalls**
5. **Humbie Dean**
6. **Inveresk Village**
7. **Longniddry Gardens**
8. **Longwood**
9. **Shepherd House**
10. **Stenton Village**
11. **Tyninghame House and The Walled Garden**
12. **Winton Castle**

East Lothian

OUR VOLUNTEER ORGANISERS

District Organisers:	Joan Johnson	The Round House, Woodbush, Dunbar EH42 1HB
		E: eastlothian@scotlandsgardens.org
Area Organisers:	Elizabeth Eckles	
	Frank Kirwan	Humbie Dean, Humbie EH36 5PW
	Ian Orr	6 Grannus Mews, Inveresk EH21 7TT
	Judy Riley	The Old Kitchen, Tyninghame House, EH42 1XW
Treasurer:	Colin Wilson	5 Tenterfield Drive, Haddington, EH41 3JF

GARDENS OPEN ON A SPECIFIC DATE

Shepherd House, Inveresk, Musselburgh	Saturday/Sunday, 22/23 February
Winton Castle, Pencaitland	Sunday, 29 March
Humbie Dean, Humbie	Sunday, 5 April
Humbie Dean, Humbie	Saturday, 18 April
Shepherd House, Inveresk, Musselburgh	Saturday/Sunday, 25/26 April
Humbie Dean, Humbie	Sunday, 3 May
Tyninghame House and The Walled Garden, Dunbar	Sunday, 10 May
Belhaven House, Edinburgh Road, Belhaven, Dunbar	Sunday, 31 May
Humbie Dean, Humbie	Saturday, 6 June
Longwood, Humbie	Saturday, 6 June
Stenton Village, Stenton, Dunbar	Sunday, 7 June
Dirleton Village, Dirleton	Saturday/Sunday, 13/14 June
Humbie Dean, Humbie	Saturday, 20 June
Inveresk Village, Inveresk, Musselburgh	Saturday/Sunday, 20/21 June
Tyninghame House and The Walled Garden, Dunbar	Sunday, 28 June
Humbie Dean, Humbie	Sunday, 5 July
Longniddry Gardens, Longniddry	Sunday, 5 July
Gifford Village and Broadwoodside, Gifford	Sunday, 12 July
Greywalls, Gullane	Saturday, 1 August
Humbie Dean, Humbie	Sunday, 16 August

GARDENS OPEN REGULARLY

Shepherd House, Inveresk, Musselburgh	11 - 28 February (Tuesdays & Thursdays)
	& 21 April - 23 July (Tuesdays & Thursdays)

East Lothian

BELHAVEN HOUSE
Edinburgh Road, Belhaven, Dunbar EH42 1NS
Mr and Mrs Bruneau

Belhaven House has four acres of formal Georgian gardens. It comprises of raised herbaceous borders with topiary features for structure, beautiful abundant rose archways and a walled vegetable and fruit garden with box edged borders. There is also a woodland area with specimen trees dating from the early 20th century and in springtime this area is carpeted with daffodils and bluebells. The garden has been associated with a succession of people interested in plants since the 19th century, most notably by Sir George Taylor, a former director of Kew gardens.

Open: Sunday 31 May, 2pm - 5pm, admission £5.00, children free. Wheelchair access is possible to most parts of the garden apart from the vegetable garden, where the pathways would be too narrow for a wheelchair. Unfortunately, we don't have a wheelchair accessible toilet.

Directions: By car — approaching Dunbar from the A1 at Thistleycross roundabout take the A199 then the A1087. After one-and-a-half miles Belhaven House is opposite Brewery Lane on the junction with Duke Street. Parking is on the street. Public transport — bus X7 to Dunbar from Edinburgh.

· East Lothian Special Needs Playschemes

Belhaven House

Broadwoodside

East Lothian

2 DIRLETON VILLAGE
Dirleton EH39 5EH
The Gardeners of Dirleton and Historic Scotland

Dirleton is widely recognised as one of Scotland's prettiest conservation villages. Its traditional houses are clustered around the extensive village green, medieval castle dating from the 13th century, and a 400-year-old parish church. Expect the village to be a blaze of colour on the opening weekend, when some 18 of its gardens will be open to the public for charity. These are scattered throughout the village, each within a short walking distance of the village green, where ample free parking is available. The gardens can all be visited on a single ticket. They are very different in size and style and you will find that their owners love to share their knowledge and answer questions. Compact gardens around the village centre contrast with larger ones on Chapelhill, which provide extensive views south over the surrounding countryside. Your ticket will also admit you to the castle gardens. These contain an impressive formal parterre and a herbaceous border extending to over 200 yards in length, claimed to be one of the longest such borders in the world.

Open: Saturday/Sunday, 13/14 June, 2pm - 5:30pm, admission £6.00, children free. Parking, tickets and village map are available at the Green. Delicious teas will be served in the church hall by RNLI supporters and church helpers.

Directions: By car - two miles west of North Berwick off the A198. By public transport — East Coast buses X5 and 124 from Edinburgh.

· *Dirleton Village Association & RNLI*

3 GIFFORD VILLAGE AND BROADWOODSIDE
Gifford EH41 4QY
The Gardeners of Gifford and Mr & Mrs Dalrymple

Gifford Village: The gardens vary in size and type, from the compact and informal to the large and formal, with a wide range of plants, shrubs and trees. Gifford was laid out early in the 18th century and has retained much of its original charm. The village includes a beautiful church built in 1708, the Lime Avenue of Yester House, a community woodland and a wide range of gardens — all within walking distance of each other.
Broadwoodside: The garden at Broadwoodside is planted in and around a farm steading rescued from dereliction. While people often talk of starting a new garden with a blank canvas, Broadwoodside was more like painting by numbers – planting the garden has been like an exercise in 'colouring in', with the layout determined by the footprint of the existing buildings and the old walls surrounding them. But, unlike a picture in a frame, a garden is always work in progress.

Open: Sunday 12 July, 1pm - 5pm, admission £6.00, children free.

Directions: Gifford sits between the A1 and the A68 roads about five miles south of Haddington. The village is well signposted from Haddington, Pencaitland and Duns. Broadwoodside is on the B6355 going out of Gifford towards Pencaitland, at the Golf Course junction.

· *Gifford Horticultural Society & Gifford Community Land Company*

East Lothian

GREYWALLS
Gullane EH31 2EG
Mr & Mrs Giles Weaver and Mr & Mrs Dominic Hoar
W: greywalls.co.uk

Six-acre formal garden, attributed to Gertrude Jekyll, surrounding Greywalls Hotel, with stunning views over East Lothian and the Forth. Late season colour as featured in *The Beechgrove Garden* in September 2015. Highlights of the garden are straight and curved walls which create rooms and vistas, and radiating paths which link entrances and exits. Everywhere there are places to sit, in the sun and in the shade.

Open: Saturday 1 August, 2pm - 5pm, admission £5.00, children free.

Directions: Signposted on the A198 south east of Gullane. From Edinburgh take the A1 south, then the A198 to Gullane last turning on left side. From south take the A1 north to Haddington, *Gullane* is signposted. Further information is on our website.

· *Leuchie*

Humbie Dean

HUMBIE DEAN
Humbie EH36 5PW
Frank Kirwan
E: frank.kirwan@gmail.com

A two-acre ornamental and woodland garden sandwiched between two burns at 600 feet with interest throughout a long season. A limited palette of plants with hosta, hellebores, perennial geranium, primula, meconopsis, martagon lilies, spring bulbs, ground cover, herbaceous and shrub planting, bluebell meadow, mature and recent azalea and rhododendron planting. A short woodland walk has been created, only accessible by a series of steps.

Open: Sunday 5 April, Saturday 18 April, Sunday 3 May, Saturday 6 June, Saturday 20 June, Sunday 5 July & Sunday 16 August, 10am - 2pm. Admission £5.00, children free.

East Lothian

Directions: Enter Humbie from the A68, pass the school and village hall on the left then immediately turn right just before the Humbie Hub. Take second left and Humbie Dean is on the left between two small bridges. Limited parking.

· *Mamie Martin Fund*

INVERESK VILLAGE
Inveresk, Musselburgh EH21 7TT
The Gardeners of Inveresk
E: ianorrgardens@gmail.com
....

Inveresk has said goodbye to two very loyal garden openers, but is presenting two new gardens. One is a moderate sized garden attached to a Victorian villa, the other is a small newly developed garden attached to a gatehouse cottage. These are in addition to previously displayed gardens — one a television star, one complementing an eco house where teas will be served with home cooking of high repute, and one surrounding the house of the previous area coal mine manager. The National Trust Scotland property, Inveresk Lodge Garden will provide children's entertainment. Pond dipping is an ever-popular pursuit at this venue. Musselburgh's highly-rated allotments will also be open within the circuit trail which passes a very interesting topiary hedge outside a cottage in Double Dykes. The mix of large and small gardens, some of which are wrapped round by high stone walls and others of which are more exposed to the wind and relative dry climate will offer visitors many ideas to think over when they return home. The Romans recognised the quality of the soil in this area when they settled here during the Antonine era between 140 and 165 AD and some of the land may well have been in continuous cultivation since then. The village gardens are open over two days for the first time. Enthusiasts can visit on both days if they retain their village map and a sticky badge. Full catering will only be available on one day — updated information is available on the SGS website.

Open: Saturday/Sunday, 20/21 June, 2pm - 5pm, admission £7.00, children free.

Directions: Southside of Musselburgh, on the A6124.

· *LMN Scotland*

'Wasps help control some pests
such as leaf-rolling caterpillars,
leaf beetles and weevils'

East Lothian

7

LONGNIDDRY GARDENS
Longniddry EH32 0LF
The Gardeners of Longniddry

Longniddry is an attractive village with extensive green spaces and outstanding sea views. Our gardens are tended by enthusiastic gardeners some of whom are old hands and some recent converts to gardening. The gardens exhibit a wonderful variety of size, layout and planting ensuring something for every visitor to enjoy. One of the smaller gardens is modern and shows what can be achieved with attractive and innovative hard landscaping. This contrasts with a fabulous lush garden including a water feature — small can be beautiful! Larger gardens include new and mature trees and herbaceous planting ranging from self-seeding cottage style to more formal. There are veggie plots and potagers, containers of all sorts, alpine beds and ponds. Outbuildings range from working greenhouses to summer houses and gazebos. A new addition this year is professionally designed and though aimed at attracting wildlife, is anything but wild with a large modern sway of varied grasses. Lots to see so please join us!

Open: Sunday 5 July, 1pm - 5pm, admission £7.00, children free. Tickets and maps will be available at the gardens at the entrances to Longniddry. These gardens will be well signposted.

Directions: On the A198 from North Berwick (east) or Edinburgh (west). Access also from the B1348 (the coast road from Port Seton/Cockenzie) and the B1377 (from Drem). Longniddry is also on the North Berwick train line from Edinburgh Waverley.

· *St Columbas Hospice & Maggie's*

8

LONGWOOD
Humbie EH36 5PN
Linda Flockhart and Sandra Gentle

An extensive, long-established country garden at 800 feet, undergoing renewal. There are ducks and hens, stream and ponds as well as areas of wild garden and borders including roses, vegetables, lawns and woodlands. Stunning views over the Forth.

Open: Saturday 6 June, 10am - 2pm, admission £5.00, children free.

Directions: From the B6368 (Humbie to Haddington road) about one mile east of Humbie take the direction south to *Blegbie Farm* (signposted). Follow the road for circa two miles, passing Humbie Mains Farm as you go. You will find Blegbie Farm at a hard right-hand bend. The drive for Longwood will be straight in front of you, right beside Blegbie. Go straight up the drive and park at the bottom of the cottages. Do not turn right or left.

· *Médecins Sans Frontières*

'Money raised supports over 250
different charities annually'

East Lothian

SHEPHERD HOUSE
Inveresk, Musselburgh EH21 7TH
Sir Charles and Lady Fraser
T: 0131 665 2570 E: annfraser@talktalk.net
W: www.shepherdhousegarden.co.uk

A constantly evolving artist's garden that never stands still, with lots of surprises including a shell house built in 2014, lavender parterres, a rill and fountains. At its heart are the plants filling every border, spilling over arches and lining paths, which are the inspiration for Ann's paintings. The season starts with the snowdrop collection of over 70 cultivars, moves on through hellebores, tulips, irises and roses. One of the garden's features is a mirror steel diamond sculpture to commemorate the Frasers' diamond wedding anniversary and 60 years in this garden.

Open: Saturday/Sunday, 22/23 February, 11am - 4pm and 11 February - 28 February (Tuesdays & Thursdays), 2pm - 4pm for Snowdrops and Winter Walks. Also open Saturday/Sunday, 25/26 April, 11am - 4pm. And open 21 April - 23 July (Tuesdays & Thursdays), 2pm - 4pm. Admission £5.00, children free. Groups welcome all year by appointment, email: ann@shepherdhousegarden.co.uk. The garden will also be open as part of the Inveresk Village opening on 21/22 June, 2pm -5pm.

Directions: The garden is near Musselburgh. From the A1 take the A6094 exit signposted *Wallyford and Dalkeith* and follow signs to *Inveresk*.

· *LMN Scotland: Live Music Now Scotland*

Shepherd House, photo by Ann Fraser

East Lothian

Tyninghame Walled Garden, photo by Jannie Bos

STENTON VILLAGE
Stenton, Dunbar EH42 1TE
Gardeners of Stenton Village

Stenton (Stane Toon) with its ancient cottages of purple-hued sandstone and pantiled roofs has been awarded *Outstanding Conservation* status. There is a thriving Horticultural Society and the gardens, large and small, are of extraordinary variety and interest. A couple of examples include:
Ruchlaw Walled Garden NEW is an impressive 17th-century laird's house built by Archibald Sydserff. Of interest is the handsome walled garden situated to the south of the property. It has a south-facing aspect and a combination of well-maintained rubble walls and a thick holly hedge creating a monastic ambience. The most eye-catching element is the path that runs north to south through the centre of the garden. This forms an avenue that passes between venerable and substantial pleached fruit trees. The visitors' eye is drawn on past parallel herbaceous borders which the current owner has restored and enhanced. The garden is in its prime between May and June when the tulips, alliums and catmint form a riot of colour and are arranged to a great effect. Within the garden are two sundials; one of particular historic note with its octagonal shaft.
Tron House NEW has a small walled garden divided into separate areas by low stone dykes. The garden has been planted intensively to provide interest and colour throughout the year. There are several large shrubs giving structure and lots of spring bulbs and hellebores, followed by rhododendrons and azaleas before roses and perennials take over. In the autumn, several shades of hesperantha, Michaelmas daisies and fuchsias keep the interest going.

Open: Sunday 7 June, 2pm - 5:30pm, admission £6.00, children free. Map to the gardens will be supplied at the village hall in Stenton. The village is also renowned for its generous teas on open days.

Directions: Follow signs from the A199/A1. There is a local bus that runs twice daily from Dunbar, information on www.eveinfo.co.uk.

· *St Columbas Hospice*

East Lothian

11

TYNINGHAME HOUSE AND THE WALLED GARDEN
Dunbar EH42 1XW
Mrs C Gwyn and Tyninghame Gardens Ltd

The formal walled garden combines the lawn, sculpture and yew hedges, an Apple Walk, extensive herbaceous planting including roses and peonies with an informal arboretum. Splendid 17th-century sandstone Scottish baronial house, remodelled in 1829 by William Burn. The gardens include herbaceous border, formal rose garden, Lady Haddington's Secret Garden with old fashioned roses and an extensive Wilderness spring garden with rhododendrons, azaleas, flowering trees and bulbs. Grounds include a one-mile beech avenue to the sea. The Romanesque ruin of St Baldred's Church commands views across the Tyne Estuary and Lammermuir Hills. Tyninghame has been awarded 'Outstanding' for every category in the *Inventory of Gardens and Designed Landscapes of Scotland*.
Champion Trees: Two British and seven Scottish.

Open: Sunday 10 May, 1pm - 5pm. Also open Sunday 28 June, 1pm - 5pm. Admission £6.00, children free. Dogs are not allowed in the Walled Garden.

Directions: Gates on the A198 at Tyninghame Village. Bus 120.

· *Lynton Day Centre (Sunday 10 May) & Tyninghame Village Hall (Sunday 28 June)*

12

WINTON CASTLE
Pencaitland EH34 5AT
Sir Francis Ogilvy, Winton Trust
T: 01875 340222
W: www.wintoncastle.co.uk

The gardens continue to develop and improve. In addition to the natural areas around Sir David's Loch and the Dell, extensive mixed borders are taking shape for the terraces and walled garden. In spring a glorious covering of daffodils makes way for cherry and apple blossoms. Enjoy an informative tour of this historic house and walk off delicious lunches and home baking around the estate. A visit to Winton Castle is a wonderful family day out.

Open: Sunday 29 March, noon - 4:30pm, admission £5.00, children free.

Directions: Entrance off the B6355 Tranent/Pencaitland Road.

· *Marie Curie*

EDINBURGH, MIDLOTHIAN & WEST LOTHIAN

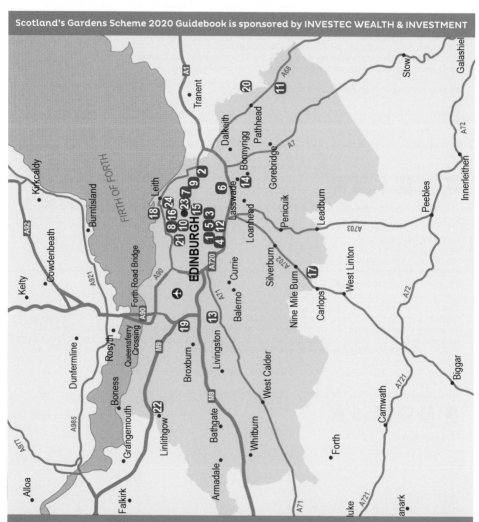

Scotland's Gardens Scheme 2020 Guidebook is sponsored by INVESTEC WEALTH & INVESTMENT

1. 101 Greenbank Crescent
2. 14 East Brighton Crescent
3. 2 Pentland Crescent
4. 4 Harelaw Road
5. 5 Greenbank Crescent
6. 89 Ravenscroft Street
7. Craigentinny Telferton
8. Dean Gardens
9. Dr Neil's Garden
10. Even More Gardens of the Lower New Town
11. Frostineb
12. Hunter's Tryst
13. Jupiter Artland & Bonnington House
14. Kevock Garden
15. Meadow Place
16. Moray Place & Bank Gardens
17. Newhall
18. Newhaven Heritage Community Garden
19. Newliston
20. Preston Hall Walled Garden
21. Redcroft
22. Rivaldsgreen House
23. The Archivists' Garden
24. The Glasshouses at the RBGE

Edinburgh, Midlothian & West Lothian

OUR VOLUNTEER ORGANISERS

District Organiser:	Victoria Reid Thomas	Riccarton Mains Farmhouse, Currie EH14 4AR E: edinburgh@scotlandsgardens.org
Area Organisers:	Jerry & Christine Gregson Caroline Pearson	101 Greenbank Crescent, Edinburgh EH10 5TA 42 Pentland Avenue, Edinburgh EH13 0HY
District Photographers:	Philip Gillespie Robert Pereira Hind	5/6 Hawkhill Court, Restalrig, Edinburgh EH7 6UT 38 Marchmont Crescent, Edinburgh EH9 1HG
Treasurers:	Michael Pearson	42 Pentland Avenue, Edinburgh EH13 0HY

GARDENS OPEN ON A SPECIFIC DATE

Dr Neil's Garden, Duddingston Village	Saturday/Sunday, 2/3 May
Kevock Garden , 16 Kevock Road, Lasswade	Saturday/Sunday, 9/10 May
Redcroft, 23 Murrayfield Road, Edinburgh	Sunday, 10 May
Moray Place and Bank Gardens, Edinburgh	Sunday, 17 May
101 Greenbank Crescent, Edinburgh	Sunday, 17 May
Jupiter Artland & Bonnington House, Wilkieston	Wednesday, 20 May
101 Greenbank Crescent, Edinburgh	Saturday/Sunday/Monday, 23/24/25 May
Redcroft, 23 Murrayfield Road, Edinburgh	Sunday, 24 May
Hunter's Tryst, 95 Oxgangs Road, Edinburgh	Sunday, 31 May
14 East Brighton Crescent, Portobello, Edinburgh	Sunday, 31 May
Rivaldsgreen House, 48 Friars Brae, Linlithgow	Saturday, 6 June
The Glasshouses at the RBGE, 20A Inverleith Row, Edinburgh	Sunday, 7 June
Dean Gardens, Edinburgh	Sunday, 7 June
89 Ravenscroft Street, Edinburgh	Saturday, 13 June
Preston Hall Walled Garden, Pathhead	Sunday, 14 June
89 Ravenscroft Street, Edinburgh	Wednesday, 17 June
89 Ravenscroft Street, Edinburgh	Saturday, 20 June
Even More Gardens of the Lower New Town, Edinburgh	Sunday, 21 June
2 Pentland Crescent, Edinburgh	Sunday, 21 June
5 Greenbank Crescent, Edinburgh	Sunday, 28 June
4 Harelaw Road, Edinburgh	Saturday, 4 July
Meadow Place, 19 Meadow Place	Sunday, 5 July
The Archivists' Garden, 2 Princes Street, Edinburgh	Saturday, 25 July
Craigentinny Telferton Allotments, Edinburgh	Sunday, 26 July
Newhaven Heritage Community Garden, Edinburgh	Sunday, 26 July
Newhaven Heritage Community Garden, Edinburgh	Saturday, 29 August

GARDENS OPEN REGULARLY

Newliston, Kirkliston	1 May - 4 June (not Mondays & Tuesdays)

Edinburgh, Midlothian & West Lothian

GARDENS OPEN BY ARRANGEMENT

Hunter's Tryst, 95 Oxgangs Road, Edinburgh	1 January - 31 December
Frostineb, by Fala, Pathhead	1 January - 31 December
101 Greenbank Crescent, Edinburgh	12 April - 27 September
4 Harelaw Road, Edinburgh	1 May - 31 July
Newhall, Carlops	1 June - 31 August
Redcroft, 23 Murrayfield Road, Edinburgh	1 September - 31 October

Edinburgh, Midlothian & West Lothian

101 GREENBANK CRESCENT

Edinburgh EH10 5TA
Jerry and Christine Gregson
T: 0131 447 6492 E: jerry_gregson@yahoo.co.uk

The house is on a busy bus route but hides a fascinating garden on a steeply sloped site. There are views over Braidburn Valley Park to the Pentland hills. Paths wind down from the new oval lawn, past a handsome magnolia tree, to a terrace which overlooks a water feature and established flowering shrubs. Less common species include *Neillia thibetica* and dierama. Further steps lead past a scree bed of azalea and rhododendron to a productive area of vegetable beds and fruit trees. A neatly concealed composting area includes wood and earth piles as a home for wildlife. We aim to have colour, contrast, and interest all year round.

Open: Sunday 17 May, 2pm - 5pm. Also open Saturday/Sunday/Monday, 23/24/25 May, 2pm - 5pm for the May Weekend Festival. And open by arrangement 12 April - 27 September. Admission £4.00, children free.

Directions: From the city centre take the A702 through Morningside. Continue uphill and turn right at Greenbank Church on to Greenbank Crescent. Buses 5 and 16 and the stop is for Greenbank Row.

· *Shelter Scotland*

14 EAST BRIGHTON CRESCENT

Portobello, Edinburgh EH15 1LR
Mr & Mrs Jim and Sue Hurford

Roughly two-thirds of an acre suburban garden, developed over 35 years. People have said the following about it: 'A little bit of countryside in the town'; 'Booming with green', 'A bosky bower' and 'There is such a wide range of plant material and every little corner holds a new gem'. There are some new features since the last opening.

Open: Sunday 31 May, 2pm - 5pm, admission £4.00, children free. Plant sale by Macplants. Apple-pressing demonstration.

Directions: Buses 21, 42 and 49 to Brighton Place, and 15, 26, 40 and 45 to Portobello High Street. Brighton Place intersects Portobello High Street just east of the bus stops.

· *Action Porty*

Edinburgh, Midlothian & West Lothian

2 PENTLAND CRESCENT
Edinburgh EH10 6ND
Jan Polley
T: 07801 439299 E: jpolley@blueyonder.co.uk

A colourful urban garden that contains a wide variety of shrubs and herbaceous planting, including roses, peonies, cranesbill, geums, azaleas, clematis, camellias, delphiniums and cotoneasters. The garden surrounds the house on four sides with planting designed to provide colour all year round, and to cope with varying degrees of sun and shade. It includes a rockery, herbaceous borders, archway, raised beds. Various sitting areas and a pergola framed 'gin and tonic' patio from which to enjoy sunsets.

Open: Sunday 21 June, 2pm - 5pm, admission £4.00, children free.

Directions: From the city centre take the A702 through Morningside, continue uphill and turn right at Comiston Springs Avenue. Pentland Crescent is first left. Bus 11 (get off at the Comiston Springs Avenue stop).

· *Marie Curie*

4 HARELAW ROAD
Edinburgh EH13 0DR
Mrs Kathleen Tait
T: 0131 441 4802 E: katait04@outlook.com

An attractive, well-designed garden featuring a delightful pond and statuary with a collection of unusual ferns and herbaceous plants and a variety of acers. A large rockery is an interesting new addition. Numerous pots of all shapes and sizes adorn the lower and upper garden.

Open: Saturday 4 July, 2pm - 5pm. Also open by arrangement 1 May - 31 July. Admission £5.00, children free.

Directions: From the city take the left fork at the traffic lights at the top of Colinton village. Buses 10, 16, 45, 400

· *Parkinsons UK*

5 GREENBANK CRESCENT
Edinburgh EH10 5TE
Sandy Corlett
T: 0131 447 1119 E: sandycorlett@hotmail.co.uk

South-facing, newly designed, sloping terraced garden with views over Braidburn Valley Park to the Pentlands. Colourful chaos of herbaceous plants, shrubs, roses and small trees. Hard features include a gazebo, pergola, greenhouse and water feature.

Open: Sunday 28 June, 2pm - 5pm, admission £4.00, children free. Afternoon teas in the architect designed extension. Children are very welcome and there will be activities for them.

Directions: From the city centre take the A702 through Morningside, continue uphill on Comiston Road, turn right at Greenbank Church on to Greenbank Crescent. Buses 5, 16, 11.

· *Parkinsons UK*

Edinburgh, Midlothian & West Lothian

89 RAVENSCROFT STREET
Edinburgh EH17 8QS
Andrew and Alex Gray Muir

A large walled garden, full of surprises, in the old mining village of Gilmerton. Planting includes mature trees, roses and herbaceous borders. There is also a potager. Andrew and Alex Gray Muir have been there for over 50 years but say the garden is still a work in progress. There are plenty of seats so bring a thermos and sit and enjoy the garden.

Open: Saturday 13 June, Wednesday 17 June & Saturday 20 June, 2pm - 5pm. Admission £4.00, children free. Plant stall on 13 and 20 June only.

Directions: Buses 29 and 3 come to the end of the street - look out for *Tanz* on the left and get off at the next stop. It is a nine-minute walk up Ravenscroft Street. Buses 7 and 11 come to Hyvots Bank. A short walk up Ravenscroft Place will bring you to Ravenscroft Street, where you turn right up a short stretch of unmetalled road. If you come by car, park on the public road and walk up the last 50 yards. If necessary, passengers can be dropped off in the yard in front of the house.

· *Scottish Association For Mental Health*

89 Ravenscroft Street

Edinburgh, Midlothian & West Lothian

CRAIGENTINNY TELFERTON ALLOTMENTS
Telferton Road, off Portobello Road, Edinburgh EH7 6XG
The Gardeners of Craigentinny and Telferton
W: ctallotments@gmail.com

Established in 1923, this independent allotment site is a tranquil and charming space, hidden away in a built-up area, where the local community benefit from growing their own vegetables and fruit. Yarn bombing of allotments, and display of scarecrows. Come and enjoy tea, home baking and a chat with our friendly plot-holders.

Open: Sunday 26 July, 2pm - 5pm, admission £3.00, children free.

Directions: Park on Telferton Road. Buses 15, 26, 45.

· *Craigentinny Telferton Allotments*

DEAN GARDENS
Edinburgh EH4 1QE
Dean Gardens Management Committee
W: www.deangardens.org

Nine acres of semi-woodland garden with spring bulbs on the steep banks of the Water of Leith in central Edinburgh. Founded in the 1860s by local residents, the Dean Gardens contain part of the great structure of the Dean Bridge, a Thomas Telford masterpiece of 1835. Lawns, paths, trees, and shrubs with lovely views to the weir in the Dean Village and to the St Bernard's Well. There is also a children's play area.

Open: Sunday 7 June, 2pm - 5pm, admission £4.00, children free.

Directions: Entrance at Ann Street or Eton Terrace.

· *All proceeds to SGS Beneficiaries*

DR NEIL'S GARDEN
Duddingston Village EH15 3PX
Dr Neil's Garden Trust
E: info@drneilsgarden.co.uk
W: www.drneilsgarden.co.uk

Wonderful, secluded, landscaped garden on the lower slopes of Arthur's Seat including conifers, heathers, alpines, a physic garden, herbaceous borders and ponds. Also Thompson's Tower with the Museum of Curling and beautiful views across Duddingston Loch.

Open: Saturday/Sunday, 2/3 May, 2pm - 5pm, admission £3.00, children free.

Directions: Park at the kirk car park on Duddingston Road West and then follow signposts through the manse garden.

· *Dr. Neils Garden Trust*

Edinburgh, Midlothian & West Lothian

EVEN MORE GARDENS OF THE LOWER NEW TOWN
St Stephen's Church, Edinburgh EH3 5AB
Gardeners of Lower New Town
E: jw.homeoffice@gmail.com

Not to be missed - an even wider variety of horticultural creations than last year bringing fresh air and wildlife into the heart of the city. Comprises a steeply-terraced town garden, densely-planted courtyard gardens, imaginative back lane, patio and basement gardens, a traditional tenement green and a hidden roof garden, glorious mews lane planting and spectacular pot gardens, and newly landscaped front and back in a cul-de-sac. The collection provides lots of creative solutions to gardening in the city with year-round interest through a mix of seasonal planting and structural evergreens which the gardeners will be on hand to talk about.

Open: Sunday 21 June, 1pm - 5pm, admission £7.00, children free. Please check our entry on the Scotlands Gardens Scheme website nearer the time for details of where to get tickets and route maps. Gardens run between Logie Green Gardens and Northumberland Street Lane NW. Refreshments at St Stephen's Church and plants for sale at the gardens.

Directions: Buses 23, 27 to Dundas Street and Canonmills, 8 to Rodney Street and Canonmills, 36 to Hamilton Place and Broughton Road.

· *Shelter Scotland & Médecins Sans Frontières*

FROSTINEB
by Fala, Pathhead EH37 5TB
Mr and Mrs Henry Gibson
T: 07833 287367

Developed over the past 25 years this farmhouse garden, sitting at 750 feet, is constantly evolving. A half-acre garden by the house consists of mixed borders of herbaceous plants, ornamental trees and shrubs, including rhododendrons and azaleas. It is a relaxed garden where plants are allowed to seed freely resulting in some interesting plant combinations. Further from the house is a wildlife pond, ornamental trees and a cedar greenhouse . Peripheral areas of the garden are deliberately left wild to encourage birds, insects and wildlife. A large paddock has been planted with 42 different apple trees plus pears and plums. There is a mixed woodland area planted in 2000 and a conservatory with two 30-year-old vines, bougainvillea, jasmine and numerous geraniums. Frostineb has featured on *The Beechgrove Garden* and in various publications.

Open: by arrangement 1 January - 31 December, admission by donation.

Directions: Off the A68, three miles south of Pathhead. Before Fairshiels B&B turn right up farm road. Proceed for one mile and Frostineb is the first house on the left.

· *Euan Macdonald Centre for Motor Neurone Disease Research*

Edinburgh, Midlothian & West Lothian

Jupiter Artland and Bonnington House, photo by Allan Pollok Morris, courtesy of Jupiter Artland

HUNTER'S TRYST
95 Oxgangs Road, Edinburgh EH10 7BA
Jean Knox
T: 0131 477 2919 E: jean.knox@blueyonder.co.uk

Well-stocked and beautifully designed, mature, medium-sized town garden comprising herbaceous and shrub beds, lawn, fruit and some vegetables, water features, seating areas, trees and an example of cloud pruning. This is a wildlife-friendly garden that has been transformed from a wilderness 35 years ago and continues to evolve. In 2017 two raised beds were added to the front garden. This hidden treasure of a garden was featured on *The Beechgrove Garden* in June 2015 and on *The Instant Gardener* in June 2016.

Open: Sunday 31 May, 2pm - 5pm. Also open by arrangement 1 January - 31 December. Admission £4.00, children free.

Directions: From Fairmilehead crossroads head down Oxgangs Road to Hunter's Tryst roundabout and it's the last house on the left. Buses 4, 5, 27, 400. The bus stop is at Hunter's Tryst and the garden is opposite.

· *St Columbas Hospice & Lothian Cat Rescue*

Edinburgh, Midlothian & West Lothian

JUPITER ARTLAND & BONNINGTON HOUSE
Bonnington House Steadings, Wilkieston EH27 8BY
Robert and Nicky Wilson
T: 01506 889900
W: jupiterartland.org

Bonnington House is surrounded by Jupiter Artland, an award-winning contemporary sculpture park founded in 2009 by Robert and Nicky Wilson. Set in over 100 acres of parkland, Jupiter Artland is home to sculptures by Charles Jencks, Anish Kapoor, Cornelia Parker, Antony Gormley, Andy Goldsworthy and many more. The gardens of about five acres surrounding Bonnington House were designed by Nicky Wilson and Arabella Lennox-Boyd, comprising a parterre, laburnum arch, labyrinth, terrace gardens and a lawn tennis court. A swimming pool designed by Joana Vasconcelos and the surrounding garden designed by Nicky Wilson and Thomas Underdorfer were opened in 2019 and featured in many publications, both national and international.

Open: Wednesday 20 May, 10am - 5pm, admission £10.00. Friends of Jupiter Artland £5,00, Children under 3 years free, tickets can be purchased at the gate. Bonnington House gardens are only open on 20 May 2020, Jupiter Artland is open daily from 9 May - 27 September, from 10am - 5pm, please check on the website for updates.

Directions: Follow the postcode EH27 8BY and access via the main entrance to Jupiter Artland on the B7015, just off the A71. There is no access via Bonnington village. Jupiter Artland is well signposted and there is ample parking within the grounds. Frequent bus services from Edinburgh. Buses X27and X28. For further details please visit our website.

· *Prostate Scotland*

KEVOCK GARDEN
16 Kevock Road, Lasswade EH18 1HT
David and Stella Rankin
T: 0131 454 0660 E: stella@kevockgarden.co.uk
W: www.kevockgarden.co.uk

A lot has changed since this garden was last opened. Lawns have been relaid, surrounding borders have been planted, and there is a new rock garden. This wonderful hillside garden has magnificent views over the North Esk Valley and the steep slope creates a range of different habitats with a wide diversity of plants, ranging from those that love hot, sunny conditions to those that prefer the cool, damp places near the pond and woodland glades. Mature specimen trees, rhododendrons, azaleas and unusual shrubs are underplanted with many rare woodland plants. Kevock Garden has featured in many magazine articles and gardening programmes. The associated nursery, Kevock Garden Plants, which will provide the plant stall, has won many Chelsea gold medals.

Open: Saturday/Sunday, 9/10 May, 2pm - 5pm, admission £5.00, children free. Teas will be available at Drummond Grange Nursing Home, 7 Kevock Road. Only disabled parking on Kevock Road please.

Directions: Kevock Road lies to the south of the A678 Loanhead/Lasswade Road. Five minutes from the city bypass Lasswade Junction and on the 31 Lothian Bus route to Polton/Bonnyrigg. Parking available in Drummond Grange Nursing Home, 7 Kevock Road. Only disabled parking on Kevock Road please.

· *Fischy Music*

Edinburgh, Midlothian & West Lothian

15 MEADOW PLACE
19 Meadow Place EH9 1JR
Jan Wilson
T: 0131 229 8316 E: janwilson1920@gmail.com

....

The secret garden of Meadow Place is a walled garden of a Georgian house that was built in 1816. The owner has been tending the garden for 46 years and the garden is now patios, pots and flower beds rather than the lawn and roses of yesteryear. The planting is a mixture of trees, shrubs and herbaceous flowers.

Open: Sunday 5 July, 1:30pm - 4:30pm, admission £4.00, children free.

Directions: The garden is down the lane off Roseneath Terrace. Look for the brown garage door. Buses 24, 41.

· *Maggie's: Edinburgh*

16 MORAY PLACE AND BANK GARDENS
Edinburgh EH3 6BX
The Residents of Moray Place and Lord Moray's Feuars
T: 0131 225 5363 E: gracedurham@btinternet.com

....

Bank Gardens (The Residents of Bank Gardens): Nearly six acres of secluded wild gardens with lawns, trees and shrubs with banks of bulbs down to the Water of Leith. Stunning vistas across the Firth of Forth.
Moray Place (The Residents of Moray Place): Private garden of three-and-a-half acres in the Georgian New Town. Shrubs, trees and beds offer an atmosphere of tranquillity in the city centre.

Open: Sunday 17 May, 2pm - 5pm, admission £5.00, children free.

Directions: **Bank Gardens** Enter by the gate at the top of Doune Terrace. **Moray Place** Enter by the north gate in Moray Place.

· *Euan Macdonald Centre for Motor Neurone Disease Research*

17 NEWHALL
Carlops EH26 9LY
John and Tricia Kennedy
T: 01968 660206 E: tricia.kennedy@newhalls.co.uk

....

Traditional 18th-century walled garden with huge herbaceous border, shrubberies, fruit and vegetables. Stunning glen running along the North Esk river in the process of restoration (stout shoes recommended). Large pond with evolving planting. Young arboretum and collection of *Rosa spinosissima*. Featured in *Good Gardens Guide 2010*, *Scottish Field*, *Gardens Monthly* and *Scotland on Sunday*.

Open: by arrangement for groups (minimum 6). 1 June - 31 August, admission £5.00, children free.

Directions: On the A702 Edinburgh/Biggar road, half-a-mile after Ninemileburn and a mile before Carlops. Follow signs.

· *All proceeds to SGS Beneficiaries*

Edinburgh, Midlothian & West Lothian

18

NEWHAVEN HERITAGE COMMUNITY GARDEN
Newhaven Main Street, Edinburgh EH5 4LL
Heather Yang
T: 07985 006007 E: greenfingersnh@gmail.com

An oasis on the edge of the city that offers a wonderful wander around the gardens of the historical fishing village of Newhaven. Walk in the footsteps of Darwin to discover the tranquil garden spots. Visit the Old Burial Ground where sage and rosemary and a wildflower meadow bloom then stroll in the fern woodland and the community garden and vegetable plot.

Open: Sunday 26 July, 2pm - 4pm. Also open Saturday 29 August, 2pm - 4pm. Admission £3.00, children free. There will be a walking tour and storytelling reflecting the history of the area.

Directions: Lothian buses 11, 16, 7, 10 to Newhaven Harbour. The garden is behind Fishmarket Square. At the bottom of Newhaven Road, turn left and the garden is on the right at Auchinleck Court.

· *Maggie's*

19

NEWLISTON
Kirkliston EH29 9EB
Mr and Mrs R C Maclachlan
T: 0131 333 3231 E: newliston@gmail.com

A well preserved 18th-century parkland/designed landscape rather than a garden as such, full of mature rhododendrons and azaleas, fine vistas and allees of trees. The walk around the woods and lake is a carpet of wild garlic and bluebells in the spring. The wood to the east of the house is in the pattern of the Union Jack, best appreciated by standing in the centre where all the radiating paths meet. The house, designed by Robert Adam, is also open.

Open: 1 May - 4 June (not Mondays & Tuesdays), 2pm - 6pm, admission £5.00, children free.

Directions: Four miles south of the Forth Road Bridge, entrance off the B800.

· *Children's Hospice Association Scotland*

20

PRESTON HALL WALLED GARDEN
Pathhead EH37 5UG
William and Henrietta Callander
T: 07971 028697 E: henrietta@prestonhall.co.uk
W: www.prestonhall.co.uk

Preston Hall Walled Garden is a beautiful example of an 18th-century walled garden. The current restoration began in 2011 and wonderfully demonstrates what can be achieved in a few years. An imposing brick wall surrounds the two-acre garden, which features two impressive gazebo structures that give spectacular views of the garden, a rose garden, a partly restored Victorian greenhouse, fruit and vegetables patches, and a stunning flower garden.

Open: Sunday 14 June, 2pm - 5pm, admission £6.00, children free.

Directions: Located 12 miles south of Edinburgh on the A68, one mile east of Pathhead village.

· *My Name'5 Doddie Foundation*

Edinburgh, Midlothian & West Lothian

21

REDCROFT
23 Murrayfield Road, Edinburgh EH12 6EP
James and Anna Buxton
T: 0131 337 1747 E: annabuxtonb@aol.com

Redcroft is a mature walled garden surrounding an attractive Arts and Crafts house. It is a hidden haven off a busy road with a variety of different features and habitats: an orchard, a rockery, a pond, shrubberies, a large lawn and contrasting longer grass. It is well maintained with many clipped shrubs and some cloud pruning. Early May is very colourful with rhododendrons and many other flowering shrubs and wall plants, and the greenhouse is full of tender plants. There will be tulips in pots and many other bulbs. Children are very welcome and there will be plenty of activities. We hope older children will enjoy our new treehouse.

Open: Sunday 10 May, 2pm - 5pm. Also open Sunday 24 May, 2pm - 5pm for the May Weekend Festival. And open by arrangement 1 September - 31 October. Admission £5.00, children free. We will have a very good plant sale thanks to members of Scotland's Gardens Scheme.

Directions: Murrayfield Road runs north from Corstorphine Road to Ravelston Dykes. There is easy parking available which is free. Buses 12, 26, 31, get off at Murrayfield Stadium, bus 38 which goes down Murrayfield Road.

· *Royal Caledonian Horticultural Society: Greenhouse at Saughton*

22

RIVALDSGREEN HOUSE
48 Friars Brae, Linlithgow EH49 6BG
Dr Ian Wallace
T: 01506 845700 E: Ianwjw1940@gmail.com

Mature two-acre garden with lovely mixed herbaceous, rose and tree planting.

Open: Saturday 6 June, 2pm - 5pm, admission £5.00, children free.

Directions: From the west end of the High Street turn into Preston Road, after crossing the canal turn left into Priory Road and at the T junction turn left down Friars Brae. There is car parking available.

· *St John Scotland*

23

THE ARCHIVISTS' GARDEN
HM General Register House, 2 Princes Street, Edinburgh EH1 3YY
T: 0131 334 0380 E: customerservices@scotlandspeople.gov.uk
W: www.nrscotland.gov.uk/research/archivists-garden

The Archivists' Garden is planted with about 60 species, including heather, iris, birch, hawthorn, violet, male fern, rosemary and Scotch thistle. The plants are all connected in some way to Scotland's collective memory, whether through myth and folklore, heraldry or by association with famous Scots. A visit to the garden shows the role that plants play in our national heritage.

Open: Saturday 25 July, 2pm - 5pm, admission £3.00, children free.

Directions: The garden lies behind General Register House and next to New Register House, at the east end of Princes Street. Enter through the courtyard gates on West Register Street (next to the Guildford Arms). Close to Waverley Station and many bus routes.

· *Cancer Research UK*

Edinburgh, Midlothian & West Lothian

24

THE GLASSHOUSES AT THE ROYAL BOTANIC GARDEN EDINBURGH

20A Inverleith Row, Edinburgh EH3 5LR
Royal Botanic Garden Edinburgh
T: 0131 248 2909
W: www.rbge.org.uk

The Royal Botanic Garden Edinburgh celebrates its 350th anniversary in 2020. For more information, visit www.rbge.org.uk/350. The Glasshouses with their ten climatic zones are a delight all year round. The Orchids and Cycads House brings together primitive cycads which dominated the land flora some 65 million years ago, and a diverse range of orchids, the most sophisticated plants in the world. In summer, giant water lilies, *Victoria amazonica*, are the star attraction in the Tropical Aquatic House. Plants with vibrant flowers and fascinating foliage thrive in the Rainforest Riches House and the complex ecosystems of life in the world's deserts are explored in the Arid Lands House. A large collection of gingers, *Zingiberaceae*, one of the largest collections of vireya rhododendrons in the world and a case housing carnivorous plants are among other attractions.

Open: Sunday 7 June, 2pm - 5pm, admission details can be found on the garden's website.

Directions: Located off the A902, one mile north of the city centre. Entrances at Inverleith Row and Arboretum Place. Lothian Buses 8, 23 and 27 stop close to the East Gate entrance on Inverleith Row. *The Majestic Tour Bus* stops at Arboretum Place.

· *Donation to SGS Beneficiaries*

The Glasshouses at the Royal Botanic Garden Edinburgh

FIFE

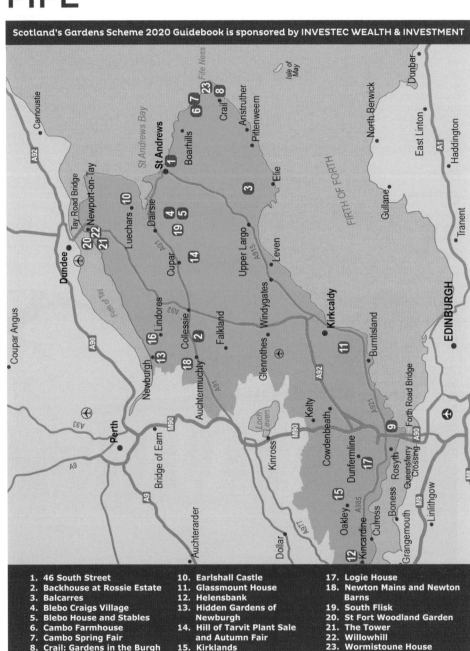

Scotland's Gardens Scheme 2020 Guidebook is sponsored by INVESTEC WEALTH & INVESTMENT

1. 46 South Street
2. Backhouse at Rossie Estate
3. Balcarres
4. Blebo Craigs Village
5. Blebo House and Stables
6. Cambo Farmhouse
7. Cambo Spring Fair
8. Crail: Gardens in the Burgh
9. Dalgety Bay Gardens
10. Earlshall Castle
11. Glassmount House
12. Helensbank
13. Hidden Gardens of Newburgh
14. Hill of Tarvit Plant Sale and Autumn Fair
15. Kirklands
16. Lindores House
17. Logie House
18. Newton Mains and Newton Barns
19. South Flisk
20. St Fort Woodland Garden
21. The Tower
22. Willowhill
23. Wormistoune House

Fife

OUR VOLUNTEER ORGANISERS

District Organisers:	David Buchanan-Cook	Helensbank, 56 Toll Road, Kincardine FK10 4QZ
	Julia Young	South Flisk, Blebo Craigs, Cupar KY15 5UQ
		E: fife@scotlandsgardens.org
Area Organisers:	Alison Aiton	Craigview Cottage, Blebo Craigs, Cupar KY15 5UQ
	Jeni Auchinleck	2 Castle Street, Crail KY10 3SQ
	Oenone Baillie	
	Pauline Borthwick	96 Hepburn Gardens, St Andrews KY16 9LP
	Evelyn Crombie	Keeper's Wood, Over Rankeilour, Cupar KY15 4NQ
	Anne Lumgair	Falside Cottage, Falside Mill, Kingsbarns KY16 8PT
	Caroline Macpherson	Edenside, Strathmiglo KY14 7PX
	Barbara Pickard	Straiton Farmhouse, Balmullo, St Andrews KY16 0BN
	Fay Smith	37 Ninian Fields, Pittenweem, Anstruther KY10 2QU
Treasurer:	David Buchanan-Cook	Helensbank, 56 Toll Road, Kincardine FK10 4QZ

GARDENS OPEN ON A SPECIFIC DATE

Lindores House, by Newburgh	Sunday, 23 February
Cambo Spring Fair, Kingsbarns	Sunday, 12 April
South Flisk, Blebo Craigs, Cupar	Sunday, 26 April
The Tower, 1 Northview Terrace, Wormit	Saturday, 2 May
Earlshall Castle, Leuchars	Sunday, 3 May
Balcarres, Colinsburgh	Sunday, 17 May
The Tower, 1 Northview Terrace, Wormit	Saturday/Sunday/Monday, 23/24/25 May
Kirklands, Saline	Saturday/Sunday, 23/24 May
St Fort Woodland Garden, St Fort Farm, Newport-on-Tay	Sunday, 24 May
South Flisk, Blebo Craigs, Cupar	Sunday/Monday, 24/25 May
Cambo Farmhouse, Kingsbarns	Monday, 25 May
St Fort Woodland Garden, St Fort Farm, Newport-on-Tay	Sunday, 31 May
Lindores House, by Newburgh	Sunday, 31 May
Newton Barns and Newton Mains, Auchtermuchty	Saturday/Sunday, 6/7 June
Earlshall Castle, Leuchars	Sunday, 7 June
Blebo House and Blebo Stables, Cupar	Sunday, 14 June
Blebo Craigs Village Gardens, Blebo Craigs, Cupar	Saturday/Sunday, 20/21 June
Helensbank, Kincardine	Saturday, 20 June
Hidden Gardens of Newburgh, Newburgh	Sunday, 21 June
The Tower, 1 Northview Terrace, Wormit	Saturday, 27 June
Backhouse at Rossie Estate, by Collessie	Sunday, 28 June
46 South Street, St Andrews	Sunday, 28 June
Crail: Gardens in the Burgh, 2 Castle Street, Crail	Saturday/Sunday, 18/19 July
Dalgety Bay Gardens, Dalgety Bay	Saturday/Sunday, 18/19 July
Willowhill, Forgan, Newport-on-Tay	Saturday, 1 August
Wormistoune House, Crail	Sunday, 2 August
Willowhill, Forgan, Newport-on-Tay	Saturday, 8 August

Fife

The Tower, 1 Northview Terrace, Wormit	Saturday, 15 August
Willowhill, Forgan, Newport-on-Tay	Saturday, 15 August
Willowhill, Forgan, Newport-on-Tay	Saturday, 22 August
Willowhill, Forgan, Newport-on-Tay	Saturday, 29 August
Hill of Tarvit Plant Sale and Autumn Fair, Hill of Tarvit	Sunday, 4 October

GARDENS OPEN REGULARLY

Glassmount House, by Kirkcaldy	1 April - 30 September (not Sundays)

GARDENS OPEN BY ARRANGEMENT

Kirklands, Saline	1 April - 30 September
St Fort Woodland Garden, St Fort Farm, Newport-on-Tay	1 April - 31 October
South Flisk, Blebo Craigs, Cupar	15 April - 30 June
Logie House, Crossford, Dunfermline	1 May - 30 September
Helensbank, Kincardine	1 June - 31 August

Fife

46 SOUTH STREET
St Andrews KY16 9JT
Mrs June Baxter
T: 01334 474 995

Renowned town garden in medieval long rig, with orchard underplanted with wildflowers and bulbs. Many unusual flowering shrubs will be looking their best. Roses and other climbers clothe the surrounding high walls. Shrub roses planted in a delightful central parterre fill the air with scent. An historic and unique feature in St Andrews, but also a wonderfully planted space where different styles of planting complement the range of plants used. Historic doocot.

Open: Sunday 28 June, 2pm - 5pm, admission £5.00, children free.

Directions: Entry for the garden is off Greenside Place. Parking is available at the Boys Brigade Hall, on the corner of Kinnessburn Road and Langlands Road, KY16 8BW.

· *Friends of Craigtoun*

BACKHOUSE AT ROSSIE ESTATE
by Collessie KY15 7UZ
Andrew and Caroline Thomson
E: info@backhouserossie.co.uk
W: www.backhouserossie.co.uk

The longest interrupted rose archway in Scotland smothered by rambling roses over a DNA pathway form the heart of the walled garden. A formal pond, water feature, grass labyrinth, yew-backed herbaceous borders with wispy grasses and unusual perennials, parterre filled with roses, cut flowers, soft fruits and herbs. Old espalier fruit trees trained against the walls, new orchard and Victorian glasshouse complete the walled garden. Alpine scree and gravel plantings, walk to a covenanter's tomb, short Bear Walk for little children, nine hole family putting. Heritage and Education Centre Exhibition.
National Plant Collection: Narcissus (Backhouse cvs.).

Open: Sunday 28 June, 2pm - 5pm, admission £5.00, children free. The Backhouse Cafe will be serving SGS teas only during the opening.

Directions: On A91, between Auchtermuchty and Collesie, and one-and-a-quarter miles east of Auchtermuchty, at the Backhouse Rossie banner and the single sign to *Charlottetown*, 300 yards down single track road, turn right into Backhouse Rossie estate.

· *Backhouse Rossie Heritage and Education Centre Ltd*

'Donate your plants to a local plant stall and help us to raise money for charity'

Fife

BALCARRES
Colinsburgh KY9 1HN
Lord and Lady Balniel
T: 01333 340205 (Estate Office)

Balcarres House has been owned by the Lindsay family since the late 16th century and each generation has made their mark on the house and gardens. The formal gardens with their magnificent yew hedges and terraces where laid out by Sir Coutts Lindsay in the 1870s. Since then other changes have been made but the largest impact has come from Lady Crawford (aged 95). She has been the inspiration of the garden and the driving force of much of what has been created in the past fifty years. The gardens are at their very best in the spring. Many of the magnolias and rhododendrons will be in full bloom and the borders bursting into life with daffodils, tulips, primulas and polyanthus. The woodland area and the Chapel Walk will also be at their best with many different hostas, smilacina, trilliums and other diverse plants, shrubs and trees. Enjoy the walks to the Sawmill Pond planting, the Den and the Balcarres Craig.

Open: Sunday 17 May, 2pm - 5pm, admission £6.00, children free.

Directions: Half a mile north of Colinsburgh off A942. Bus to Colinsburgh.

· *Colinsburgh Community Trust Ltd*

Balcarres, photo by Angus Blackburn

Fife

BLEBO CRAIGS VILLAGE GARDENS
Blebo Craigs, Cupar KY15 5UG
The Gardeners of Blebo Craigs
E: blebovh@gmail.com

The village of Blebocraigs welcomes you to visit a selection of varied gardens that will be open over the weekend. Come along and enjoy the wonderful views, lovely cottages/houses and our history trail bringing the past history of the village to life as you walk around.

Open: Saturday/Sunday, 20/21 June, 1pm - 5pm, admission £5.00, children free. Tea/coffee and home baking will be available in the village hall on both days from 2pm - 4.30pm. Wheelchair access is limited but parking is available opposite the village hall. Disabled toilet available in the village hall. Dogs must be kept on leads at all time and are welcome in the village but sadly not inside the hall.

Directions: From St Andrews: B939 for five miles, village sign on your left at the bus stop pointing right, taking you directly into the village. From Cupar: B940 to Pitscottie, turn left onto the B939 and after a couple of miles turn left into the village. Please bear left when you reach the top of the hill at the phone box and you will be guided to the car park.

· *Blebo Craigs Village Hall 2000 Trust*

BLEBO HOUSE AND BLEBO STABLES
Cupar KY15 5TZ
Mary-Frances Morris (House) and Jenny & Sal March (Stables)
T: 07955 275296

Blebo House sits in a beautiful formal garden surrounded by ancient yew hedges and walls covered with espaliered plum trees. Formal mixed beds of herbaceous plants and roses overlook parkland and Fife countryside. Many huge specimen trees including a statuesque Cedar of Lebanon. Beautiful summer house and a one-hole golf course. The house is surrounded by acres of flower-filled woodland which you are free to explore.
Blebo Stables is to the south of Blebo House. This charming organic garden, in the original walled garden of the big house, is a cornucopia of delights with mature fruit trees, borders brimming over with flowers, heavily scented roses and an ornamental pond. The garden is shared by pygmy goats, hens, ducks and turkeys! There is also a very productive 'no-dig' vegetable garden and a Victorian glasshouse sporting figs, peaches and grapes.

Open: Sunday 14 June, 1pm - 5pm, admission £5.00, children free.

Directions: Five miles west of St Andrews off the B939 between Pitscottie and Strathkinness. Bus from St Andrews or Cupar.

· *Alzheimer Scotland & Dogs Trust*

Fife

---

6 CAMBO FARMHOUSE
Kingsbarns KY16 8QD
Sir Peter and Lady Erskine

A new walled garden in development. Started in a derelict garden in 2015 with nothing but two mature plum trees and all weeds known to gardeners. In 2020 it will be showing signs of maturity and with the adjacent mill pond and woodlands it has promise!

Open: Monday 25 May, 2pm - 5pm for the May Weekend Festival, admission £5.00, children free.

Directions: On A917 between Kinsgbarns and Cambo House.

· Unicorn Preservation Society

---

7 CAMBO SPRING FAIR
Kingsbarns KY16 8QD
Trustees of Cambo Heritage Trust
T: 01333 451040 E: cambo@camboestate.com
W: www.camboestate.com

Invited nurseries will join Cambo to provide a wide range of rare and interesting plants. A variety of craft and food stalls are also taking part. A great day out for the family. Children's activities, daffodil meadow, walled garden and woodland walk to the sandy beach. Enjoy the exhibitions in the recently restored Georgian Stables, which make up the Cambo Visitor Centre. Refreshments are available in The Cambo Garden Cafe, with delicious menus based on local homegrown produce.

Open: Sunday 12 April, noon - 3pm, admission details can be found on the garden's website. Entry to the Spring Fair is free but normal admission charges to Cambo Gardens apply.

Directions: A917 between Crail and St Andrews.

· Cambo Heritage Trust

---

8 CRAIL: GARDENS IN THE BURGH
2 Castle Street, Crail KY10 3SQ
The Gardeners of Crail
T: 01333 450538 E: sueellen.jerdan@gmail.com
W: www.crailfestival.com

Take an enjoyable stroll around this quintessential East Neuk village and explore its many beautiful gardens. A number of gardens in varied styles: cottage, historic, plantsman's and bedding. The stunning coastal location of the gardens presents some challenges for planting but also allows for a great range of more tender species to flourish.

Open: Saturday/Sunday, 18/19 July, 1pm - 5pm, admission £5.50, children free. Tickets and maps available on the day from Mrs Jeni Auchinleck, 2 Castle Street or from the Crail Festival Box Office, Town Hall, Marketgate. Advance ticket sales are available from www.crailfestival.com. If purchasing tickets in advance please present your ticket at any of the gardens to receive your map and sticker. Crail gardens open in association with the Crail Festival, 15-25 July.

Directions: Approach Crail from either St Andrews or Anstruther via the A917. Parking available in Marketgate.

· Crail Preservation Society

Fife

DALGETY BAY GARDENS

Dalgety Bay KY11 9HH
Mrs Sybil Cobban and Dalgety Bay Horticultural Society (DBHS)
T: 01383 825 349

17 Inchview Gardens Dalgety Bay KY11 9SA (Mrs Sybil Cobban): This compact garden was designed and created by Sybil, who won *Fife Garden Competition* in 2006. Having held seven annual garden parties for Marie Curie Nurses and three for her local church, Sybil is now opening for SGS! The garden has a selection of herbaceous and bedding plants. She does not have a favourite flower, but top of her list are heucheras, acers and hostas.

DBHS Allotments Western Approach Road, Dalgety Bay KY11 9HH (Dalgety Bay Horticultural Society): The allotment site has grown and developed over the last 44 years. All allotments are taken and it is really nice to see them in production in the month of July. The Annual Show is in September and a lot of the produce you see will be on the show benches. Allotment holders will be on site to chat and you may get the secret of the huge marrow or gigantic cabbage.

Open: Saturday/Sunday, 18/19 July, 2pm - 5pm, admission £5.00, children free. Admission charge at 17 Inchview Gardens only, and includes refreshments. Refreshments in return for donation available at the allotments.

Directions: Inchview Gardens are accessed off Moray Way South. The allotments are behind Peter Vardy Vauxhall, Western Approach Road, Dalgety Bay.

· *Marie Curie*

EARLSHALL CASTLE

Leuchars KY16 0DP
Paul and Josine Veenhuijzen
T: 01334 839205

Extensive, exquisitely designed garden, which perfectly complements the Castle also restored by Sir Robert Lorimer in the 1890s. Fascinating topiary lawn, the finest in Scotland and for which Earlshall is renowned, rose terrace, croquet lawn with herbaceous borders, shrub border, box garden, orchard, kitchen and herb garden. Spectacular spring bulbs.

Open: Sunday 3 May, 2pm - 5pm. Also open Sunday 7 June, 2pm - 5pm. Admission £5.00, children free.

Directions: On Earlshall Road, three-quarters of a mile east of Leuchars Village (off A919). Bus/train to Leuchars.

· *Royal Scots Dragoon Guards Regimental Trust (Sunday 3 May) & Leuchars St Athernase Parish Church (Sunday 7 June)*

'I've had my hands in the soil all my life and I swear it's kept my immune system tip top' Fife Gardener

Fife

GLASSMOUNT HOUSE
by Kirkcaldy KY2 5UT
Peter, James and Irene Thomson
T: 01592 890214 E: mcmoonter@yahoo.co.uk

Densely planted walled garden with surrounding woodland. An A-listed sun dial, Mackenzie & Moncur greenhouse and historical doocot are complemented by a number of newer structures. Daffodils are followed by a mass of candelabra and cowslip primula, meconopsis and *Cardiocrinum giganteum*. Hedges and topiary form backdrops for an abundance of bulbs, clematis, rambling roses and perennials, creating interest through the summer into September. The garden is now extending beyond the walls, with new areas of naturalistic planting blending the boundary between the surrounding fields and the woodland.

Open: 1 April - 30 September (not Sundays), 2pm - 5pm, admission £5.00, children free.

Directions: From Kirkcaldy, head west on the B9157. Turn left immediately after the railway bridge on the edge of town. Follow the single track road for one-and-a-half miles and cross the crossroads. Glassmount House is the first turning on your right.

· *Parkinsons UK*

Glassmount House

HELENSBANK
Kincardine FK10 4QZ
David Buchanan-Cook and Adrian Miles
T: 07739 312912 E: Helensbank@aol.com
W: www.helensbank.com

Hidden away from public view, this is an 18th-century walled garden, with main feature a Cedar of Lebanon, reputedly planted in 1750 by the sea captain who built the house. The tree is registered as a 'Notable Tree' and while it provides challenges for planting, in terms of shade and needle fall, the garden exhibits the owners' passion for growing unusual and exotic plants. Distinctive garden 'rooms' in part of the garden comprise a perennial blue and white cottage garden, a formal rose garden and an Italian garden with citrus trees in pots. A 'hot' courtyard contains exotics including varieties of banana, acacia, iochroma, melianthus and brugmansia. A shaded walk along the bottom of the garden leads to a Japanese pagoda. A large conservatory/greenhouse houses various climbing plants including varieties of passiflora.

Fife

Open: Saturday 20 June, 2pm - 5pm. Also open by arrangement 1 June - 31 August. Admission £5.00, children free. Opening on 20 June will coincide with the Kincardine Gala. Cream teas and lunches available on request for small or large groups which are visiting by arrangement.

Directions: The garden is down a lane off the main Toll Road. For the 20th June opening, visitors are advised to park on Toll Road, or other adjoining streets, and then walk to the garden, following the yellow *SGS* signs.

· Scottish Veterans Residences (1 June - 31 August) & Kincardine Children's Gala (Saturday 20 June)

13 HIDDEN GARDENS OF NEWBURGH

Newburgh KY14 6AH
The Gardeners of Newburgh
T: 07763 340362 E: judilaugh@gmail.com

Hidden behind the 18th-century facades of Newburgh High Street lies a jumble of wonderful old gardens, some of them dating back centuries. Many have spectacular views of the Tay estuary. We are opening for the third time. The gardens will include some previously opened, and some for the first time. Those previously opened will have developed considerably, and as before there will be a wide mix of flowers, vegetables, herbaceous borders, orchards and a fair few hens and ducks.

Open: Sunday 21 June, 2pm - 5pm, admission £5.00, children free. Admission includes tea/coffee with home baking (with optional donations). Newburgh, at the northern end of the coastal path, sits on a hill, and access to some of the gardens is up closes and down vennels. Some allow for disabled access, but not all.

Directions: On the A913 between Perth and Cupar. There is a car park at each end of the town, with tickets and teas available nearby.

· Newburgh Community Trust

14 HILL OF TARVIT PLANT SALE AND AUTUMN FAIR

Hill of Tarvit, Cupar KY15 5PB
The National Trust for Scotland/Scotland's Gardens Fife
T: 01334 850859
W: scotlandsgardens.org or www.nts.org.uk

This long established plant sale is a fantastic opportunity to purchase bare root and potted plants from an enormous selection on offer. We also welcome donations of plants prior to the sale and on the day - 'bring and buy'. Participating local nurseries will also be be offering a choice selection of plants. Bulbs for autumn planting will be available, including Scottish grown daffodils from Grampian Growers. Cecilia's jam will also be on sale. Hill of Tarvit is one of Scotland's finest Edwardian mansion houses. Surrounding the mansion house are spectacular gardens designed by Robert Lorimer, woods, open heath and parkland to explore.

Open: Sunday 4 October, 10:30am - 2:30pm, admission £2.00, children free.

Directions: Two miles south of Cupar off A916.

· The Rotary Club of St Andrews: End Polio Now

Fife

15 KIRKLANDS
Saline KY12 9TS
Peter and Gill Hart
T: 07787 115477 E: gill@i-comment360.com
W: www.kirklandshouseandgarden.co.uk

Kirklands, built in 1832, has been the Hart family home for 41 years. Over the years we have re-instated the walled garden from a paddock and constructed terraces with raised beds. There are 18 espalier apple trees against the walls and box hedging with a display of tulips. The woodland garden starts with snowdrops and bluebells, then rhododendrons, trilliums, fritillaries, meconopsis, erythroniums and candelabra primulas follow. The rockery displays dwarf rhododendrons and azaleas. The herbaceous borders reach their peak in the summer. The bog garden by the Saline Burn is home to giant *Gunnera manicata*. Over the bridge we have 20 acres of woodland with a pathway by the burn. To keep the grandchildren occupied, Peter built a tree house, zip wire and rope swing, though we hope they will take an interest in gardening too!

Open: Saturday/Sunday, 23/24 May, 2pm - 5pm for the May Weekend Festival. Also open by arrangement 1 April - 30 September. Admission £5.00, children free.

Directions: Junction 4, M90, then B914. Parking in the centre of the village, then a short walk to the garden. Limited disabled parking at Kirklands.

· *Saline Environmental Group*

16 LINDORES HOUSE
by Newburgh KY14 6JD
Mr and Mrs R Turcan
T: 01337 840369

Lindores House overlooks the loch. Woodland walk beside the loch and stunning views from the garden. Herbaceous borders, wonderful snowdrops, leucojums, trilliums, primulae, rhododendrons and species trees including *Nothofagus* and *Davidia involucrata*, the handkerchief tree. Don't miss the 17th-century yew, believed to be the largest in Fife, which you can walk inside!

Open: Sunday 23 February, 11:30am - 2pm for Snowdrops and Winter Walks with homemade bread and soup. Also open Sunday 31 May, 2pm - 5pm with tea and cakes. Admission £4.00 (Sunday 23 February) and £5.00 (Sunday 31 May) with children free for both.

Directions: Off A913 two miles east of Newburgh. Bus from Cupar.

· *Bumblebee Conservation Trust (Sunday 23 February) & 1st North East Fife (Newburgh) Scout Group (Sunday 31 May)*

17 LOGIE HOUSE
Crossford, Dunfermline KY12 8QN
Mr and Mrs Jonathan Hunt
T: 07867 804020

Central to the design of this walled garden is a path through a double mixed border. Long rows of vegetables and fruit also contribute to colour and design when seen from the house and terrace. A long border of repeat flowering roses and rose and annual beds contribute to an extended season of colour and interest. There is a magnificent and very productive Mackenzie & Moncur greenhouse in excellent condition with fully working vents and original benches and central heating system. The garden is surrounded by a belt of mixed woodland with walks.

Fife

Open: by arrangement 1 May - 30 September (Monday/Tuesday and Thursday/Friday), admission £5.00, children free.

Directions: M90 exit 1 for Rosyth and Kincardine Bridge (A985). After about two miles turn right to Crossford. At traffic lights, turn right and the drive is on the right at the end of the village main street.

· *Scottish Veterans Residences*

 18

NEWTON BARNS AND NEWTON MAINS
Auchtermuchty KY14 7HR
John & Jess Anderson and Tony & Ruth Lear
T: 01337 827345

Newton Barns Auchtermuchty KY14 7HR (John & Jess Anderson): The borders at Newton Barns are planted with choice shrubs, trees and rhododendrons. Central to the garden is a huge rockery and stream. Sweeping lawns and generous borders slope towards Pitmedden Wood and there are breathtaking views across the top of the garden towards the Lomond Hills.
Newton Mains Auchtermuchty KY14 7HR (Tony and Ruth Lear): Confronted with the challenge of an exposed south facing site, visited frequently by deer and hares in search of a tasty snack, sheltered areas have been created and planted with a variety of trees, shrubs and perennials. Curving dry stone walls outline beds, pathways and seating areas that merge into the naturalised field. Wonderful views across the Eden Valley to the Lomond Hills.

Open: Saturday/Sunday, 6/7 June, 11am - 4pm, admission £6.00, children free.

Directions: On A91 from Cupar, turn right in Auchtermuchty on to B936 and follow *SGS* signs.

· *Diabetes UK*

19

SOUTH FLISK
Blebo Craigs, Cupar KY15 5UQ
Mr and Mrs George Young
T: 01334 850859 E: julia@standrewspottery.co.uk
W: www.standrewspottery.co.uk

The spectacular views over Fife to Perthshire and Angus and the large flooded quarry full of fish and planted with impressive marginals make the garden at South Flisk very special in the area. Flights of old stone steps, cliffs, huge boulders, exotic ferns and mature trees form a backdrop for carpets of primroses, bluebells, spring bulbs and woodland plants like trilliums, camassia and colourful primulas. There are different rhododendrons in flower in the garden from March until July. In front of the house is a charming, mature walled garden with traditional cottage-garden planting and next to the house is the St Andrews Pottery where George will be demonstrating his pottery skills for those who need a break from the garden!

Open: Sunday 26 April, 2pm - 5pm. Also open Sunday/Monday, 24/25 May, 2pm - 5pm for the May Weekend Festival. And open by arrangement 15 April - 30 June. Admission £5.00, children free.

Directions: Six miles west of St Andrews off the B939 between Strathkinness and Pitscottie. There is a small stone bus shelter opposite the road into the village and a small sign saying *Blebo Craigs*. Or check out the map on our website. Bus to Blebo Craigs.

· *Book Aid International*

Fife

20 ST FORT WOODLAND GARDEN
St Fort Farm, Newport-on-Tay DD6 8RE
Mr and Mrs Andrew Mylius
T: 07974 083110
W: www.stfort.co.uk

Inspired by a visit to Ruskin's woodland garden at Brantwood. Azaleas and specimen rhododendrons are the principal plants. Created from an area of mixed woodland, the garden has been substantially redesigned and enlarged over the last year with an enhanced woodland walk. The rhododendrons include a wide selection of both specimen and hybrids. Azaleas are mainly *Azalea pontica* chosen for scent and autumn colour. Around 30 acres, Northwood is home to red squirrels, and offers spectacular views northwards over the River Tay. Also of interest are eucryphia, cercidiphyllum, tulip tree, various red acers, rowans, liquidambar, metasequoia and magnolias. Spectacular late autumn foliage, when the garden potentially surpasses its spring glory in terms of colours!

Open: Sunday 24 May, 1pm - 5pm for the May Weekend Festival. Also open Sunday 31 May, 1pm - 5pm. And open by arrangement 1 April - 31 October. Admission £5.00, children free.

Directions: One-and-three-quarters miles south of the Tay Road Bridge off the A92, between the Forgan and Five Roads roundabouts. St Fort is approached with a woodland walk of about 400 yards from the car park and garden entrance.

· *Brooke Action for Working Horses & Donkeys*

21 THE TOWER
1 Northview Terrace, Wormit DD6 8PP
Peter and Angela Davey
T: 01382 541635 M: 07768 406946 E: adavey541@btinternet.com

Situated four miles south of Dundee, this one-acre Edwardian landscaped garden has panoramic views over the River Tay. Set on a hill, a series of paths meander around ponds and a small stream, rockeries featuring hellebores and low-level planting, a curved lawn and larger borders. Original woodland paths lead to a granite grotto with waterfall pool. At the rear of the house the vegetable garden features raised beds made from granite sets. Rhododendrons have recently been removed to create more space for seating and flower beds. The garden is colourful throughout the summer, with many architectural plants accentuating the clever hard landscape design.

Open: Saturday/Sunday/Monday, 23/24/25 May, 1pm - 5pm for the May Weekend Festival. Also open Saturday 2 May, Saturday 27 June and Saturday 15 August, 1pm - 5pm. Admission £5.00, children free.

Directions: From B946 park on Naughton Road outside Spar shop and walk up path on left following signs.

· *Dundee Chamber Music Club*

22 WILLOWHILL
Forgan, Newport-on-Tay DD6 8RA
Eric Wright and Sally Lorimore
T: 01382 542890 E: e.g.wright@dundee.ac.uk
W: www.willowhillgarden.weebly.com

An evolving three-acre garden. The house is surrounded by a series of mixed borders designed with different vibrant colour combinations for effect all season. Spectacular mix of roses, herbaceous perennials and annuals planted through the wide borders are a highlight in late summer. A new 'no dig' 160-foot border in shades of white, blue, purple and pale yellow has been created in 2019/2020. Come and see!

Open: Saturdays in August (1, 8, 15, 22, 29), 2pm - 5pm, admission £5.00, children free.

Directions: One-and-a-half miles south of Tay Road Bridge. Take the B995 to Newport off the Forgan roundabout. Willowhill is the first house on the left-hand side next to the Forgan Arts Centre.

· *Forgan Arts Centre SCIO*

WORMISTOUNE HOUSE
Crail KY10 3XH
Baron and Lady Wormiston
T: 07561262239 E: gemmawormiston@aol.com

The ongoing restoration and transformation of this 'pocket' estate's 17th-century Scot's tower house and gardens continues to evolve and delight. Within the walled garden, imaginatively clipped yew hedges enclose 'rooms' filled with luxuriantly planted herbaceous borders, a productive potager garden, wildflower meadows, an intricate box parterre, water features and a magical shade garden which is home to four of Scotland's largest *Griselinia littoralis* specimens. In recent years planting has extended into the wider woodland policies and highlights include a new Nuttery (inspired by Sissinghurst), extensive wildflower meadows and waterside plantings surrounding an impressively landscaped pond.

Open: Sunday 2 August, 2pm - 5pm, admission £5.00, children free.

Directions: One mile north of Crail on the A917 Crail to St Andrews road. Crail/St Andrews bus.

· *Crail Preservation Society & Crail Community Partnership*

Wormistoune House

GLASGOW & DISTRICT

Scotland's Gardens Scheme 2020 Guidebook is sponsored by INVESTEC WEALTH & INVESTMENT

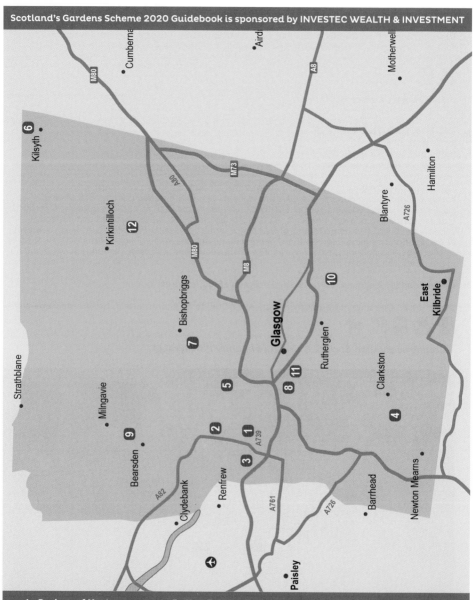

1. **Duchess of Montrose Memorial Garden**
2. **Gartnavel Secret Garden**
3. **Horatio's Gardens**
4. **Kamares**
5. **Kew Terrace Gardens: Back to Front**
6. **Kilsyth Gardens**
7. **Milton Community Garden**
8. **Strathbungo Garden**
9. **The Gardens of Kilmardinny Crescent**
10. **The Good Life Gardens**
11. **The Hidden Gardens**
12. **Woodbourne House**

Glasgow & District

OUR VOLUNTEER ORGANISERS

District Organiser:	Heidi Stone	glasgow@scotlandsgardens.org
Area Organisers:	Caroline Anderson	64 Partickhill Road, Glasgow G11 5NB
	Lucia Comerford	luciacomerford@hotmail.com
	Kaitlyn DeBiasse	Langside Garden, 336 Langside Road G42 8XR
	Audrey Mason	Hillend House, Drakemyre, Dalry KA24 5JR
	Jim & Anne Murray	44 Gordon Road, Netherlee, Glasgow G44 3TW
	John & Margaret Redmond	68 Kilmardinny Crescent, Bearsden G61 3NW
Treasurer:	To be advised	

GARDENS OPEN ON A SPECIFIC DATE

Gartnavel Secret Garden, Gartnavel Royal Hospital	Sunday, 3 May
Kilsyth Gardens, Allanfauld Road, Kilsyth	Sunday, 31 May
Kew Terrace Gardens: Back to Front, Kew Terrace Lane	Saturday, 6 June
The Hidden Gardens, 25 Albert Drive, Glasgow	Sunday, 14 June
The Good Life Gardens, Cambuslang, Glasgow	Sunday, 21 June
Strathbungo and Langside Gardens, March Street, Glasgow	Sunday, 28 June
Milton Community Garden, Liddesdale Square, Milton, Glasgow	Saturday, 4 July
Duchess of Montrose Memorial Garden, 8 Aboukir Street	Sunday, 5 July
Woodbourne House, Seven Sisters, Lenzie, Glasgow	Sunday, 12 July
Kamares, 18 Broom Road, Newton Mearns, Glasgow	Sunday, 19 July
The Gardens of Kilmardinny Crescent , Bearsden, Glasgow	Sunday, 26 July
Horatio's Gardens, Queen Elizabeth University Hospital	Sunday, 23 August
Gartnavel Secret Garden, Gartnavel Royal Hospital	Sunday, 30 August

GARDENS OPEN BY ARRANGEMENT

Kilsyth Gardens, Allanfauld Road, Kilsyth	1 April - 30 August

Glasgow & District

DUCHESS OF MONTROSE MEMORIAL GARDEN
8 Aboukir Street, Glasgow G51 4QX
Agnes Bowie
T: 07703294798 E: little.carbeth@btinternet.com

....

A delightful and peaceful new garden created from the derelict site of a former shipyard. The garden is in memory of the late Cathy, Duchess of Montrose, who was first President of the Preshal Trust Charity. Security fencings have become living walls of colour and lovely mixed planting abounds giving colour all year round. There is a rare maple tree, as Cathy was Canadian, with sensory planting around it, a vegetable garden and tiny tots play area. The Preshal Trust provides a unique service helping vulnerable people and families in the Community. The garden has provided huge therapeutic benefits for everyone who has visited it.

Open: Sunday 5 July, 2pm - 4pm, admission £3.00, children free. The Preshal Trust building will be open for strawberry cream teas; books, plants and homemade cakes will also be on sale.

Directions: From the north, head south through Clyde Tunnel, take exit immediately at end of the tunnel signposted *Govan*; turn left past Cressy Street, then Aboukir Street is next on left. Coming from the south, pass BAE systems on Govan Road opposite Elder Park, then go round traffic light controlled roundabout taking the last exit to Aboukir Street.

· *Preshal Trust*

GARTNAVEL SECRET GARDEN
Gartnavel Royal Hospital, 1055 Great Western Road, Glasgow G12 0XH
Gartnavel Royal Hospital Growing Spaces Volunteers
T: 0141 211 3681 M: 07977 406900

....

Gartnavel Royal's hidden walled garden forms part of the original 200-year-old hospital and was the private garden of the hospital's superintendent. The basic infrastructure was restored six years ago by the Green Exercise Partnership with new raised beds and growing spaces being installed. It is cared for by a group of loyal volunteers and is an oasis of calm for hospital patients, staff, visitors and the public. We do a little bit of everything at Gartnavel; in collaboration with our TCV friends, we grow both edibles and ornamentals and, as a hospital garden, we feature lots of sensory and medicinal plants too.

Open: Sunday 3 May, 2pm - 5pm. Also open Sunday 30 August, 2pm - 5pm. Admission £6.00, children free.

Directions: From Great Western Road (car, bus or foot): Enter Gartnavel Hospital site and turn right at the traffic lights onto Shelley Road. Follow yellow *SGS Open* signs, continue past pond and beyond car park on your left; at the fork bear left up the hill. Pass The Calman Centre on your left as you enter a wooded area. Continue up the hill to T junction, turn right along the front of West House and park in the spaces there. Once parked continue to follow the signs to the gardens at the rear of West House.

· *The Charity for Gartnavel Royal Hospital*

Glasgow & District

3

HORATIO'S GARDENS
National Spinal Injuries Unit, Queen Elizabeth University Hospital, 1345 Govan Road, Glasgow G51 4TF
Horatio's Gardens
E: sallie@horatiosgarden.org.uk
W: Horatiosgarden.org.uk

Opened in 2016, award-winning Horatio's Garden at the Scottish National Spinal Injuries Unit, was designed by acclaimed garden designer and RHS judge, James Alexander-Sinclair. This fully accessible garden creates a peaceful sanctuary using planting, a wealth of variety and colour and seasonality in every corner. Visit to see how this high-profile national charity has created a beautiful, cleverly designed, contemporary, accessible garden in the heart of Greater Glasgow and Clyde NHS, for the benefit of patients, relatives and staff.

Open: Sunday 23 August, 2pm - 5pm, admission £7.00, children free.

Directions: From the east or west of the city: On the M8 motorway to Junction 25, follow signs for the *Clyde Tunnel* (A739) for three-quarters of a mile, then follow signs for the *Queen Elizabeth Hospital*. Turn left into Govan Road and the hospital is on the left. From north of the River Clyde: Go through the Clyde tunnel (A739) and follow signs for the hospital. Please look at our website for the hospital estate map for directions to the garden and available parking.

· *Horatio's Garden*

4

KAMARES
18 Broom Road, Newton Mearns, Glasgow G77 5DN
Derek and Laura Harrison
E: laurah6367@gmail.com

Sitting in two-thirds of an acre, Kamares is a hacienda-style house surrounded by mature trees and a beautiful beech hedge. The garden has much of interest including a well-established pond, acers, Japanese grasses, colourful mixed shrubs, herbaceous borders and rare US sequoias. There are several patio gardens and a delightful courtyard with a rockery and miniature waterfall. Sculptures and topiary can be found around the garden where you are also welcome to visit the garden shed known as 'Owl Cottage'. The artist owner and her husband have had fun playing with spaces, colour and contrasting textures as an alternative canvas. A very well-stocked plant stall with home-grown established plants will be available.

Open: Sunday 19 July, 2pm - 5pm, admission £7.00, children free.

Directions: From the A77 heading south, turn left into Broom Estate and sharp left again into Broom Road. Kamares is the last house on the left near the top of the hill. On road parking is available beyond the house on Broom Road, Broomcroft Road, Sandringham Road and Dunvegan Avenue.

· *Jewish Care Scotland*

Glasgow & District

5

KEW TERRACE GARDENS: BACK TO FRONT
Kew Terrace Lane, Glasgow G12 0TE
Professor George G Browning and other Owners

....

The previous opening of Kew Terrace gardens included some of the south-facing rear gardens initially planned as drying greens. Access to these is from cobbled, tree-lined and partially gardened Kew Lane. Funds from previous openings have been used to plant and maintain Kew Terrace front gardens on Great Western Road. In 2020 we have slightly moved the emphasis of the opening from at least four of the back gardens to include the front gardens. The gardening of the lane has increased considerably since the first opening in 2008 and has spread to Grosvenor Lane. The gardening of the Kew Terrace front gardens has inspired the residents of Belhaven Terrace to start a similar scheme.

Open: Saturday 6 June, 2pm - 5pm, admission £7.00, children free.

Directions: From the M8 take Junction 17 (A82) and turn west onto Great Western Road. Drive west to the traffic lights at Kirklee and turn left into Horslethill Road. You are now in the Dowanhill controlled parking area, where parking spaces are usually available. Access to Kew Terrace is down the first road on the left.

· *Friends Of Glasgow West & The Coach House Trust*

6

KILSYTH GARDENS
Allanfauld Road, Kilsyth G65 9DE
Mr & Mrs George Murdoch and Mr & Mrs Alan Patrick
T: 07743 110908 E: alan.patrick3@googlemail.com

....

Aeolia (Mr and Mrs George Murdoch) A third-of-an-acre woodland garden developed since 1960 and designed to have something in flower every month of the year. The garden contains a large variety of mature specimen trees and shrubs, maples, primulas, hardy geraniums and herbaceous plants. Spring bulbs provide early colour, lilies and dahlias provide late season interest. There are a couple of small ponds for wildlife, two greenhouses and a fruit production area. The owners are members of the *Scottish Rhododendron Society* with a collection of over 100 specimens, some grown from seed. Areas of the garden are often under development to provide something new to see and provide material for the extensive plant sale, which is home grown.
Blackmill (Mr and Mrs Alan Patrick) Across the road from Aeolia is Blackmill through which the Garrel Burn flows, the garden includes the magnificent 23 feet waterfall with it's ever-changing moods throughout the year. On the side of the property, on the site of an old water-powered sickle mill, is an acre of mature specimen trees, rhododendrons and shrubs with an ornamental pond and a rock pool built into the remains of the mill building. Across the burn there is a further two acres of woodland glen with paths along the waterside offering glimpses of the many cascading waterfalls. A large area of wildflowers has been newly introduced alongside the burn. A micro hydro scheme is on view, along with many different examples of dry stone walls. Visitors remark on the sense of tranquility and peace they experience in the garden and appreciate the works of art created from repurposed stone and salvaged material.

Open: Sunday 31 May, 2pm - 5pm. Also open by arrangement 1 April - 30 August. Admission £7.00, children free. There is a minimum of six visitors for the 'by arrangement' openings. WC not suitable for disabled visitors.

Directions: Turn off the A803 into Parkburn Road up to crossroads (parking attendant will advise you on parking). Bus: 89 Glasgow-Kilsyth has a stop up at the crossroads a couple of minutes walk to the gardens. Trains: the nearest station is Croy, bus 147 or 344 to Kilsyth.

· *Strathcarron Hospice*

Glasgow & District

7

MILTON COMMUNITY GARDEN
Liddesdale Square, Milton, Glasgow G22 7BT
North Glasgow Community Food Initiative
T: 07422 375524 E: gardens@ngcfi.org.uk
W: www.ngcfi.org.uk

This community garden is a wildlife and visitor friendly organic growing space in the heart of Milton. It offers a peaceful environment for the local community to walk through or sit in, to volunteer to help develop the space or to spend time with our gardener and landscaper to learn how to 'grow your own' or build things from recycled wood. It features a pond, a green roof, a Ridan composter, a children's garden complete with mud kitchen and willow sculptures as well as lots of raised beds bursting with fruit, vegetables and flowers.

Open: Saturday 4 July, 2pm - 5pm, admission by donation. Children's activities will include pond dipping, bug hunts, seed bomb making, a garden trail and more.

Directions: From the M8 leave at Junction 15 onto Springburn Road (A803). After two miles turn left into Colston Road then at the T junction turn right onto Ashgill Road. At the roundabout take the first left into Shillay Street then left into Liddesdale Place. Turn left into Liddesdale Square, garden is at the opposite corner. Parking in the square or there is on street parking. By bus take the 75 bus to Ashgill Road, get off at the back of St Augustine's Church and the square is a short walk through an alley-way.

· *Milton Community Garden and Food Hub*

Blackmill, Kilsyth Gardens

Glasgow & District

68 Kilmardinny, The Gardens of Kilmardinny Crescent

STRATHBUNGO AND LANGSIDE GARDENS
March Street, Glasgow G41 2PX
Frank Burns (Strathbungo) and Kaitlyn DeBiasse (Langside)
W: http://www.facebook.com/strathbungogarden

Strathbungo Garden March Street, Glasgow G41 2PX (Frank Burns): Nestled behind Glasgow's busy main road artery to the Southside, you will happen upon a hidden walled terrace garden which marks the historical boundary to Strathbungo. It's an unexpected cottage-style city garden, showing how a piece of ground can be turned into a lovely colourful space for all the occupants of the terrace to enjoy. Inventive container planting is a key feature of this distinct urban retreat, which holds year-round interest. There's a range of fruit trees, some of which are trained as minarettes and stepovers, and an extensive collection of herbaceous perennials. Why not visit Strathbungo Gardens on Facebook and see what's been happening in the garden over the past months?

Langside Garden NEW 336 Langside Road, Glasgow G42 8XR (Kaitlyn DeBiasse): The second garden is another shared courtyard, a stone throw away from the City's Queens Park. Developed in 2019 from an overgrown skeleton of a few shrubs and trees, but mostly wilderness, several tonnes of large stones now define a colourful main raised bed, flanked by lawn and raised sleeper beds full of veg and herbs. A second deeper bed hosts a snowberry, a rambling yellow rose and many more perennial favourites.

Open: Sunday 28 June, 2pm - 5pm, admission £5.00, children free.

Directions: Strathbungo Garden: From the south take the M74 to Junction 1A Polmadie. Turn left onto Polmadie Road, then turn right at the next traffic lights onto Calder Street. Proceed to Nithsdale Drive, then turn left into March Street where ample parking can be found. From the north take the M8 and join the M74, turn right into Polmadie Road at Junction 1A. At the bottom of March Street you will see a sign for *World Foods* – and a banner for the garden opening.
Langside Garden: A 10 minute 'walking bus' will take you to and from the second garden every half hour.

· *ALVO Rural South Lanarkshire*

Glasgow & District

9

THE GARDENS OF KILMARDINNY CRESCENT
Bearsden, Glasgow G61 3NW
Colin & Joan McMinn, John & Margaret Redmond and John & Nancy Heath

....

64 Kilmardinny (Colin and Joan McMinn) The garden is dominated by a large lawn with a flower bed with mixed planting. There is also a mature lime, lilac and cherry trees. There is a border with a profusion of planting including lavatera, fuchsias, pampas grass and hydrangeas. Overlooking the lawn is a 'sitooterie'. At the rear of the property is a delightful bijoux courtyard garden.

68 Kilmardinny (John and Margaret Redmond) The front garden has a curved lawn which has borders of mixed trees, shrubs, perennials and annual plants including a scented path. Statues are delightfully placed in the garden. There are various pots in the gravel area and the lower patio area. The borders either side of the house contain peonies hellebores, hostas, shrubs and a magnolia tree.

70 Kilmardinny (John and Nancy Heath) The front garden contains a colourful variety of shrubs and trees. There is an eye-catching carved wooden sculpture of an eagle surrounded by shrubs which include berberis, pieris, azaleas and hostas. The small lawn at the front of the house is bordered with shrubs. There is a water feature at the corner of the lawn.

Open: Sunday 26 July, 2pm - 5pm, admission £6.00, children free. Live music, weather permitting.

Directions:
From Glasgow via Canniesburn Toll Roundabout take the A81 (Milngavie Road). Just past Kilmardinny Estate Self Catering Cottages on the right-hand side take a left into Kilmardinny Avenue then second left into Kilmardinny Crescent. By bus 60A from Glasgow or 10A Balfron bus. Bus stop near junction of Milngavie Road and Kilmardinny Avenue. By train to Hillfoot station then a short bus ride.

· *Children's Hospice Association Scotland*

10

THE GOOD LIFE GARDENS
Cambuslang, Glasgow G72 8BJ
Paul & Sheona Brightey and Andy & Amanda Bateman

....

12 Chatelherault Avenue (Paul and Sheona Brightey) The front garden is split into a gravel garden and a small white woodland garden. Go through the gate and you will find a garden where the aim is to grow as many different edibles as possible; herbs, fruit arches, vegetable beds and edible hedging. There are herbaceous perennials and a cut-flower bed, a wildlife pond, a pizza oven and around the corner is a food smoker.

14 Chatelherault Avenue (Andy and Amanda Bateman) An established garden that has been revived since the owners arrived four years ago. As the overgrowth was removed more and more beautiful surprises emerged. The garden is now a lovely calm sanctuary, artistically planted with a wide range of herbaceous perennials surrounded by beautiful trees.

Open: Sunday 21 June, 2pm - 5pm, admission £6.00, children free.

Directions: M74 Glasgow to Cambuslang at Junction 2, exit onto Cambuslang Road/A724 towards Rutherglen. At the roundabout, take the first exit and stay on Cambuslang Road/A724. Continue to follow A724. Turn right onto Buchanan Drive, then right onto Richmond Drive, which turns left and becomes Chatelherault Avenue.

· *Macmillan Cancer Support: Nurses*

Glasgow & District

THE HIDDEN GARDENS
25 Albert Drive, Glasgow G41 2PE
The Hidden Gardens Trust
T: 0141 433 2722 E: info@thehiddengardens.org.uk
W: www.thehiddengardens.org.uk

The Hidden Gardens has been designed to reflect the legacy of this historic site as well as the ever-changing character and needs of the local area. The north to south borders echo the layout of the site when it was a tree nursery in the 1800s, whilst the retained tramlines and the chimney reflect its industrial past. A number of artworks are integrated into the overall design, for example the Xylotheque, a library of wooden books detailing native Scottish trees. The Hidden Gardens is an independent charity offering learning and social activities and opportunities for the whole community to participate in its development. It is a calm, green space where you can relax away from the busy city streets, take a walk around the formal lawn, brush past the aromatic herb border, admire the white wall border with its herbaceous plantings and espalier fruit trees, stroll through the wildlife area, connect with nature in the woodland glade and enjoy the naturalistic planting of the grassy meadow.

Open: Sunday 14 June, 1pm - 4pm, admission £6.50 to include tour and cream tea. Guests will be guided around The Hidden Gardens by our knowledgeable Head Gardener: tours hourly, beginning at 1pm. Children's activities available and visit our plant sale kiosk.

Directions: Free street parking on Albert Drive is available if coming by car. The Hidden Gardens are very accessible by public transport; the 3, 4, 5, 6, 7, 38, 57 and 59 buses take you within walking distance; enter either through Tramway or from Pollokshaws Road. Trains to Pollokshields East station are every 15 minutes from Glasgow Central Station. At the top of the stairs at Pollokshields East station turn right and enter the Hidden Gardens through Tramway.

· *The Hidden Gardens Trust: Glasgow*

The Hidden Gardens

Glasgow & District

WOODBOURNE HOUSE
Seven Sisters, Lenzie, Glasgow G66 3AW
Alice May

This is a landscaped garden on several levels; about the size of half a football pitch and roughly triangular with a traditional Victorian villa at its centre. A work in progress, it features a wildlife pond and a 'wigloo' – an igloo made from living willow and climbers – alongside rare and unusual perennials. These include cold-hardy tropicals and colourful tender ones. On one side a woodland-style border gives way to a bog garden and exotic slope, while paths and steps lead up to decking and gravel planting along the rear drive.

Open: Sunday 12 July, 2pm - 5pm, admission £6.00, children free.

Directions: From the M80 exit Junction 3 onto the A806. After two mini-roundabouts turn left onto Woodilee Road at the Old Gatehouse pub. Park in the pub. Walk back onto Woodilee Road and turn left along it, then left again onto Seven Sisters and continue right to the very end to Woodbourne House.

· *David Sheldrick Wildlife Trust*

Woodbourne House

INVERNESS, ROSS, CROMARTY & SKYE

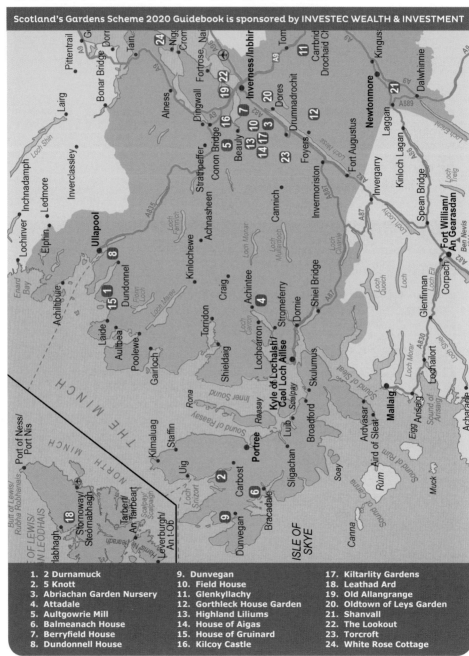

Scotland's Gardens Scheme 2020 Guidebook is sponsored by INVESTEC WEALTH & INVESTMENT

1. 2 Durnamuck	9. Dunvegan	17. Kiltarlity Gardens
2. 5 Knott	10. Field House	18. Leathad Ard
3. Abriachan Garden Nursery	11. Glenkyllachy	19. Old Allangrange
4. Attadale	12. Gorthleck House Garden	20. Oldtown of Leys Garden
5. Aultgowrie Mill	13. Highland Liliums	21. Shanvall
6. Balmeanach House	14. House of Aigas	22. The Lookout
7. Berryfield House	15. House of Gruinard	23. Torcroft
8. Dundonnell House	16. Kilcoy Castle	24. White Rose Cottage

Inverness, Ross, Cromarty & Skye

OUR VOLUNTEER ORGANISERS

District Organiser:	Lucy Lister-Kaye	House of Aigas, Aigas, Beauly IV4 7AD E: inverness@scotlandsgardens.org
Area Organiser:	Emma MacKenzie	Glenkyllachy, Tomatin IV13 7YA
Treasurer:	Sheila Kerr	Lilac Cottage, Struy, By Beauly IV4 7JU

GARDENS OPEN ON A SPECIFIC DATE

Dundonnell House, Little Loch Broom, Wester Ross	Thursday, 16 April
White Rose Cottage, Pitcalnie, Tain	Sunday, 24 May
Dundonnell House, Little Loch Broom, Wester Ross	Thursday, 28 May
House of Gruinard, Laide, by Achnasheen	Wednesday, 3 June
Gorthleck House Garden, Stratherrick	Friday/Saturday/Sunday, 5/6/7 June
Field House, Belladrum, Beauly	Sunday, 7 June
Old Allangrange, Munlochy	Sunday, 14 June
House of Aigas and Field Centre, by Beauly	Sunday, 28 June
2 Durnamuck, Little Loch Broom, Wester Ross	Saturday, 18 July
House of Aigas and Field Centre, by Beauly	Sunday, 26 July
Kiltarlity Gardens, Kiltarlity, Beauly	Sunday, 9 August
Kilcoy Castle, Redcastle, by Muir of Ord	Sunday, 16 August
Dundonnell House, Little Loch Broom, Wester Ross	Thursday, 20 August
2 Durnamuck, Little Loch Broom, Wester Ross	Sunday, 23 August
Old Allangrange, Munlochy	Sunday, 30 August

GARDENS OPEN REGULARLY

Oldtown of Leys Garden, Inverness	1 January - 31 December
Highland Liliums, 10 Loaneckheim, Kiltarlity	1 January - 31 December
Abriachan Garden Nursery, Loch Ness Side	1 February - 30 November
Attadale, Strathcarron	1 April - 31 October
Dunvegan Castle and Gardens, Isle of Skye	1 April - 15 October
Glenkyllachy, Tomatin	1 April - 30 October (Mondays only)
Leathad Ard, Upper Carloway, Isle of Lewis	1 May - 30 September (not Sundays)
Balmeanach House, Balmeanach, nr Struan, Isle of Skye	4 May - 8 October (Mondays & Thursdays)
The Lookout, Kilmuir, North Kessock	1 June - 31 August (Sundays only)
5 Knott, Clachamish, Portree, Isle of Skye	26 June - 21 September (Mons, Fris & Suns)
Torcroft, Balnain, Glenurquhart	1 July - 31 August (Mondays only)

GARDENS OPEN BY ARRANGEMENT

Old Allangrange, Munlochy	1 January - 31 December
Torcroft, Balnain, Glenurquhart	1 March - 31 October
Berryfield House, Lentran, Inverness	1 April - 4 October

Inverness, Ross, Cromarty & Skye

The Lookout, Kilmuir, North Kessock	1 April - 30 September

GARDENS OPEN BY ARRANGEMENT CONTINUED

Aultgowrie Mill, Aultgowrie, Urray, Muir of Ord	1 April - 1 September
House of Aigas and Field Centre, by Beauly	1 April - 31 October
Leathad Ard, Upper Carloway, Isle of Lewis	1 April - 30 April (not Sundays)
Dundonnell House, Little Loch Broom, Wester Ross	1 April - 31 October
Glenkyllachy, Tomatin	1 April - 30 October
2 Durnamuck, Little Loch Broom, Wester Ross	1 June - 30 September
5 Knott, Clachamish, Portree, Isle of Skye	1 June - 30 September
Shanvall, Glentruim, Newtonmore	1 June - 31 August

Inverness, Ross, Cromarty & Skye

2 DURNAMUCK
Little Loch Broom, Wester Ross IV23 2QZ
Will Soos and Susan Pomeroy
T: 01854 633761 E: sueandwill@icloud.com

Our garden is south-east facing on the edge of Little Loch Broom. It is a coastal plantsman's garden with a rich mix of herbaceous borders, trees and shrubs, vegetables, drystone wall planting, South African plants, Mediterranean plants, a wild meadow and stunning views. Many of the plants have been collected from all over the world, and growing them in Durnamuck has provided obvious challenges but with an overall pleasing outcome. Featured on *Gardeners' World* (2016), *Garden Magazine, The Scottish Field* and *Country Life* in 2018. 2019 saw entries in *Gardens Illustrated, Homes & Gardens,* and *The Beechgrove Garden.*

Open: Saturday 18 July, & Sunday 23 August, noon - 5pm. And open by arrangement 1 June - 30 September. Admission £5.00, children free (Saturday 18 July & Sunday 23 August) and by donation (1 June - 30 September). Homemade teas on 18 July and 23 August only.

Directions: On the A832, between Dundonnell and Ullapool, take the turning along the single-track road signed *Badcaul*, continue to the yellow salt bin, turn right, go to the bottom of the hill and 2 Durnamuck is the house with the red roof. There is parking down by the house if needed.

· *Scottish Association For Marine Science*

5 KNOTT
Clachamish, Portree, Isle of Skye IV51 9NZ
Brian and Joyce Heggie
T: 01470 582213 E: jbheggie@hotmail.co.uk
W: knottcottageselfcatering.co.uk

An informal, organic garden on a gently sloping half-acre site. Perimeter hedging has enabled a sheltered, tranquil oasis to be created. Winding paths meander through densely planted borders filled with a diverse range of perennials, annuals and shrubs. The house overlooks a sheltered bay with regular sightings of otters, sea eagles and harbour porpoises. There is a separate vegetable and herb area with a large polytunnel and raised beds. Garden seating in several locations. The garden is situated in an easily reached, particularly quiet and scenic area of Skye.

Open: 26 June - 21 September (Mondays, Fridays & Sundays), 2pm - 5pm. Also open by arrangement 1 June - 30 September. Admission £3.00, children free.

Directions: From Portree, take the A87 to Uig/Dunvegan. After approximately three miles, take the A850 towards Dunvegan. Six miles on, past the *Treaslane* sign, look for the red phone box on the right. Turn right on the bend at the signpost for *Knott.*

· *Crossroads Care Skye & Lochalsh*

Inverness, Ross, Cromarty & Skye

ABRIACHAN GARDEN NURSERY
Loch Ness Side IV3 8LA
Mr and Mrs Davidson
T: 01463 861232 E: info@lochnessgarden.com
W: www.lochnessgarden.com

This is an outstanding garden with over four acres of exciting plantings with winding paths through native woodlands. Seasonal highlights include snowdrops, hellebores, primulas, meconopsis, hardy geraniums and colour-themed summer beds. Views over Loch Ness.

Open: 1 February - 30 November, 9am - 7pm (including for Snowdrops and Winter Walks), admission £3.00, children free.

Directions: On the A82 Inverness/Drumnadrochit road, about eight miles south of Inverness.

· *Highland Hospice*

ATTADALE
Strathcarron IV54 8YX
Mr Ewen Macpherson
T: 01520 722603 E: info@attadalegardens.com
W: www.attadalegardens.com

The Gulf Stream, surrounding hills and rocky cliffs create a microclimate for 20 acres of outstanding water gardens, old rhododendrons, unusual trees and a fern collection in a geodesic dome. There is also a sunken fern garden developed on the site of an early 19th-century drain, a waterfall into a pool with dwarf rhododendrons, sunken garden, peace garden and kitchen garden. Other features include a conservatory, Japanese garden, sculpture collection and giant sundial.

Open: 1 April - 31 October, 10am - 5:30pm, admission £8.00, children £1.00, OAPs £6.00. Self-service teas with home-baking.

Directions: On the A890 between Strathcarron and South Strome.

· *Strathcarron Project: Howard Doris Centre*

AULTGOWRIE MILL
Aultgowrie, Urray, Muir of Ord IV6 7XA
Mr and Mrs John Clegg
T: 01997 433699 E: john@johnclegg.com

Aultgowrie Mill is an 18th century converted water mill set in gardens, river and woodlands of 13 acres. Features include a wooded island, a half-acre wildflower meadow and a wildlife pond, all with views of the surrounding hills. The maturing gardens have terraces, lawns, two mixed orchards and raised vegetable beds with glasshouse and a third-of-a-mile river walk. *The Beechgrove Garden* featured this garden in July 2014.

Open: by arrangement 1 April - 1 September, admission £4.50, children free. Teas available by arrangement.

Directions: From the south, turn left at Muir of Ord Distillery, Aultgowrie Mill is then about three miles. From the north and west, after Marybank Primary School, Aultgowrie Mill is about one-and-a-half miles up the hill.

· *RNLI*

Inverness, Ross, Cromarty & Skye

6

BALMEANACH HOUSE
Balmeanach, nr Struan, Isle of Skye IV56 8FH
Mrs Arlene Macphie
T: 01470 572320 E: info@skye-holiday.com
W: www.skye-holiday.com

Approximately a third of an acre of open croft land was fenced and a garden started, some 30 ears ago. Now well established, there are glorious herbaceous borders, with a small azalea and rhododendron walk, a rose garden, arbour area, a small sunken pond and a well established woodland, complete with statues and fairies. Two additional ponds and a small shrubbery provide shelter for wildlife. Visitors are welcome to sit, or even picnic, in the numerous seating areas provided - remembering, to take all litter away, please.

Open: 4 May - 8 October (Mondays & Thursdays), 10:30am - 3pm, admission £3.00, children free.

Directions: A87 to Sligachan, turn left, Balmeanach is five miles north of Struan and five miles south of Dunvegan.

· *Scottish SPCA*

7

BERRYFIELD HOUSE
Lentran, Inverness IV3 8RJ
Lynda Perch-Nielsen
T: 01463 831346 M: 07547 960341 E: lyndazpn@gmail.com

An open garden of trees and bushes with views across the Beauly Firth to Ben Wyvis. There are large swathes of bulbs: crocus, dogs tooth violets and heritage daffodils. A three-acre wildflower meadow with meandering paths adjoins the garden giving interest until the start of autumn foliage and crocus.

Open: by arrangement 1 April - 4 October, admission by donation.

Directions: Halfway between Inverness and Beauly on the A862. From Inverness - 4 and a quarter miles on the left from crossing over the Clachnaharry railway bridge. From Beauly - 1 and a quarter miles on the right from The Old North Inn.

· *Action Medical Research*

Berryfield House

Inverness, Ross, Cromarty & Skye

DUNDONNELL HOUSE
Little Loch Broom, Wester Ross IV23 2QW
Dundonnell Estates
T: 07789 390028

Camellias, magnolias and bulbs in spring, rhododendrons and laburnum walk in this ancient walled garden. Exciting planting in new borders gives all year colour centred around one of the oldest yew trees in Scotland. A new water sculpture, midsummer roses, recently restored unique Victorian glass house, riverside walk, arboretum - all in the valley below the peaks of An Teallach. Champion Trees: Yew and Holly.

Open: Thursdays 16 April, 28 May and 20 August, 2pm - 5pm. And open by arrangement 1 April - 31 October. Admission £5.00, children free (Thursday 16 April, Thursday 28 May & Thursday 20 August) and by donation (1 May - 31 October). Homemade teas are only available on the 28 May.

Directions: Turn off the A835 at Braemore on to the A832. After 11 miles take the Badralloch turn for a half mile.

· *The Wild Camel Protection Foundation & Population Matters*

Dundonnell House

DUNVEGAN CASTLE AND GARDENS
Isle of Skye IV55 8WF
Hugh Macleod of Macleod
T: 01470 521206 E: info@dunvegancastle.com
W: www.dunvegancastle.com

Five acres of formal gardens dating from the 18th century. In contrast to the barren moorland of Skye, the gardens are an oasis featuring an eclectic mix of plants, woodland glades, shimmering pools fed by waterfalls and streams flowing down to the sea. After the water garden with its ornate bridges and islands replete with a rich and colourful plant variety, wander through the elegant

Inverness, Ross, Cromarty & Skye

surroundings of the formal round garden. The walled garden is worth a visit to see its colourful herbaceous borders and recently added Victorian-style glasshouse. In what was formerly the castle's vegetable garden, there is a garden museum and a diverse range of plants and flowers which complement the features including a waterlily pond, a neoclassical urn and a larch pergola. Replanting and landscaping have taken place over the last 30 years to restore and develop the gardens.

Open: 1 April - 15 October, 10am - 5:30pm, admission details can be found on the garden's website.

Directions: One mile from Dunvegan village, 23 miles west of Portree. Follow the signs for *Dunvegan Castle.*

· **Donation to SGS Beneficiaries**

FIELD HOUSE
Belladrum, Beauly IV4 7BA
Mr and Mrs D Paterson
W: www.dougthegarden.co.uk

An informal country garden in a one-acre site with mixed borders, ponds and some unusual plants - a plantsman's garden. Featured on the *The Beechgrove Garden.*

Open: Sunday 7 June, 2pm - 4:30pm, admission £4.00, children free. Home-baking and teas.

Directions: Four miles from Beauly on the A833 Beauly to Drumnadrochit road, then follow signs to *Belladrum.*

· **Highland Disability Sport: Swim Team**

GLENKYLLACHY
Tomatin IV13 7YA
Mr and Mrs Philip Mackenzie
E: emmaglenkyllachy@gmail.com

In a magnificent Highland glen, at 1200 feet above sea level, Glenkyllachy offers a glorious garden of shrubs, herbaceous plants, rhododendrons, trees and spectacular views down the Findhorn River. There are some rare specimens and a newly planted arboretum. Rhododendrons and bulbs flower in May/June, herbaceous plants bloom through July/August. Experience the annual wildflower meadow in summer and glorious autumn colours from September. Original sculptures and a Highgrove-inspired wall provide year-round interest. As featured on *The Beechgrove Garden* in 2018.

Open: 1 April - 30 October (Mondays only), 2pm - 5pm. Also open by arrangement 1 April - 30 October. Admission £5.00, children free. Individuals and groups welcome by arrangement

Directions: Turn off the A9 at Tomatin and take the Coignafearn/Garbole single-track road down the north-side of the River Findhorn, there is a cattle grid and gate on the right 500 yards AFTER the humpback bridge and the sign to *Farr.*

· **Marie Curie**

Inverness, Ross, Cromarty & Skye

GORTHLECK HOUSE GARDEN
Stratherrick IV2 6UJ
Steve and Katie Smith
T: 07710 325903 E: gorthleckgarden@gmail.com

Gorthleck is an unusual 20-acre woodland garden built in an unlikely place, on and around an exposed rocky ridge which offers long views of the surrounding countryside in the 'borrowed landscape' tradition of Japanese gardens. The layout of the garden works with the natural features of the landscape with numerous paths, hedges and shelter belts creating clearly defined areas where a large collection of trees and shrubs are thriving. The garden includes over 400 different varieties of rhododendrons, half of which are species, and a large variety of bamboos. It is a large garden so allow sufficient time to see it properly.

Open: Friday/Saturday/Sunday, 5/6/7 June, 10am - 8pm, admission £5.00, children free.

Directions: From the A9, join the B862. Go through the village of Errogie where there is a sharp left-hand bend on the road. After approximately one mile, there is a small church on the left. The Gorthleck drive is directly opposite the church and the house can be seen on the hill to the left as you follow the drive to the left of the new house. Visitors can park on the verges at the top of the drive.
· *Maggie's*

HIGHLAND LILIUMS
10 Loaneckheim, Kiltarlity IV4 7JQ
Neil and Frances Macritchie
T: 01463 741365 E: accounts@highlandliliums.co.uk
W: www.highlandliliums.co.uk

Highland Liliums is a working retail nursery with spectacular views over the Beauly valley and Strathfarrar hills. A wide selection of home-grown plants available including alpines, ferns, grasses, herbaceous, herbs, liliums, primulas and shrubs.

Open: 1 January - 31 December, 9am - 5pm. Also open as part of the Kiltarlity Gardens on Sunday 9 August.

Directions: Signposted from Kiltarlity village, which is just off the Beauly to Drumnadrochit road (A833), approximately 12 miles from Inverness.

· *Donation to SGS Beneficiaries*

HOUSE OF AIGAS AND FIELD CENTRE
by Beauly IV4 7AD
Sir John and Lady Lister-Kaye
T: 01463 782443 E: info@aigas.co.uk
W: www.aigas.co.uk

The House of Aigas has a small arboretum of named Victorian specimen trees and modern additions. The garden consists of extensive rockeries, herbaceous borders, ponds and shrubs. Aigas Field Centre rangers lead regular guided walks on nature trails through woodland, moorland and around a loch.
Champion Trees: Douglas fir, Atlas cedar and *Sequoiadendron giganteum*.

Open: Sunday 28 June, 2pm - 5pm. Also open Sunday 26 July, 2pm - 5pm. And open by arrangement 1 April - 31 October. Admission £4.00, children free.

Directions: Four and a half miles from Beauly on the A831 Cannich/Glen Affric road.

· *Highland Hospice: Aird branch*

Inverness, Ross, Cromarty & Skye

15

HOUSE OF GRUINARD
Laide, by Achnasheen IV22 2NQ
The Hon Mrs A G Maclay
T: 01445 731235 E: office@houseofgruinard.com

Superb hidden and unexpected garden developed in sympathy with stunning west coast estuary location. Wide variety of interesting herbaceous and shrub borders with water garden and extended wild planting.

Open: Wednesday 3 June, 2pm - 5pm, admission £4.00, children free.

Directions: On the A832 12 miles north of Inverewe and nine miles south of Dundonnell.

· *Macmillan Cancer Support*

16

KILCOY CASTLE
Redcastle, by Muir of Ord IV6 7RX
Kilcoy Castle Estate
T: 07766 445511

To the front of the castle are steps which lead on to grass terraces surrounded by shrubs and trees: the walled garden leads off to the east. The area farthest from the castle has been restyled based on the poem *Solitude* by Thomas Merton. The shape is rhomboid with a central point taken from which the design radiates planted with pleached hornbeam, underplanted with willow. Box holly and yew hedges are still to grow to fruition. Work is ongoing with new herbaceous border and different planting using annuals and herbaceous plants; the garden will host a further vibrant display of colourful plants within the walled garden along with a greenhouse in full production.

Open: Sunday 16 August, 2pm - 4:30pm, admission £6.00, children under 12 free.

Directions: From the Tore roundabout, take the A832, go past Fettes Sawmill on the left. Turn right at Kilcoy Kindergarten (an old church) heading towards Kilcoy. Go along the single road for about a quarter-mile and you will see the Kilcoy Castle entrance on the left.

· *Nansen Highland*

'Opening with the scheme helps me
meet like-minded people, and I can
raise money for charity while doing so'
Inverness Gardener

Inverness, Ross, Cromarty & Skye

17 **KILTARLITY GARDENS**
Kiltarlity, Beauly IV4 7JQ
Sheila Ross, Sue Mullins, Neil and Frances Macritchie
T: 01463 741365 E: accounts@highlandliliums.co.uk
W: www.highlandliliums.co.uk

Aird View 30a Camault Muir IV4 7JH (Sheila Ross): The garden at Aird View offers a mix of borders, a water feature, an arbour and a newly added herbaceous border. There are also fruit trees and vegetable beds.
Foinaven Loaneckheim IV4 7JQ (Sue Mullins): Foinaven is approximately half an acre in size, and is blessed with several mature Scots pine trees. This is a 'plantaholics' garden with many different varieties of shrubs, trees and herbaceous plants. There is a natural pond and the garden has untamed areas for wildlife and pollinators. Wildlife is well catered for by the selection of plants with flowers for pollinators, and the birds are fed well by the resultant berries.
Highland Liliums 10 Loaneckheim IV4 7JQ (Neil and Frances Macritchie): Highland Liliums is a working retail nursery with spectacular views over the Beauly valley and Strathfarrar hills. A wide selection of home grown plants available including alpines, ferns, grasses, herbaceous, herbs, liliums, primulas and shrubs.

Open: Sunday 9 August, noon - 5pm, admission £3.00, children free. Admission tickets available at any of the gardens. Teas (£3.00) and discounted plants at Highland Liliums.

Directions: **Aird View** Take the A833 Beauly to Drumnadrochit road, pass Brockies Lodge. Turn right at the bus shelter and follow single track road to junction at school. Turn left up the hill to the top at junction. Aird View is on the right. **Foinaven** Turn up Post Office Brae in Kiltarlity then turn right after the Free Church. Follow the road towards Highland Liliums. Foinaven is about a half mile from the church. (sixth house on the right-hand side). **Highland Liliums** Signposted from Kiltarlity village, which is just off the Beauly to Drumnadrochit road (A833), approximately 12 miles from Inverness.

· *Highland Hospice: Aird branch*

Foinaven, Kiltarlity Gardens

Inverness, Ross, Cromarty & Skye

18

LEATHAD ARD
Upper Carloway, Isle of Lewis HS2 9AQ
Rowena and Stuart Oakley
T: 01851 643204 E: stuart.oakley1a@gmail.com
W: www.leathadard.org.uk

A one-acre sloping garden with stunning views over East Loch Roag. It has evolved along with the shelter hedges that divide the garden into a number of areas giving a new view at every corner. With shelter and raised beds, the different conditions created permit a wide variety of plants to be grown. Features include herbaceous borders, cutting borders, bog gardens, grass garden, exposed beds, patios, a pond and vegetables and fruit grown both in the open ground and the Keder greenhouse. Some of the vegetables are grown to show standards.

Open: 1 May - 30 September (not Sundays), 10am - 6pm. Also open by arrangement 1 April - 30 April (not Sundays). Admission £4.00, children free.

Directions: On the A858 Shawbost-Carloway, first right after the Carloway football pitch, and the first house on the right. By bus take the Westside circular bus, exit Stornoway, head for Carloway football pitch.

· *British Red Cross*

19

OLD ALLANGRANGE
Munlochy IV8 8NZ
J J Gladwin
T: 01463 811304 E: office@blackislebeegardendesign.com

The garden surrounds an 18th-century orange lime-washed house. There is a formalish parterre in front of the house with loose planting in the individual beds, a terrace garden, lime pom pom bed planted with roses, herb garden, mound, orchard, all linked with various styles of hedges - pleached lime, yew, beech, box, holly, mixed and more recently, we have started to remove perimeter wire fences and replace with log hedges and brash bunds. The hedges are treated with different degrees of formality. There is a five-acre organic vegetable garden with two large Keder greenhouses. We have a keen interest in gardening for all wildlife with a particular focus on planting for invertebrates. No chemicals have been used since arrival in 1995. The development and improvement of the garden is on-going.
Champion Trees: Yew and sweet chestnut.

Open: Sunday 14 June, 2pm - 5pm & Sunday 30 August, 2pm - 5pm. And open by arrangement for groups (minimum 10 people). Admission £7.50, children free.

Directions: From Inverness head four miles north on the A9, and follow the directions for *Black Isle Brewery*. Park up at the Brewery and walk down to the garden. Directions will be given in the shop.

· *Black Isle Bee Gardens*

Inverness, Ross, Cromarty & Skye

20
OLDTOWN OF LEYS GARDEN
Inverness IV2 6AE
David and Anne Sutherland
T: 01463 238238 E: ams@oldtownofleys.com

Large garden established in 2003 on the outskirts of Inverness and overlooking the town. Herbaceous beds with lovely rhododendron and azalea displays in spring. There are specimen trees, three ponds surrounded by waterside planting and a small woodland area. A new rockery area was created in 2015 and is still developing.

Open: 1 January - 31 December, dawn - dusk, admission by donation.

Directions: Turn off southern distributor road (B8082) at Leys roundabout towards Inverarnie (B861). At the T junction turn right. After 50 yards turn right into Oldtown of Leys.

· *Local Charities*

21
SHANVALL
Glentruim, Newtonmore PH20 1BE
George and Beth Alder
T: 01540 673213 E: beth.alder@yahoo.co.uk

The garden is two-thirds of an acre at 900 feet above sea level, surrounding a 19th-century cottage. On the south side of the River Spey, it has lovely views of the Creag Dubh and Creag Meagaidh mountains. There are ruined buildings of an old township within the garden. To the south is a garden of roses and perennials. Within a stone wall, there are fruit cages, a small orchard and organic vegetable beds which have been cultivated for about 200 years. The garden on the north slopes has trees, shrubs, herbaceous border, wildflowers, a pond and is rich with wildlife, including woodpeckers and red squirrels.

Open: by arrangement 1 June - 31 August, admission £5.00, children free. Admission price includes tea.

Directions: Shanvall is on the minor road running along the south side of the Spey, linking the A9 south of Newtonmore at Glentruim and the A889 at Catlodge. The garden gate is on the right about one-and-a-half miles from the A9. Further details on request.

· *Laggan and Newtonmore Church of Scotland*

22
THE LOOKOUT
Kilmuir, North Kessock IV1 3ZG
David and Penny Veitch
T: 01463 731489 E: david@veitch.biz

A three-quarter-acre elevated coastal garden with incredible views over the Moray Firth which is only for the sure-footed. This award-winning garden, featured on the *The Beechgrove Garden* has been created out of a rock base with shallow pockets of ground, planted to its advantage to encourage all aspects of wildlife. There is a small sheltered courtyard, raised bed vegetable area, pretty cottage garden, scree and rock garden, rose arbour, rhododendrons, flowering shrubs, bamboos, trees and lily pond with waterside plants.

Open: 1 June - 31 August (Sundays only), noon - 4pm. Also open by arrangement 1 April - 30 September. Admission £3.00, children free.

Inverness, Ross, Cromarty & Skye

Directions: From Inverness, take the North Kessock left turn from the A9, and third left at the roundabout to go on the underpass, then sharp left onto Kilmuir Road. From Tore, take the slip road for North Kessock and immediately right for Kilmuir. Follow signs for *Kilmuir* (three miles) until you reach the shore. The Lookout is near the far end of the village with a large palm tree in front, surrounded by gravel.

· *Alzheimer Scotland*

TORCROFT
Balnain, Glenurquhart IV63 6TJ
Barbara Craig
T: 01456 476717

....

This garden is about three-quarters of an acre on a hillside overlooking Loch Meiklie in Glen Urquhart. It is a wild garden, with its own character and style. There are weeds and cardamine for the orange tip butterflies, but most of all there are plants in profusion from acer, anemone and astrantia to veronicastrum, verbascum, weigela and water lilies. A natural stream comes into the garden and meanders into various small ponds. In the spring there are masses of bog primula of all types and colours. There is a fern bed, a rockery, herbs, wooded area. New in 2018 was a stumpery, beds and another pond.

Open: 1 July - 31 August (Mondays only), 2pm - 5pm. Also open by arrangement 1 March - 31 October. Admission £3.00, children free.

Directions: From Inverness turn right at Drumnadrochit and go towards Cannich. After four miles, sign *Balnain*, there is a very sharp right-hand bend with a high retaining wall on the right. At the end of the wall take the turning to right signposted *Torcroft Lodges*.

· *Munlochy Animal Aid & Send a Cow*

WHITE ROSE COTTAGE
Pitcalnie, Tain IV20 1XJ
Mr and Mrs S Miles
T: 01862 851292 E: lambdon@hotmail.co.uk

....

A garden full of surprises from secret dens to hidden gems. Colourful rhododendron displays plus unusual trees, shrubs and flowers in woodland, seaside and traditional settings.

Open: Sunday 24 May, 2pm - 5pm, admission £4.00, children free.

Directions: Turn right at Nigg roundabout over the railway crossing, through Nigg Station and Arabella. Turn left to Shandwick up a slight hill (the cemetery is on the left). White Rose Cottage is immediately after the Old Schoolhouse on the left opposite junction to Pitcalnie. Stagecoach Buses from Tain, 30A or 30C. Request stop.

· *Nigg Old Trust & Cromarty Firth Men's Shed*

KINCARDINE & DEESIDE

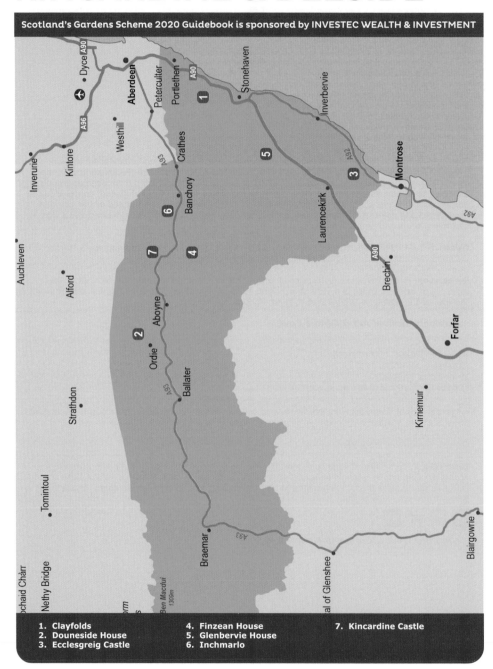

Scotland's Gardens Scheme 2020 Guidebook is sponsored by INVESTEC WEALTH & INVESTMENT

1. Clayfolds
2. Douneside House
3. Ecclesgreig Castle
4. Finzean House
5. Glenbervie House
6. Inchmarlo
7. Kincardine Castle

Kincardine & Deeside

OUR VOLUNTEER ORGANISERS

District Organisers:	Catherine Nichols	Westerton Steading, Dess, Aboyne AB34 5AY
	Julie Nicol	Cedarwood Lodge, Aboyne AB34 5JB
		E: kincardine@scotlandsgardens.org
Area Organisers:	Wendy Buchan	Inneshewen, Dess, Aboyne AB34 5BH
	Gavin Farquhar	Ecclesgreig Castle, St Cyrus DD10 0DP
	Hilary Greensill	Broomhill, Tarland, Aboyne, AB34 4UJ
	Tina Hammond	Sunnybank, 7 Watson Street, Banchory AB31 5UB
	Liz Inglesfield	2 Earlspark Circle, Bieldside, Aberdeen AB15 9BW
	David & Patsy Younie	Bealltainn, Ballogie, Aboyne AB34 5DL
District Photographer:	Hilary Greensill	Broomhill, Tarland, Aboyne, AB34 4UJ
Treasurers:	Michael Buchan	Inneshewen, Dess, Aboyne AB34 5BH

GARDENS OPEN ON A SPECIFIC DATE

Ecclesgreig Castle, St Cyrus	Sunday, 1 March
Inchmarlo Retirement Village Garden, Inchmarlo, Banchory	Sunday, 17 May
Kincardine Castle, Kincardine O'Neil	Sunday, 14 June
Finzean House, Finzean, Banchory	Sunday, 21 June
Douneside House, Tarland	Sunday, 12 July
Glenbervie House, Drumlithie, Stonehaven	Sunday, 2 August
Clayfolds, Bridge of Muchalls, Stonehaven	Sunday, 9 August

GARDENS OPEN BY ARRANGEMENT

Glenbervie House, Drumlithie, Stonehaven	1 May - 15 September

Kincardine & Deeside

CLAYFOLDS
Bridge of Muchalls, Stonehaven AB39 3RU
Andrea Sinclair
E: andreaysinclair@outlook.com

An informal country garden extending to a half-acre, with a further six acres of wildflowers, native trees and a pond. The main garden is laid out with lawn and mixed borders, which are filled with shrubs and a wide range of hardy perennials and includes a 'hot' border with various flaxes and a variety of 'hot'-coloured plants. Small cottage-style garden to the front of the house. Follow the tracks through the recently developed six-acre Wilderness Garden and see what native fauna and flora you can spot.

Open: Sunday 9 August, 2pm - 5pm, admission £4.00, children free.

Directions: SatNav - AB39 3RU but travel inland a further one-and-a-half miles to Clayfolds. Travelling in either direction on the A92, three miles north of Stonehaven, take the road signposted *Netherley 3*, continue travelling inland for approximately one-and-a-half miles and you will then be directed where to park.

· *Scottish SPCA*

Clayfolds

Kincardine & Deeside

2

DOUNESIDE HOUSE
Tarland AB34 4UD
The MacRobert Trust
W: www.dounesidehouse.co.uk
....

Douneside is the former home of Lady MacRobert, who developed these magnificent gardens in the early to mid-1900s. Ornamental borders and water gardens surround a spectacular infinity lawn overlooking the Deeside hills. A large walled garden supplies vegetables and cut flowers and also houses a large ornamental greenhouse. A new arboretum displays over 130 trees amongst mown grass paths and walking trails behind Douneside, which offer breathtaking views across the Howe of Cromar and beyond.

Open: Sunday 12 July, 2pm - 5pm, admission £5.00 (concession £3.00), children free. There will be a local pipe band and raffle.

Directions: On the B9119 towards Aberdeen. Tarland one mile.

· *Perennial*

3

ECCLESGREIG CASTLE
St Cyrus DD10 0DP
Mr Gavin Farquhar
T: 01224 214301 E: enquiries@ecclesgreig.com
W: www.ecclesgreig.com
....

Ecclesgreig Castle, Victorian Gothic on a 16th-century core, is internationally famous as an inspiration for Bram Stoker's *Dracula*. The snowdrop walk (over 150 varieties of snowdrop) starts at the castle, meanders around the estate, along woodland paths and the pond, ending at the garden. In the Italian balustraded gardens there is a 140-foot-long herbaceous border, classical statues and stunning shaped topiary with views across St Cyrus to the sea. Started from a derelict site, development continues. Also to be found in the grounds is the well of St Cyrus.

Open: Sunday 1 March, 1pm - 4pm for Snowdrops and Winter Walks, admission £4.00, children free.

Directions: *Ecclesgreig* will be signposted from the A92 Coast Road and from the A937 Montrose/Laurencekirk Road.

· *Girlguiding Montrose District: Montrose Guide Camp Fund*

4

FINZEAN HOUSE
Finzean, Banchory AB31 6NZ
Mr and Mrs Donald Farquharson

....

Finzean House was the family home of Joseph Farquharson, the Victorian landscape painter, and the garden was the backdrop for several of his paintings. The garden has lovely views over the historic holly hedge to the front of Clachnaben. There is a spring woodland garden, extensive lawns with herbaceous and shrub borders and a working cut-flower garden for late summer, alongside a recently restored pond area. A new vegetable garden is planned for 2020.

Open: Sunday 21 June, 2pm - 5pm, admission £5.00, children free, OAP's £4.00.

Directions: On the B976, South Deeside Road, between Banchory and Aboyne.

· *The Forget-Me-Not Club*

Kincardine & Deeside

5 GLENBERVIE HOUSE
Drumlithie, Stonehaven AB39 3YA
Mr and Mrs A Macphie

The nucleus of the beautiful present-day house dates from the 15th century with additions in the 18th and 19th centuries. There is a traditional Scottish walled garden on a slope with roses, herbaceous and annual borders along with fruit and vegetables. One wall is taken up with a Victorian-style greenhouse with many species of pot plants and climbers including peach and figs. A woodland garden by a burn is punctuated with many varieties of plants, primula to name but one.

Open: Sunday 2 August, 2pm - 5pm. Also garden visits by arrangement 1 May - 15 September, apply in writing. Admission £5.00, children free. Please note some steep pathways and tree roots can make walking difficult in places. Gravel pathways are not accessible for electric wheelchairs. Please no dogs.

Directions: Drumlithie one mile. Garden is one-and-a-half miles off the A90.

· *Scotland's Charity Air Ambulance*

Glenbervie House

6 INCHMARLO RETIREMENT VILLAGE GARDEN
Inchmarlo, Banchory AB31 4AL
Skene Enterprises (Aberdeen) Ltd
T: 01330 826242 E: info@inchmarlo-retirement.co.uk
W: www.inchmarlo-retirement.co.uk

Beautiful five-acre woodland garden filled with azaleas and rhododendrons beneath ancient Scots pines, Douglas firs and silver firs (some over 140 feet tall). Also beeches, rare and unusual trees including pindrow firs, Pere David's maple, Erman's birch and a mountain snowdrop tree. The Oriental Garden features a Karesansui, a dry slate stream designed by Peter Roger, a *RHS Chelsea* gold medal winner. The Rainbow Garden, within the keyhole-shaped purple *Prunus cerasifera* hedge, has been designed by Billy Carruthers, an eight-times gold medal winner at the *RHS Scottish Garden Show*.

Kincardine & Deeside

Open: Sunday 17 May, 1:30pm - 4:30pm, admission £5.00, children free.

Directions: From Aberdeen via North Deeside Road on the A93, one mile west of Banchory turn right at the main gate to the Inchmarlo Estate.

· *Alzheimer Scotland & The Forget-Me-Not Club*

KINCARDINE CASTLE
Kincardine O'Neil AB34 5AE
Mr and Mrs Andrew Bradford

A superb series of gardens around a Victorian castle with great views across Deeside. Walled garden with a world-class laburnum walk, a mixture of herbaceous and shrub borders, vegetables and fruit trees. Extensive lawns, wildflower meadows and a thought-provoking Planetary Garden. A woodland garden with 120 varieties of rhododendrons and azaleas, many of recent planting, set amongst mature trees. Sculpture by Lyman Whittaker of Utah. A great day out.

Open: Sunday 14 June, 1:30pm - 5pm, admission £5.00, children free.

Directions: Kincardine O'Neil on the A93. Gates and lodge are opposite the village school.

· *Christ Church, Kincardine O'neil & Children 1st*

KIRKCUDBRIGHTSHIRE

Scotland's Gardens Scheme 2020 Guidebook is sponsored by INVESTEC WEALTH & INVESTMENT

Thornhill

A76

Dumfries

New Abbey

SOLWAY FIRTH

3

14

Crocketford

Dalbeattie

13

Moniaive

5

Castle Douglas

9

8

11

17 15

Kirkcudbright

7

18

16

10

A75

New Galloway

Loch Ken

Carsphairn

St John's Town of Dalry

1

Gatehouse
of Fleet

6

Clatteringshaws
Loch

12

2

Loch
Doon

4

Creetown

town

1. 3 Millhall	8. Crofts	14. Southwick House
2. Anwoth Old Schoolhouse	9. Dalbeattie Community	15. Stockarton
3. Arbigland House	Allotments Association	16. The Limes
4. Barholm Castle	10. Danevale Park	17. The Waterhouse Gardens
5. Brooklands	11. Kings Grange House	at Stockarton
6. Cally Gardens	12. Luckie Harg's	18. Threave Garden
7. Corsock House	13. Seabank	

Kirkcudbrightshire

OUR VOLUNTEER ORGANISERS

District Organisers:	Theodora & Julian Stanning	Seabank, Merse Rd, Rockcliffe, Dalbeattie DG5 4QH
		E: kirkcudbrightshire@scotlandsgardens.org
Area Organisers:	Hedley Foster	Deer Park, Fleet Forest, Gatehouse of Fleet DG7 2DN
	May Lockhart	25 Victoria Park, Kirkcudbright DG6 4EN
	Norman McClure	142 Cotton Street, Castle Douglas DG7 1DG
	Lesley Pepper	Anwoth Old Schoolhouse, Gatehouse of Fleet DG7 2EF
	Audrey Slee	Holmview, New Galloway, Castle Douglas DG7 3RN
	George Thomas	Savat, Meikle Richorn, Dalbeattie DG5 4QT
Treasurer:	Duncan Lofts	Balcary Tower, Auchencairn, Castle Douglas DG7 1QZ

GARDENS OPEN ON A SPECIFIC DATE

Danevale Park, Crossmichael	Sunday, 23 February
3 Millhall, Shore Road, Kirkcudbright	Sunday, 12 April
Cally Gardens, Cally Avenue, Gatehouse of Fleet	Sunday, 10 May
Arbigland House, Kirkbean, Dumfries	Sunday, 17 May
Corsock House, Corsock, Castle Douglas	Sunday, 24 May
The Limes, Kirkcudbright	Sunday, 31 May
Seabank, The Merse, Rockcliffe	Sunday, 7 June
Threave Garden, Castle Douglas	Friday/Saturday/Sunday, 12/13/14 June
Southwick House, Southwick	Sunday, 5 July
Dalbeattie Community Allotments, Port Road, Dalbeattie	Sunday, 19 July
Crofts, Kirkpatrick Durham, Castle Douglas	Sunday, 26 July
Cally Gardens, Cally Avenue, Gatehouse of Fleet	Sunday, 2 August
Kings Grange House, Castle Douglas	Sunday, 9 August
3 Millhall, Shore Road, Kirkcudbright	Sunday, 30 August

GARDENS OPEN BY ARRANGEMENT

The Limes, Kirkcudbright	1 January - 31 December
Stockarton, Kirkcudbright	1 January - 31 December
Anwoth Old Schoolhouse, Anwoth, Gatehouse of Fleet	15 February - 15 November
Barholm Castle, Gatehouse of Fleet	15 February - 15 October
Corsock House, Corsock, Castle Douglas	1 April - 30 June
Luckie Harg's, Anwoth, Gatehouse of Fleet, Castle Douglas	1 April - 31 July
Brooklands, Crocketford	1 May - 30 September
The Waterhouse Gardens at Stockarton, Kirkcudbright	1 May - 30 September

Kirkcudbrightshire

Arbigland House

1 3 MILLHALL
Shore Road, Kirkcudbright DG6 4TQ
Mr Alan Shamash
T: 01557 870352 E: shamash@freeuk.com

....

Impressive five-acre garden with a large collection of mature shrubs, including over 200 rhododendron species, many camellias, perennials, over 300 hydrangeas and many rare Southern Hemisphere plants. The garden has several interesting paths and is on a hillside running along the rocky shore of the Dee Estuary in Kirkcudbright Bay.

Open: Sunday 12 April, 2pm - 5pm. Also open Sunday 30 August, 2pm - 5pm. Admission £4.00, children free.

Directions: On the B727 between Kirkcudbright and Borgue on the west shore of the Dee Estuary. Parking at Dhoon beach public car park, about three miles south of Kirkcudbright. There is a five-minute walk to the house.

· *Kirkcudbright Hospital League Of Friends & Alzheimer's Research UK*

2 ANWOTH OLD SCHOOLHOUSE
Anwoth, Gatehouse of Fleet DG7 2EF
Mr and Mrs Pepper
T: 01557 814444 E: lesley.pepper@btinternet.com

....

Two acres of delightful cottage-style gardens behind the old schoolhouse and cottage in a picturesque setting opposite Anwoth Old Church (in ruins) and graveyard. Winding paths alongside a burn, informally planted with unusual woodland perennials and shrubs. Wildlife pond, fish pond, rock garden, vegetable garden, wildflower area and viewpoint.

Open: by arrangement 15 February - 15 November, admission £3.00, children free.

Kirkcudbrightshire

Directions: Driving west on the A75, take the Anwoth turn off about half a mile after Gatehouse of Fleet. Anwoth Church is about half a mile along the road and Anwoth Old Schoolhouse is a little further along, opposite Anwoth Old Church (in ruins).

· *Dogs for Good*

3 ARBIGLAND HOUSE
Kirkbean, Dumfries DG2 8BQ
Alistair Alcock and Wayne Whittaker
T: 01387 880764 E: alcockalistair@gmail.com
W: www.arbiglandhouseandgardens.co.uk
....

Arbigland House is an Adam-style 18th-century mansion surrounded by 24 acres of woodland gardens running down to a beach on the Solway Firth. The gardens date from the 18th century but the more formal areas were developed in the late 19th and early 20th centuries and are currently undergoing a programme of restoration and development. There are 200 year old trees lining the Broad Walk which runs down to the Solway and a huge variety of rhododendrons and azaleas; within the woodland are a range of features including a stream-fed lake and a Japanese garden, with a more formal sundial garden and sunken rose garden, all in the process of renewal. Amongst these are a diverse collection of mature trees and shrubs

Open: Sunday 17 May, 2pm - 5pm, admission £5.00, children free. Short tours available of the principal rooms of the House.

Directions: Take the A710 to Kirkbean. In the village turn off towards Carsethorn and, after 200 yards, turn right and follow signs to *John Paul Jones Cottage*. After a mile or so, turn left at the T junction through white gates and down the drive through ornamental gates to Arbigland House.

· *Absolute Classics*

4 BARHOLM CASTLE
Gatehouse of Fleet DG7 2EZ
Drs John and Janet Brennan
E: barholmcastle@gmail.com
....

Barholm Castle, a 16th-century tower, was restored from a ruin in 2006. The gardens surrounding the tower have been mostly developed from scratch and are now mature. There is a recently extended walled garden, with a gate designed by the artist blacksmith Adam Booth; a courtyard garden; a wooded ravine with huge hybrid rhododendrons from Benmore, a pond and a large fernery with over 90 varieties of fern, including very large tree ferns; a large Victorian style greenhouse filled with succulents and tender perennials; and a large open garden with island beds of shrubs and perennials and a pond. Directly around the castle are rockeries and shrub borders. Views over Wigtown Bay are magnificent. The garden is planted for year round colour, from February, when the castle ravine is a river of snowdrops, to October, when autumn colour is splendid.

Open: by arrangement 15 February - 15 October for Snowdrops and Winter Walks, admission £4.00, children free.

Directions: Off the A75 at the Cairn Holy turn off, fork right three times up a steep narrow road for half a mile.

· *Home-Start Wigtownshire*

Kirkcudbrightshire

Corsock House

 BROOKLANDS
Crocketford DG2 8QH
Mr and Mrs Robert Herries
T: Head Gardener: Kate Redding 07870 481286

Large old walled garden with a wide selection of plants, including some interesting shrubs and climbers, fruit trees and a kitchen garden. Mature woodland with many established rhododendrons and azaleas.

Open: by arrangement 1 May - 30 September, admission £4.00, children free.

Directions: Turn off the A712 Crocketford to New Galloway Road one mile outside Crocketford at the Gothic gatehouse (on the right travelling north).

· **All proceeds to SGS Beneficiaries**

 CALLY GARDENS
Cally Avenue, Gatehouse of Fleet DG7 2DJ
Kevin Hughes
T: 01557 815228 E: info@callygardens.co.uk
W: www.callygardens.co.uk

Cally Gardens and Specialist Plant Centre is a treasure trove of exotic and rare hardy plants gathered from around the globe. The towering 18th-century walls of what was once the kitchen garden and pleasure garden of Cally House now provide shelter to thousands of rare and exotic plants. The informal garden, which was created by the famous plant collector Michael Wickenden, is now in the care of the plantsman Kevin Hughes. Kevin took ownership of Cally in 2018 and has since brought his own large collection of magnolias, daphnes and trilliums and has also added more collections including galanthus, paeonies and nerines. As an ecologist and environmentalist, Kevin has decided to make Cally a haven for birds, insects and all things wild.

Open: Sunday 10 May, 10am - 5pm. Also open Sunday 2 August, 10am - 5pm. Admission £5.00, children free.

Directions: From Dumfries take the Gatehouse of Fleet turning off the A75, follow the B727 and turn left through the Cally Palace Hotel gateway from where the gardens are well signposted. A regular bus service will stop at the end of Cally Drive if requested.

· **WWF-UK**

Kirkcudbrightshire

CORSOCK HOUSE
Corsock, Castle Douglas DG7 3DJ
The Ingall family
T: 01644 440250

Corsock House garden includes an amazing variety of designed landscape, from a strictly formal walled garden, through richly planted woodlands full of different vistas, artfully designed water features and surprises to manicured lawns showing off the Bryce baronial mansion. This is an Arcadian garden with pools and temples, described by Ken Cox as 'perhaps my favourite of Scotland's many woodland gardens'.

Open: Sunday 24 May, 2pm - 5pm for the May Weekend Festival. Also open by arrangement 1 April - 30 June. Admission £5.00, children free.

Directions: Off the A75, Dumfries is 14 miles, Castle Douglas is ten miles, Corsock Village is a half mile on the A712.

· Corsock & Kirkpatrick Durham Church Of Scotland

CROFTS
Kirkpatrick Durham, Castle Douglas DG7 3HX
Mrs Andrew Dalton
T: 01556 650235 E: jenniedalton@mac.com

Victorian country-house garden with mature trees, a walled garden with fruit and vegetables and glasshouses, hydrangea garden and a pretty water garden. Delightful woodland walk, colourfully planted with bog plants, and a stream running through.

Open: Sunday 26 July, 2pm - 5pm, admission £4.00, children free.

Directions: A75 to Crocketford, then three miles on the A712 to Corsock and New Galloway.

· Corsock & Kirkpatrick Durham Church Of Scotland

DALBEATTIE COMMUNITY ALLOTMENTS ASSOCIATION
Port Road, Dalbeattie DG5 4AZ
Dalbeattie Community Allotments Association
T: 01556 612208

Dalbeattie Community Allotments Association was formed in 2008 and the site was officially opened in August 2010. A local land owner has leased the land for 25 years at £1 per year, initially providing for 47 plots. The initial results were so successful that the area is now increased to provide for 81 productive plots where local residents can grow their own fruit, vegetables and flowers. Come and enjoy a stroll around the site, chat to members or relax in one of the community areas. Information will be available and photos of the development of the site will be on display.

Open: Sunday 19 July, 2pm - 5pm, admission £3.00, children free.

Directions: The allotment site can be found on the Dalbeattie bypass (A710) next to Craignair Health Centre.

· Dalbeattie Community Initiative

Kirkcudbrightshire

 DANEVALE PARK
Crossmichael DG7 2LP
Mrs M R C Gillespie
T: 01556 670223 E: danevale@tiscali.co.uk

First opening for snowdrops in 1951, these mature grounds have a wonderful display of snowdrops as well as aconites and many other wildflowers. Walks through the woods and alongside the River Dee make this a memorable afternoon. In celebration of this 50th Year of opening under Scotland's Gardens Scheme, complete your visit with an old fashioned afternoon tea in the house.

Open: Sunday 23 February, 1pm - 4pm for Snowdrops and Winter Walks, admission £3.00, children free.

Directions: On the A713 two miles from Castle Douglas and one mile short of Crossmichael

· *Earl Haig Fund Poppy Scotland*

 **KINGS GRANGE HOUSE**
Castle Douglas DG7 3EU
Christine and Peter Hickman

An extensive garden surrounded by mature trees and shrubberies, with views to the south west over the surrounding countryside. Originally Victorian, the garden is being restored by the present owners with a colourful variety of herbaceous mixed borders, beds and rockeries, mainly to the front of the house.

Open: Sunday 9 August, 2pm - 5pm, admission £4.00, children free. Homemade teas with vintage music.

Directions: Take the B794 north off the A75, two miles east of Castle Douglas. Kings Grange House is approximately one mile on the left.

· *RNLI & Marie Curie*

 LUCKIE HARG'S
Anwoth, Gatehouse of Fleet, Castle Douglas DG7 2EF
Drs Carole and Ian Bainbridge
T: 01557 814141 E: luckiehargs@btinternet.com

A new and developing garden on the outskirts of Gatehouse. A rock and spring herbaceous garden with a wide range of alpines, Himalayan and New Zealand plants, rock garden, crevices, troughs, large alpine house and bulb frame. Under the extension new beds and woodland area are being developed. Small productive vegetable and fruit garden, plus a bluebell bank in May.

Open: by arrangement 1 April - 31 July, admission £4.00, children free.

Directions: From Gatehouse High Street, turn north onto Station Road, immediately west at the Fleet Bridge by the *Ship Inn*. After almost one mile turn left signed to *Anwoth Old Church*. Luckie Harg's is the first on the right after 400 yards. The nearest bus stop is on Gatehouse High Street, walk about 15 minutes to Luckie Harg's.

· *Scottish Rock Garden Club*

Kirkcudbrightshire

13 ▼

SEABANK
The Merse, Rockcliffe DG5 4QH
Julian and Theodora Stanning
T: 01556 630244

This one-and-a-half-acre garden extends to the high water mark with views across a small wildflower meadow to the Urr Estuary, Rough Island and beyond. Mixed shrub and herbaceous borders surround the house and there is a new walled garden with fruit, vegetables and flowers. A plantswoman's garden with a range of interesting and unusual plants.

Open: Sunday 7 June, 2pm - 5pm, admission £4.00, children free.

Directions: Park in the public car park at Rockcliffe. Walk down the road about 50 yards towards the sea and turn left along The Merse, a private road. Seabank is the sixth house on the left.

· Marie Curie: DG5 Fundraising Group

14 ▼

SOUTHWICK HOUSE
Southwick DG2 8AH
Mr and Mrs R H L Thomas

The extensive gardens at Southwick House comprise three main areas. The first is a traditional formal walled garden with potager and large glasshouse producing a range of fruit, vegetables and cutting flowers. Adjacent to this is a hedged formal garden with herbaceous, shrub and rose beds centred around a lily pond, with roses being a notable feature. Outwith the formal gardens there is a large water garden with two connected ponds with trees, shrubs and lawns running alongside the Southwick Burn.

Open: Sunday 5 July, 2pm - 5pm, admission £5.00, children free.

Directions: On the A710 near Caulkerbush. Dalbeattie seven miles, Dumfries 17 miles.

· Loch Arthur

Luckie Harg's

Kirkcudbrightshire

15

STOCKARTON
Kirkcudbright DG6 4XS
Lt Col and Mrs Richard Cliff
T: 01557 330430

This garden was started in 1995 by Carola Cliff, a keen and knowledgeable plantswoman, and contains a collection of unusual shrubs and small trees, which are growing well. Her aim has been to create different informal gardens around a Galloway farm house, leading down to a lochan. Above the lochan there is a sweet cottage, used for holiday retreats, with its own interesting garden. In 1996 a three-acre arboretum was planted as a shelter belt and it now contains some rare oak trees.

Open: by arrangement 1 January - 31 December, admission £4.00, children free.

Directions: On the B727 Kirkcudbright to Gelston Road. Kirkcudbright three miles, Castle Douglas seven miles.

· *Great Ormond Street Hospital Children's Charity*

16

THE LIMES
Kirkcudbright DG6 4XD
David and Carolyn McHale
E: carolyn.mchale@btinternet.com

This one-and-a-quarter-acre plantsman's garden has a variety of different plant habitats: woodland, dry sunny gravel beds, rock garden, crevice garden and mixed perennial and shrub borders. There is also a large productive vegetable garden. The McHales like to grow most of their plants from seed obtained through various international seed exchanges. You can expect to see a large number of unusual and exciting plants. In late May and early June the meconopsis should be at their best.

Open: Sunday 31 May, 2pm - 5pm. Also open by arrangement 1 January - 31 December. Admission £4.00, children free.

Directions: In Kirkcudbright go straight along St Mary Street towards Dundrennan. The Limes is on the right, about half-a-mile from the town centre crossroads, on the edge of the town.

· *Friends Of Kirkcudbright Swimming Pool*

Kirkcudbrightshire

17 THE WATERHOUSE GARDENS AT STOCKARTON
Kirkcudbright DG6 4XS
Martin Gould and Sharon O'Rourke
T: 01557 331266 E: waterhousekbt@aol.com
W: www.waterhousekbt.co.uk

One acre of densely planted terraced-cottage-style gardens attached to a Galloway cottage. Three ponds surround the oak-framed eco-polehouse 'The Waterhouse'. Climbing roses, clematis and honeysuckles are a big feature as well as a pond-side walk. Over 50 photos on their website. Featured on *The Beechgrove Garden* in 2007.

Open: by arrangement 1 May - 30 September, admission £4.00, children free. The Waterhouse Gardens are adjacent to Stockarton, providing an opportunity to combine visits by arrangement.

Directions: On the B727 Kirkcudbright to Gelston/Dalbeattie road. Kirkcudbright is three miles and Castle Douglas is seven miles.

· *Loch Arthur*

18 THREAVE GARDEN
Castle Douglas DG7 1RX
The National Trust for Scotland
T: 01556 502 575 E: rapolley@nts.org.uk
W: www.nts.org.uk/visit/places/Threave-Garden-and-Estate

Threave Gardening Show 2020 will mark 60 years since the foundation of Threave's School of Heritage Gardening. The three day event will offer the opportunity to gain advice and ideas from people who have innovated, transformed, and developed these outstanding gardens. Exhibitors will be arranged throughout the main paths across the garden, displaying new plants, sculptures, tools and services from landscape design to garden maintenance. There will be talks and daily demonstrations from the School of Heritage Gardening on key horticultural skills and many opportunities to take tours of the garden and glasshouses. Threave House will be opening its doors to another flower 'extravaganza' which visitors can wonder at and admire. Food and drink will be supplied by Threave's catering team, with new venues throughout the garden. Don't miss out on Scotland's newest and most exciting garden festival.
Champion Trees: *Acer platanoides* 'Princeton Gold'; *Carpinus caroliniana; X Cuprocyparis leylandii* 'Picturesque' and a further 25 Scottish Champion Trees.

Open: Friday/Saturday/Sunday, 12/13/14 June, 10am - 5pm, admission £5.00, children free. Demonstrations cost £5.00 each or £10.00 for three on the same day of entry. Advanced ticket booking on Threave's website or at the gift shop.

Directions: Off the A75, one mile west of Castle Douglas.

· *The National Trust for Scotland: School of Heritage Gardening*

LANARKSHIRE

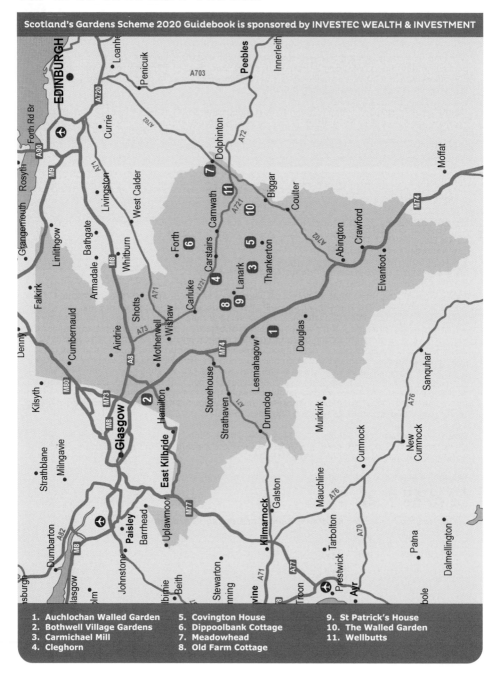

Scotland's Gardens Scheme 2020 Guidebook is sponsored by INVESTEC WEALTH & INVESTMENT

1. Auchlochan Walled Garden
2. Bothwell Village Gardens
3. Carmichael Mill
4. Cleghorn
5. Covington House
6. Dippoolbank Cottage
7. Meadowhead
8. Old Farm Cottage
9. St Patrick's House
10. The Walled Garden
11. Wellbutts

Lanarkshire

OUR VOLUNTEER ORGANISERS

District Organiser:	Vanessa Rogers	1 Snowberry Field, Thankerton ML12 6RJ
		E: lanarkshire@scotlandsgardens.org
Area Organisers:	Nicky Eliott Lockhart	Stable House, Cleghorn Farm, Lanark ML11 7RW
	Janis Sinclair	2 Meadowflatts Cottage, Meadowflatts Road,
		Thankerton ML12 6NF
District Photographer:	Alistair McNeill	Thankerton
Treasurer:	Sheila Munro Tulloch	Castlegait House, Castlegait, Lanarkshire ML10 6FF

GARDENS OPEN ON A SPECIFIC DATE

Cleghorn, Stable House, Cleghorn Farm, Lanark	Sunday, 1 March
Old Farm Cottage, The Ladywell, Nemphlar, Lanark	Sunday, 29 March
Old Farm Cottage, The Ladywell, Nemphlar, Lanark	Sunday, 5 April
St Patrick's House, Lanark	Saturday/Sunday, 23/24 May
Covington House, Covington Road, Thankerton, Biggar	Sunday/Monday, 24/25 May
Wellbutts, Elsrickle, by Biggar	Sunday/Monday, 24/25 May
Old Farm Cottage, The Ladywell, Nemphlar, Lanark	Sunday/Monday, 24/25 May
Meadowhead, Meadowhead, Dolphinton, West Linton	Sunday, 14 June
Covington House, Covington Road, Thankerton, Biggar	Sunday, 28 June
Dippoolbank Cottage, Carnwath	Sunday, 12 July
Wellbutts, Elsrickle, by Biggar	Sunday, 26 July
Bothwell Village Gardens, Bothwell	Sunday, 2 August
The Walled Garden, Shieldhill, Quothquan, Biggar	Sunday, 9 August

GARDENS OPEN BY ARRANGEMENT

Carmichael Mill, Hyndford Bridge, Lanark	1 January - 31 December
Cleghorn, Stable House, Cleghorn Farm, Lanark	9 February - 30 April
Old Farm Cottage, The Ladywell, Nemphlar, Lanark	6 April - 20 September
St Patrick's House, Lanark	1 May - 31 May
Covington House, Covington Road, Thankerton, Biggar	1 May - 31 August
The Walled Garden, Shieldhill, Quothquan, Biggar	14 June - 12 September
Auchlochan Walled Garden, New Trows Road, Lesmahagow	20 June - 1 October (not Sats & Suns)

Lanarkshire

AUCHLOCHAN WALLED GARDEN
New Trows Road, Lesmahagow, Lanarkshire ML11 0GS
MHA Auchlochan Garden Village
T: 01555 893592 E: auchlochan.enquiries@mha.org.uk

The Walled Garden at Auchlochan Garden Village was created at the turn of the century as a kitchen garden to service Auchlochan House. The garden, which is located within 50 acres of landscaped parkland and small lochan, has evolved over the years and now has interesting mixed planting. Around every corner you will find a mass of summer colour with lots of lovely shaded seating areas from which to appreciated the wide variety of plants on offer. The central walkway is of particular note. Adjacent to the garden is a large lily pond offering picturesque views of the terraces beyond.

Open: by arrangement 20 June - 1 October (not Saturdays & Sundays), admission £5.00, children free. There is a bistro/cafe adjacent to the Walled Garden open daily, serving hot and cold food and home-baked cakes.

Directions: Exit the M74 at junction 9 and follow signs to *Lesmahagow Village*. Once in the High Street take New Trows Road, opposite the Bank of Scotland, keep on this road for two miles. Follow the brown tourist signs to *Auchlochan Garden Village*.

· *MHA Auchlochan*

Auchlochan Walled Garden

Our volunteers run the
accounts and social media,
want to help?

Lanarkshire

2

BOTHWELL VILLAGE GARDENS
Bothwell G71 8PJ
Jean Murray
T: 07801 731964 E: jeanmurray4@icloud.com

....

Bothwell Village Gardens Hamilton Road, Green Street, Main Street, Blantyre Road, Bothwell G71 8LY (Community Volunteers): There are four delightful gardens developed by various local organisations in conjunction with the Local Authority to be found around the village of Bothwell. Each of these spaces has its own atmosphere created by individual plantings. You will find formal and informal gardens, managed woodland, a sensory garden, suffragette inspired planting, wildflowers, sculptures, plus quirky features such as craft bombing and fairy doors.
Bothwell Organic Growers 30 Blantyre Road Bothwell, G71 8PJ (Gardeners of Bothwell Organic Growers): Also open will be the Bothwell Organic Growers Garden. This large community-managed area has many interesting features including over 50 raised beds tended by individuals, polytunnels, wildlife areas to encourage bees and an interesting hot composting system.

Open: Sunday 2 August, 2pm - 5pm, admission by donation. Minimum suggested donation £5.00 per person. Maps available at the Sensory Garden, Main Street and the Bothwell Organic Growers Garden, Blantyre Road. Teas available at the Community Hall, 8 Fallside Road G71 8HF.

Directions: By car from the M74 take junction 5 and follow the signs to *Bothwell* (B7071) taking care not to veer off left A725 East Kilbride. At the T junction turn right into Bothwell. Buses 255 First Bus from Buchanan Bus Station to Hamilton via Bothwell. Train, alight at Uddingston Station and take the bus to Bothwell.

· *St Andrew's Hospice (Lanarkshire) & Lanarkshire Cancer Care Trust*

Bothwell Organic Growers, Bothwell Village Gardens

Lanarkshire

CARMICHAEL MILL
Hyndford Bridge, Lanark ML11 8SJ
Chris, Ken and Gemma Fawell
T: 01555 665880 E: ken.fawell@btinternet.com

Gardens developed over the last 30 years surrounding the last workable water mill in Clydesdale. The water wheel will be rotating, river levels permitting. A large collection of over 200 different ornamental trees with shrubs and herbaceous plants, as well as a large vegetable and fruit garden. The mill lade (stream) flows through the centre, providing diverse habitats including Candelabra primula in late May. Large collection of tulips and narcissus in early spring followed by glorious display of flowering cherry and crab apples. Wildlife protection and enhancement are priorities. Also visible are archaeological remains of the medieval grain milling, flax processing and a foundry. (The bell in Carmichael village was made here).

Open: by arrangement 1 January - 31 December, admission £5.00, children free.

Directions: Just off the A73 Lanark to Biggar road a half-mile east of the Hyndford Bridge.

· *All proceeds to SGS Beneficiaries*

CLEGHORN
Stable House, Cleghorn Farm, Lanark ML11 7RN
Mr and Mrs R Eliott Lockhart
T: 01555 663792 E: eliottlockhart.nicky@gmail.com
W: www.cleghornestategardens.com

Eighteenth-century garden gradually being returned to former layout. Lawns with mature trees, shrubs, abundant snowdrops and a woodland walk along the valley, formed by 12th-century dams, that were originally built to form fish ponds. The valley has been totally cleared in the last couple of years, the burn and snowdrops are now visible from both sides of the valley. Visitors are welcome to return when the daffodils are in flower.

Open: Sunday 1 March, 2pm - 4pm for Snowdrops and Winter Walks. Also open by arrangement 9 February - 30 April. Admission by donation. Prize quest to find all the characters and things not usually found in the garden.

Directions: Cleghorn Farm is situated two-miles north of Lanark off the A706.

· *Marie Curie*

COVINGTON HOUSE
Covington Road, Thankerton, Biggar ML12 6NE
Angus and Angela Milner-Brown
T: 01899 308024 E: angela@therathouse.com

Set in seven acres, Covington House stands within both traditional and formal gardens, including an 18th-century walled garden with potager, fruit cages and alpine garden. A fernery and heather garden can be found within one of two small areas of broadleaved woodland. Recently, the original Glebe lands have been acquired which will be managed as a wildflower meadow, with a delightful easy meadow walk. Biodiversity is deliberately being allowed to flourish, in part to help the honeybee apiary near the house, but also to encourage moths, bumblebees and butterflies. Covington, settled as a feudal estate by King David I, has been an important fortified location since at least the 11th century.

Lanarkshire

Open: Sunday/Monday, 24/25 May, 1pm - 4pm for the May Weekend Festival. Also open Sunday 28 June, 1pm - 5pm. And open by arrangement 1 May - 31 August. Admission £5.00, children free. On the open days there will be a honeybee stand, together with a moth expert identifying insects found in the garden.

Directions: One mile along Covington Road from Thankerton on the left.

· *Scottish Wildlife Trust Ltd & Bumblebee Conservation Trust*

DIPPOOLBANK COTTAGE
Carnwath ML11 8LP
Mr Allan Brash

Artist's intriguing cottage garden. Vegetables are grown in small beds. There are herbs, fruit, flowers and a pond in woodland area with treehouse and summerhouse. The fernery was completed in 2007. This is an organic garden that was mainly constructed with recycled materials.

Open: Sunday 12 July, 2pm - 6pm, admission £4.00, children free.

Directions: Off the B7016 between Forth and Carnwath near the village of Braehead on the Auchengray road. Approximately eight miles from Lanark. Well signposted.

· *The Little Haven (Forth)*

MEADOWHEAD
Meadowhead, Dolphinton, West Linton EH46 7AB
Andrew and Pam Taylor
E: pam.taylor1@btinternet.com

Water is a major feature of this eleven-and-a-half-acre garden with a lochan, river and many wildlife ponds. Areas of tamed wilderness provide valuable biodiversity with a wide variety of habitats for flora and fauna, including a family of swans. Many varieties of primula provide a mass of colour in the extensive bog garden and the rhododendrons and azaleas will still be in bloom. Steps from the walled garden with its Italianate ponds, waterfall, rill, fountain and sitooteries, lead up to a pleasant terrace with a small parterre. For the more energetic there are delightful woodland walks.

Open: Sunday 14 June, 2pm - 5pm, admission £4.00, children free. Stout shoes recommended. There will be a children's quiz and a variety of other activities for the young folk. Old and young alike will be fascinated by the live moths and butterflies collected from the garden and presented by a local lepidopterist.

Directions: The garden can be found just off the A702 in the village of Dolphinton.

· *Maggie's*

Lanarkshire

8

OLD FARM COTTAGE
The Ladywell, Nemphlar, Lanark ML11 9GX
Ian and Anne Sinclair
T: 01555 663345 M: 07833 204180 E: anniesinclair58@gmail.com

....

This delightful garden as featured in the *Scotland on Sunday* in September 2019, has something of interest all year round. A magnificent collection of spring bulbs (29 March and 5 April openings), shrubs and small trees attractive for their flowers, fruit and autumn foliage are all complemented by herbaceous plantings. The garden also offers a wildflower area, a pond, an apiary and small orchard. Around an acre in size it has a large grassed area with a putting green, which is particularly suitable for families. There are lots of child-friendly nooks and crannies for discovery and play. Visitors are welcome to bring a picnic as there are many sheltered places to sit and enjoy views over the Clyde Valley and district.

Open: Sunday 29 March & Sunday 5 April, 2pm - 5pm. Also open Sunday/Monday, 24/25 May, 2pm - 5pm for the May Weekend Festival. And open by arrangement 6 April - 20 September. Admission £4.00, children free.   The garden is on a spur of the Clyde Walkway. Walking Groups welcome.

Directions: Leave the A73 at Cartland Bridge (Lanark to Carluke Road) or the A72 (Clyde Valley Road) at Crossford. Both routes are well signposted. The garden is just off the West Nemphlar Road on Ladywell Lane.

· *Guide Dogs*

9

ST PATRICK'S HOUSE
Lanark ML11 9EH
Mr and Mrs Peter Sanders
T: 01555 663800 E: peterjeansanders@gmail.com

....

A May visit to St Patrick's House garden will be rewarded with a stunning display of rhododendrons, azaleas, heathers and shrubs. Created over a 50-year period, the grounds of this five-acre garden slope down to the River Clyde. Natural springs have been harnessed to create water features, a large contemporary pond with an arbour begs you to sit a while. Paths wind between beds of varied plantings and perennials, rockeries, and woodland plants, which all add to the magic of this unexpected gem.

Open: Saturday/Sunday, 23/24 May, 2pm - 5pm for the May Weekend Festival. Also open by arrangement 1 May - 31 May. Admission £4.00, children free.

Directions: A73 into Lanark, after the Police Station turn right into Friars Lane. At the bottom of the hill turn right onto St Patrick Road. The garden is a quarter of a mile on the left.

· *Lanark Community Development Trust*

10

THE WALLED GARDEN, SHIELDHILL
Quothquan, Biggar ML12 6NA
Mr and Mrs Gordon
T: 01899 221961 E: nicolagord@gmail.com

....

This 200-year-old walled garden was completely redesigned and planted in 2014/15 with contemporary features within a classic design. The garden incorporates a modern rill and banks of colour with perennial flowers in a variety of borders. The resident bees enjoy the large area of traditional meadow flowers as well as the rose garden planted with lavenders, salvias and stocks. Outside the wall you will find mature woodland including a giant sequoia and a wildlife pond. If you are interested in fruit and vegetables, take a look at the raised beds and the peach tree and vine in the greenhouse.

Lanarkshire

Open: Sunday 9 August, 2pm - 5pm. Also open by arrangement 14 June - 12 September. Admission £5.00, children free.

Directions: Turn off the B7016 between Biggar and Carnwath towards Quothquan. After about a mile, look for signs and turn right at the lodge.

· *Médecins Sans Frontières*

11

WELLBUTTS
Elsrickle, by Biggar ML12 6QZ
Nick and Lillian Slater

We started our croft garden 19 years ago on an exposed hill site of approximately two acres at an altitude of 960 feet. Our priority then was hedging, shrub and tree planting, keeping open views but creating windbreaks for herbaceous gardens, spring-fed natural duck ponds and a rill fed 'boggery'. Now established the beds are reshaped, enlarged and replanted with an extensive collection of perennials. Greenhouses and covered areas provide protection for more than 70 hanging baskets and our collection of pot grown begonias.

Open: Sunday/Monday, 24/25 May, 1pm - 5pm for the May Weekend Festival. Also open Sunday 26 July, 1pm - 5pm. Admission £4.00, children free. We have plants for sale in the garden and seating areas under cover where we serve cream teas in vintage china with the help of our special team of garden open day friends.

Directions: Parking on the main road (A721) then walk to the garden (approximately 200-yards). Adjacent field parking may be available dependent on the weather, see signs on the day.

· *Marie Curie*

St Patrick's House

MORAY & NAIRN

Scotland's Gardens Scheme 2020 Guidebook is sponsored by INVESTEC WEALTH & INVESTMENT

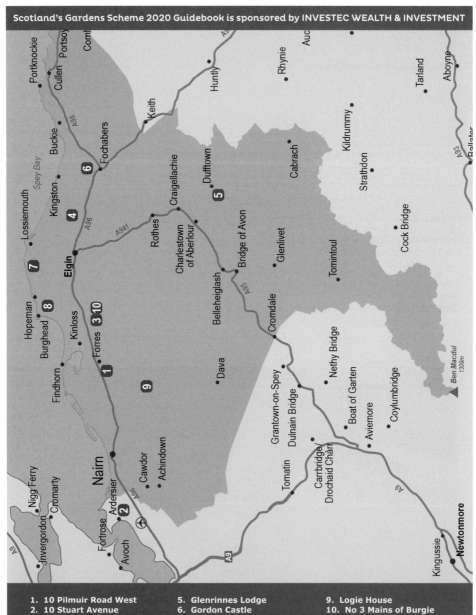

1. 10 Pilmuir Road West
2. 10 Stuart Avenue
3. Burgie
4. Glebe House
5. Glenrinnes Lodge
6. Gordon Castle
7. Gordonstoun
8. Haugh Garden
9. Logie House
10. No 3 Mains of Burgie

Moray & Nairn

OUR VOLUNTEER ORGANISERS

District Organiser:	James Byatt	Lochview Cottage, Pitgaveny, Elgin IV30 5PQ
		E: moraynairn@scotlandsgardens.org
Area Organisers:	Michael Barnett	Drumdelnies, Nairn IV12 5NT
	Lorraine Dingwall	10 Pilmuir Road West, Forres IV36 2HL
	David Hetherington	Haugh Garden, College of Roseisle IV30 5YE
	Gwynne Hetherington	Haugh Garden, College of Roseisle IV30 5YE
	Annie Stewart	33 Albert Street, Nairn IV12 4HF
Treasurer:	David Barnett	196 Findhorn, Forress IV36 3YN

GARDENS OPEN ON A SPECIFIC DATE

10 Stuart Avenue, Ardersier, Inverness	Saturday, 30 May
Gordonstoun, Duffus, near Elgin	Saturday, 30 May
Haugh Garden, College of Roseisle	Saturday, 27 June
No 3 Mains of Burgie, by Forres, Moray	Sunday, 28 June
Gordon Castle Walled Garden, Fochabers, Moray	Saturday, 18 July
Haugh Garden, College of Roseisle	Saturday, 25 July
Glenrinnes Lodge, Dufftown, Keith, Banffshire	Sunday, 26 July
Glebe House, Main Street, Urquhart	Sunday, 2 August
10 Stuart Avenue, Ardersier, Inverness	Saturday, 26 September

GARDENS OPEN REGULARLY

Logie House, Dunphail, Forres	1 January - 31 December
Gordon Castle Walled Garden, Fochabers, Moray	1 January - 31 December
Burgie, Between Forres and Elgin	1 April - 31 October

GARDENS OPEN BY ARRANGEMENT

10 Pilmuir Road West, Forres	1 February - 15 March
Haugh Garden, College of Roseisle	1 May - 31 August
10 Pilmuir Road West, Forres	1 June - 18 August

Moray & Nairn

10 PILMUIR ROAD WEST
Forres IV36 2HL
Mrs Lorraine Dingwall
T: 01309 674634 E: fixandig@aol.com

Plantswoman's small town garden with over 300 cultivars of hostas, an extensive collection of hardy geraniums together with many other unusual plants. Managed entirely without the use of artificial fertilisers or chemicals, the owner encourages hedgehogs, toads and wild birds to control slugs. In early spring there are approximately 150 named snowdrops to be seen, some of which are very rare.

Open: by arrangement 1 February - 15 March for Snowdrops and Winter Walks. Also open by arrangement 1 June - 18 August. Admission £3.00, children free.

Directions: From Tesco roundabout at Forres continue along Nairn Road. Take the first left onto Ramflat Road, then go right at the bottom and first left onto Pilmuir Road West.

· *Macmillan Cancer Support*

10 Pilmuir Road West

10 STUART AVENUE
Ardersier, Inverness IV2 7SA
Mr and Mrs Kevin Reid

A cottage style garden with vibrant rich and dense plantings of perennials and shrubs that bring colour and scent across the seasons, and makes the most of the limited space. Winner of the *Inverness Courier Garden of the Year* (medium category) in 2015, featured in *The Beechgrove Garden* in 2016 and overall winner of the *Inverness Courier Garden of the Year* in 2017.

Moray & Nairn

Open: Saturday 30 May & Saturday 26 September, 10am - 4pm, admission £3.00, children free.

Directions: From Inverness or Nairn take the A96, then the B9039 to Ardesier. After the *30mph* sign turn right to Nairn, then first left into Reaybank Road and left again. Limited parking in Stuart Avenue, more in adjoining streets.

· **Chest Heart & Stroke Scotland**

BURGIE
Between Forres and Elgin IV36 2QU
Hamish Lochore
T: 01343 850231 E: hamish@burgie.org

A rare opportunity to see a sizeable woodland garden / arboretum in its infancy. It has a good collection of rhododendrons, sorbus, alder, birch and tilia but also includes many unusual trees from around the world. The arboretum is zoned into geographic areas and species type. It includes a Japanese Garden, bog garden, bog wood, loch and Quarry Garden. First created in 2005 and is ongoing. Most plants are grown from hand collected seed and propagated in the Georgian greenhouse.

Open: 1 April - 31 October, 8am - 5pm, admission £3.00, children free. Please use honesty box. Disabled should get in touch by email so the gate can be opened for buggies.

Directions: A96 between Forres and Elgin. Four miles east of Forres. Six miles west of Elgin. Sign to *Burgie Mains* along the A96 is set in wrought iron decorated with horses and cattle. South off the main road and one mile to the Woodland Garden car park.

· **Sandpiper Trust & World Horse Welfare**

Burgie

Moray & Nairn

4

GLEBE HOUSE
Main Street, Urquhart IV30 8LG
Melanie Collett

Early 19th-century formal walled garden of the former manse by Alexander Forteath, also incorporating a unique doocot in its construction of clay dab. The garden consists of colourful herbaceous borders within the walled garden and box hedge symmetry. A wide variety of roses together with an orchard and kitchen garden area to the south.

Open: Sunday 2 August, 2pm - 4:30pm, admission £5.00, children free.

Directions: Off of the main street in Urquhart, find the walled entrance at the end of the street. Follow parking signs.

· *The Royal Air Force Benevolent Fund*

5

GLENRINNES LODGE
Dufftown, Keith, Banffshire AB55 4BS
Mrs Kathleen Locke
T: 01340 820384
W: www.glenrinnes.com

The garden and policies surrounding Glenrinnes Lodge are typical of a Victorian lodge. There is a semi-formal garden that lends itself to quiet reflection with stunning views up Glenrinnes. A walled kitchen garden with a large heated greenhouse supply plants, cut flowers and fruit and vegetables. There is also a newly developed herbaceous border displaying vibrant colours through the use of perennial and half-hardy plantings. There are delightful walks in the meadow around the pond and into the woodland, watch out for red squirrels! Some major works have been undertaken recently and much of the garden is still a 'work in progress'. In keeping with the rest of the estate, Glenrinnes Lodge is gardened following organic principles.

Open: Sunday 26 July, 2pm - 5pm, admission £4.00, children free.

Directions: In the centre of Dufftown at the Clock Tower take the B9009 road to Tomintoul for about one mile. After passing Dufftown Golf Club on your right there is a lane to the left, which leads to two stone pillars to Glenrinnes Lodge.

· *Alzheimer's Research UK*

6

GORDON CASTLE WALLED GARDEN
Fochabers, Moray IV32 7PQ
Angus and Zara Gordon Lennox
T: 01343 612317 E: info@gordoncastlescotland.com
W: www.gordoncastle.co.uk

At almost eight acres in size Gordon Castle has one of the oldest and largest walled gardens in Britain. lovingly restored to its former glory with a modern design by award-winning designer Arne Maynard, this beautiful garden is overflowing with vegetables, fruit, herbs, and cut flowers. The onsite cafe has a 'Plant,Pick,Plate' ethos using wonderful fresh produce grown in the garden. There is a children's natural play area and shop.

Open: Saturday 18 July, 2pm - 5pm. And open 1 April - 31 October, 10am - 4pm. Admission £6.00, children free. Open the rest of the year, 10am - 4pm, with admission £3.00, children free. £3.00 charge for the children's play area.

Moray & Nairn

Directions: The main entrance is at the western end of the village of Fochabers, just off the A96, nine miles east of Elgin and 12 miles west of Keith.

· *Gordon Lennox Fochabers Trust (Saturday 18 July) & Donation to SGS Beneficiaries (1 April - 31 October & 1 January - 31 March)*

Gordon Castle Walled Garden

GORDONSTOUN
Duffus, near Elgin IV30 5RF
Gordonstoun School
E: davidsonl@gordonstoun.org.uk
W: www.gordonstoun.org.uk
....

The gardens consist of good formal herbaceous borders around lawns, a terrace and an orchard. The school grounds include Gordonstoun House, a Georgian house of 1775/6 incorporating an earlier 17th-century house built for the First Marquis of Huntly, and the school chapel, both of which will be open to visitors. There is also a unique circle of former farm buildings known as the Round Square, and a scenic lake.

Open: Saturday 30 May, 2pm - 4pm, admission £5.00, children free.

Directions: Entrance off B9012, four miles from Elgin at Duffus village.

· *All proceeds to SGS Beneficiaries*

Moray & Nairn

HAUGH GARDEN
College of Roseisle IV30 5YE
Gwynne and David Hetherington
T: 01343 835790

Our garden is in the seventh year of development. From previously unmaintained woodland we have created a spring garden with informal paths and with extensive drifts of snowdrops and over 40 varieties of tulips. Colour interest continues with a collection of hellebores, daffodils, narcissi and rhododendrons. A wildlife pond is situated in a corner of the woodland close to the ruins of an 18th-century farmhouse. Extensive colourful herbaceous borders enclose the lawns, with a central rose bed and small orchard. The immature pine and birch woodland has been thinned out allowing bluebells to flower and is now planted with a wide range of shrubs to give all year round interest. Meandering paths lead round small meadow areas, a polytunnel and organic beds.

Open: Saturday 27 June & Saturday 25 July, 2pm - 5pm. Also open by arrangement 1 May - 31 August. Admission £4.00, children free.

Directions: From Elgin take the A96 west, then the B9013 Burghead Road to the crossroads at the centre of College of Roseisle. The garden is on the right, enter from the Duffus Road. Village hall car parking is to the left off Kinloss Road. Drop-off and disabled parking is available at the house.

· *Children's Hospice Association Scotland & Alzheimer Scotland*

Haugh Garden

Moray & Nairn

LOGIE HOUSE
Dunphail, Forres IV36 2QN
Alasdair and Panny Laing
E: panny@logie.co.uk
W: www.logie.co.uk

Originally a formal garden with a large area of vegetable production, Logie House garden has been developed since 1991 with emphasis on trees, shrubs and hardy perennials, giving all-year-round interest. The meandering burn and dry stone walls support the creation of a wide variety of planting habitats from dry sunny banks to damp shady areas. Many of the unusual plants are propagated for sale in the Garden Shop at Logie Steading. Also features woodland and river walks.

Open: 1 January - 31 December, 10am - 5pm, admission £2.00, children free.

Directions: Six miles south of Forres off A940. Follow signs to *Logie Steading*.

· Donation to SGS Beneficiaries

NO 3 MAINS OF BURGIE
by Forres, Moray IV36 2QZ
Mandeigh Wells-Ali
E: mandeigh@gmail.com

The hidden garden behind the hedge where cultivated and wild meet. We have no 'weeds' in this garden which is managed as a pollinator's paradise. This small cottage garden also contains a sunny courtyard, a Japanese area leading into a tiny woodland garden and onto the mixed border. Both the fish pond and wildlife pond support toads, newts, frogs and dragonflies. The main beds are an immersion in nectar-rich plants and bright colours. Various species of cultivars mingle with wild plants such as ground elder to create a species rich feast.

Open: Sunday 28 June, 10am - 4pm, admission £3.00, children free. After your visit you can take a walk around Burgie Arboretum. You will see the sign to it on your left as you go back down the drive. Details of the arboretum are in the SGS guidebook and on the website.

Directions: Located off the A96 between Forres and Elgin, four miles east of Forres - sign to *Burgie Mains/Arboretum*. Turn south off the main road and head up the hill, past the sign to *Arboretum*, keep left and up to hairpin bend right at the top. No 3 is the right-hand cottage. Parking in the field next door. Bus 10 stops on along the main road at the bottom of the lane to the cottage/arboretum.

· All proceeds to SGS Beneficiaries

PEEBLESSHIRE & TWEEDDALE

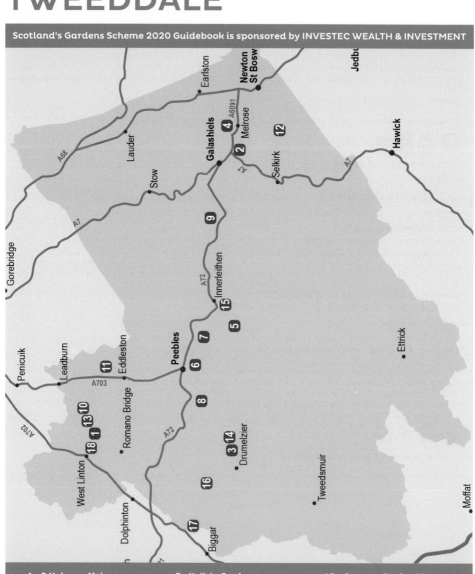

Scotland's Gardens Scheme 2020 Guidebook is sponsored by INVESTEC WEALTH & INVESTMENT

1. 8 Halmyre Mains	7. Kailzie Gardens	13. Quercus Garden Plants
2. Abbotsford	8. Kirkton Manor House	14. Stobo
3. Dawyck Botanic Garden	9. Laidlawstiel House	15. The Pines
4. Gattonside Village Gardens	10. Lamancha Community Hub	16. The Potting Shed
5. Glen House	11. Portmore	17. The Schoolhouse
6. Haystoun	12. Prieston House	18. West Linton Village

Peeblesshire & Tweeddale

OUR VOLUNTEER ORGANISERS

District Organisers:	Lesley McDavid	Braedon, Medwyn Road, West Linton EH46 7HA
	John Bracken (Deputy)	Gowan Lea, Croft Road, West Linton EH46 7DZ
		E: peeblesshire@scotlandsgardens.org
Area Organisers:	Jennifer Barr	Allerly, Gattonside, Melrose TD6 9LT
	Jenny Litherland	Laidlawstiel House, Clovenfords, Galashiels TD1 1TJ
District Photographers:	Kathy Henry	1 Kittlegairy Gardens, Peebles, EH45 9LY
Treasurers:	John Bracken	Gowan Lea, Croft Road, West Linton EH46 7DZ
	Paul Douglas	3/4 Hopefield Terrace, Leith, Edinburgh EH6 4AA

GARDENS OPEN ON A SPECIFIC DATE

Kailzie Gardens, Peebles	Sunday, 23 February
The Pines, 43, St Ronan's Terrace, Innerleithen	Sunday, 17 May
Haystoun, Peebles	Sunday, 24 May
Quercus Garden Plants, Whitmuir Farm, West Linton	Sunday, 31 May
The Potting Shed, Broughton Place, Broughton, Biggar	Tuesday, 2 June
Stobo Japanese Water Garden, Home Farm, Stobo	Tuesday/Wednesday, 2/3 June
Lamancha Community Hub Plant Sale, Lamancha	Saturday, 6 June
The Potting Shed, Broughton Place, Broughton, Biggar	Tuesday, 9 June
Prieston House, Melrose	Friday, 12 June
Prieston House, Melrose	Saturday, 20 June
8 Halmyre Mains, West Linton	Sunday, 21 June
The Potting Shed, Broughton Place, Broughton, Biggar	Tuesday, 30 June
Glen House, Glen Estate, Innerleithen	Sunday, 5 July
The Potting Shed, Broughton Place, Broughton, Biggar	Tuesday, 7 July
The Schoolhouse, Skirling by Biggar	Sunday, 19 July
West Linton Village Gardens, West Linton	Sunday, 2 August
The Pines, 43, St Ronan's Terrace, Innerleithen	Sunday, 9 August
Gattonside Village Gardens, Gattonside	Sunday, 16 August
Laidlawstiel House, Clovenfords, Galashiels	Wednesday/Thursday, 2/3 September
Kailzie Gardens, Peebles	Sunday, 6 September
Dawyck Botanic Garden, Stobo	Sunday, 11 October

GARDENS OPEN REGULARLY

Abbotsford, Melrose	1 March - 30 November
Kirkton Manor House, Peebles	20 May - 8 July (Wednesdays only)
Portmore, Eddleston	1 July - 26 August (Wednesdays only)

GARDENS OPEN BY ARRANGEMENT

Kirkton Manor House, Peebles	1 February - 31 March
The Potting Shed, Broughton Place, Broughton, Biggar	1 May - 31 October
Stobo Japanese Water Garden, Home Farm, Stobo	1 May - 31 October
Portmore, Eddleston	1 June - 31 August

Peeblesshire & Tweeddale

8 HALMYRE MAINS
West Linton EH46 7BX
Joyce and Mike Madden
T: 07774 609547 E: agentromanno@gmail.com

A half-acre organic garden with colourful herbaceous borders and a number of raised vegetable beds. There is a greenhouse, Keder house and polytunnel leading to the wildlife pond with a summer house and viewing area. There are four large composting bins, with additional hot bin, wormery and the production of comfrey liquid fertiliser on display.

Open: Sunday 21 June, 2pm - 5pm, admission £4.00, children free.

Directions: Five miles south of Leadburn Junction on the A701 (Moffat).

· *Lamancha Hub*

ABBOTSFORD
Melrose TD6 9BQ
The Abbotsford Trust
T: 01896 752043 E: enquiries@scottsabbotsford.co.uk
W: www.scottsabbotsford.com

The garden was designed by Sir Walter Scott with advice from artists, architects and friends. It is a rare surviving example of a Regency garden layout and completely different from the English landscape garden style of Capability Brown. Scott's garden aims to provide a harmonious transition between the luxury and comfort of the interiors of the house with wonders of nature in the wider estate through a series of secluded, richly detailed and sheltered 'rooms'. In its day it would have showcased the latest plants discovered from around the globe, both in its borders and 'stove houses'. Regular tours are held exploring Scott's vision for the garden and the hidden meanings of its design. Check the Abbotsford website for details.

Open: 1 March - 31 March 10am - 4pm, 1 April - 31 October 10am - 5pm & 1 November - 30 November 10am - 4pm, admission details and further information can be found on the garden's website.

Directions: Off the A6091 near Melrose. Buses X62 and 72 from Edinburgh and Peebles. Train from Waverley to Tweedbank. Minibus or one-mile walk from train station.

· *Donation to SGS Beneficiaries*

DAWYCK BOTANIC GARDEN
Stobo EH45 9JU
A Regional Garden of the Royal Botanic Garden Edinburgh
T: 01721 760254
W: www.rbge.org.uk/dawyck

Dawyck is a regional garden of the Royal Botanic Garden Edinburgh which celebrates its 350th anniversary in 2020. For more information, visit www.rbge.org.uk/350
Stunning collection of rare trees and shrubs. With over 300 years of tree planting, Dawyck is a world-famous arboretum with mature specimens of Chinese conifers, Japanese maples, Brewer's spruce, the unique Dawyck beech and sequoiadendrons from North America which are over 150 feet tall. Bold herbaceous plantings run along the burn. Range of trails and walks. Fabulous autumn colours.
National Plant Collection: *Larix* spp. and *Tsuga* spp.
Champion Trees: Numerous.

Peeblesshire & Tweeddale

Open: Sunday 11 October, 10am - 5pm, admission details can be found on the garden's website.

Directions: Eight miles south west of Peebles on the B712.

· *Donation to SGS Beneficiaries*

GATTONSIDE VILLAGE GARDENS

Gattonside TD6 9NP
The Gardeners of Gattonside
T: 07500 869041 E: jenbarr@gmx.com

Gattonside is a pretty, south-facing village beside the River Tweed and opposite the town of Melrose. Traditionally, the village was known for its fruit trees and was the garden for the monks of Melrose Abbey. Today it is a village with a variety of gardens. You can visit small, cottage type gardens with mixed herbaceous borders, dahlia enthusiasts' gardens and even ponds with fish. There are new gardens and more established gardens — with mixed borders, vegetables, fruit cages as well as many beautiful trees, copper birch and oak to name but a few.

Open: Sunday 16 August, 1pm - 5pm, admission £5.00, children free. Tickets and maps available from village hall on Main Street. Teas and plant sale will be in the village hall.

Directions: Short walk from Melrose over the chain bridge. Twenty-minute walk along River Tweed from Tweedbank Railway Station. By car access off the A68 signposted *Gattonside*.

· *Macmillan Cancer Support*

GLEN HOUSE

Glen Estate, Innerleithen EH44 6PX
The Tennant family
T: 01896 830210 E: info@glenhouse.com
W: www.glenhouse.com

Surrounding the outstanding Scots Baronial mansion designed by David Bryce in the mid-19th century, Glen House gardens are laid out on shallow terraces overhanging the glen itself, which offers one of the loveliest designed landscapes in the Borders. The garden expands from the formal courtyard through a yew colonnade, and contains a fine range of trees, long herbaceous border and a pool garden with pergola, all arranged within the curve of slopes sheltering the house.

Open: Sunday 5 July, 11am - 4pm, admission £5.00, children free.

Directions: Follow the B709 out of Innerleithen for approximately two-and-a-half miles. Right turn at signpost for *Glen Estate*.

· *CDP Worldwide: sustainable finance sculpture*

Peeblesshire & Tweeddale

HAYSTOUN
Peebles EH45 9JG
Mrs David Coltman

This sixteenth-century house (not open) has a charming walled garden with an ancient yew tree, herbaceous beds and vegetable garden. There is a wonderful burnside walk created since 1980, with azaleas, rhododendrons and primulas leading to a small ornamental loch (cleared in 1990) with stunning views up Glensax Valley.

Open: Sunday 24 May, 1:30pm - 5pm for the May Weekend Festival, admission £5.00, children free.

Directions: Cross the River Tweed in Peebles to the south bank and follow *Scotland's Gardens Scheme* sign for approximately one mile.

· *St Columbas Hospice*

KAILZIE GARDENS
Peebles EH45 9HT
Lady Buchan-Hepburn
T: 01721 720007 E: info@kailziegardens.com
W: www.kailziegardens.com

Semi-formal walled garden with shrubs and herbaceous borders, rose garden and excellent display of plants in large Victorian greenhouses. Woodland and burnside walks among spring bulbs, snowdrops, bluebells, rhododendrons and azaleas. The garden is set among fine old trees. Watch osprey with live CCTV recordings of ospreys nesting in the recently extended nature centre. Kailzie has been featured on *Landward* and *The Beechgrove Garden*.
Champion Trees: Larch planted 1725.

Open: Sunday 23 February, 10am - 4pm for Snowdrops and Winter Walks. Also open Sunday 6 September, 10am - 4pm. Admission £5.00, children free (Sunday 23 February) and £6.00, children free (Sunday 6 September). See website for other opening times.

Directions: Two-and-a-half miles east of Peebles on the B7062.

· *Erskine Hospital*

KIRKTON MANOR HOUSE
Peebles EH45 9JH
Mrs Rosemary Thorburn
T: 01721 740220 E: rpthorburn@icloud.com

Kirkton Manor House has a delightful three-acre informal country garden set in the beautiful Manor Valley. It enjoys spectacular open views and calling curlews from its riverside position. Bluebells flank the impressive entrance leading to a new shrub border. Stone steps continue through to terraced slopes filled with bulbs, roses and hellebores providing height, interest and fragrance. Grass paths meander along the burn where blue and white camassia, meconopsis, and ligularia thrive in this sunny meadow environment. Later, in June, sisyrinchiums, irises, orchids and many flowering shrubs and roses are abundant. The natural woodland includes many interesting trees.

Open: by arrangement 1 February - 31 March for Snowdrops and Winter Walks. Also open 20 May - 8 July (Wednesdays only), 2pm - 5pm. Admission £4.00, children free.

Peeblesshire & Tweeddale

Directions: Turn off the A72 west of Neidpath Castle, signposted to *Kirkton Manor*. After crossing the River Tweed, enter a garden gate which is a mile downhill, opposite a *Beware Horses* sign.

· *All proceeds to SGS Beneficiaries*

LAIDLAWSTIEL HOUSE
Clovenfords, Galashiels TD1 1TJ
Mr and Mrs P Litherland
....

Walled garden containing herbaceous border, fruit, and vegetables in raised beds. There are colourful rhododendrons and azaleas as well as splendid views down to the River Tweed.

Open: Wednesday/Thursday, 2/3 September, 1pm - 5pm, admission £4.00, children free.

Directions: A72 between Clovenfords and Walkerburn, turn up the hill signposted for *Thornielee*. The house is on the right at the top of the hill.

· *CLIC Sargent: Ciaran's House, Edinburgh*

Kirkton Manor House, photo by Kathy Henry

Peeblesshire & Tweeddale

LAMANCHA COMMUNITY HUB PLANT SALE
Old Moffat Road, Lamancha EH46 7BD
Mike Madden
T: 07774 609547 E: hello@lamanchahub.org.uk

This year's plant sale will be held in a small community garden with shrubs for year-round interest; and herbaceous and cottage garden borders. The garden is currently being developed as an organic demonstration site, following the recent erection of a Keder house, rainwater collection and composting areas. A wide variety of locally grown plants will be available for sale.

Open: Saturday 6 June, 2pm - 5pm, admission by donation. The cafe will offer teas and home-baking.

Directions: Three miles south of the Leadburn Junction on the A701.

· *Lamancha Hub*

PORTMORE
Eddleston EH45 8QU
Mr and Mrs David Reid
T: 07825 294388
W: www.portmoregardens.co.uk

Lovingly created by the current owners over the past 30 years, the gardens, surrounding the David Bryce-designed mansion house contain mature trees and offer fine views of the surrounding countryside. Large walled garden with box-edged herbaceous borders is planted in stunning colour harmonies, potager, rose garden, pleached lime walk and ornamental fruit cages. The Victorian glasshouses contain fruit trees, roses, geraniums, pelargoniums and a wide variety of tender plants. There is also an Italianate grotto and water garden with shrubs and meconopsis. The woodland walks are lined with rhododendrons, azaleas and shrub roses. Starred in *Good Gardens Guide* and featured in Kenneth Cox's book *Scotland for Gardeners* and on *The Beechgrove Gardens*.

Open: 1 July - 26 August (Wednesdays only), 1pm - 5pm. Also open by arrangement 1 June - 31 August. Admission £6.00, children free. Self-service refreshments for Wednesday openings. Homemade cream teas for groups over 15 people by prior arrangement.

Directions: Off the A703 one mile north of Eddleston. Bus 62.

· *Eddleston Parish Church of Scotland*

PRIESTON HOUSE
Melrose TD6 9HQ
Jilly Bhamra
T: 07903 560818 E: jilly.bhamra@hotmail.co.uk
W: www.theghilliebnb.com

A delightful three-and-a-half-acre garden designed around a Georgian farmhouse dating from 1720. It has a woodland area with many interesting trees and a small pond. The terraced lawns are enhanced by several secluded seating areas surrounded by yew hedges and mature shrubs including many rhododendrons and azaleas. The walls of the house are covered by old roses, clematis and wisteria and a side gate leads to a paddock and views across open countryside to the Eildon Hills and Cheviots.

Peeblesshire & Tweeddale

Open: Friday 12 June, 2pm - 5pm. Also open Saturday 20 June, 2pm - 5pm. Admission £4.00, children free.

Directions: Off the A699 Selkirk to St. Boswells road, signposted.

· *Borders Childrens Charity*

QUERCUS GARDEN PLANTS
Whitmuir Farm, West Linton EH46 7BB
Rona Dodds
T: 01968 660708 E: quercusgardenplants@gmail.com
W: www.quercusgardenplants.co.uk

We are a small independent nursery growing and selling a wide range of happy, healthy plants propagated from our nursery gardens. At just under two acres, these gardens were started in 2015 to show visitors and customers what can be grown in our conditions here on a north-west-facing hill at 850 feet above sea level. Explore our herb garden, scented garden, wildlife garden and all the other inspirational smaller borders. New areas are being developed to include prairie-style planting of grasses and perennials. Many of the plants seen in the gardens are available to buy in the nursery.

Open: Sunday 31 May, 10am - 5pm, admission £5.00, children free.

Directions: On the A701, four miles south of the Leadburn junction or two miles north of West Linton.

· *Breast Cancer Care*

STOBO JAPANESE WATER GARDEN
Home Farm, Stobo EH45 8NX
Hugh and Georgina Seymour
T: 01721 760245 E: stobo.home.farm@gmail.com

This is a mature, secluded woodland garden and is dominated by its water feature — a 60-foot waterfall. The water adds to the tranquillity of the garden throughout the year. In the spring, rhododendrons and azaleas provide a show of colour and scent. In the autumn, acers and cherries provide a riot of vivid colours while the Cercidiphyllum leaves have the aroma of burnt sugar. There are still many facets from the original Japanese garden in place which include lanterns, a tea house, humpback bridges, stepping stones as well as specialist trees and shrubs of Japanese origin. Limited disabled access due to gravel paths and steps.

Open: Tuesday/Wednesday, 2/3 June, 2pm - 5pm. Also open by arrangement 1 May - 31 October for groups of 12 or more. Admission £5.00, children free. Refreshments available locally.

Directions: Off the B712. (Peebles/Broughton road) via *Stobo Castle* entrance.

· *Diocese of Edinburgh Scottish Episcopal Church: St Peter's Church, Peebles & Stobo and Drumelzier Church of Scotland*

Peeblesshire & Tweeddale

THE PINES
43, St Ronan's Terrace, Innerleithen EH44 6RB
Fiona and Bill Jack
T: 07969 081965 E: fgbwjack@gmail.com

Camellias, rhododendrons and hydrangeas thrive in this terraced one-and-a-half-acre garden, perched on the hillside overlooking the town of Innerleithen in the Tweed Valley. Set over four levels, the gardens were created in 1905 around the Arts and Crafts house. Formal lawns, rose garden and herbaceous borders fill the lower terraces. The owners have concentrated on bee friendly flowers to encourage insects as they have a fenced in area for their apiary. On the upper level, a large walled garden with restored glasshouse, original espalier apple trees leading through to wildflower meadows and hillside woodland.

Open: Sunday 17 May, 2pm - 5pm. Also open Sunday 9 August, 2pm - 5pm. Admission £5.00, children free.

Directions: Bus X62. From Peebles turn left off the A72 on Hall Street which bears right into St Ronan's Terrace. The garden has green gates and is uphill on the left. Free car park at bottom of hill.

· *Innerleithen Pipe Band & Bees for Development*

THE POTTING SHED
Broughton Place, Broughton, Biggar ML12 6HJ
Jane and Graham Buchanan-Dunlop
T: 01899 830574 E: buchanandunlop@btinternet.com

A one-acre garden, begun from scratch in 2008, on an exposed hillside at 900 feet. It contains herbaceous plants, climbers, shrubs and trees, all selected for wind resistance and ability to cope with the poor, stony soil. There are (usually) fine views to the Southern Uplands.

Open: Tuesday 2 June, Tuesday 9 June, Tuesday 30 June & Tuesday 7 July, 11am - 5pm. Also open by arrangement 1 May - 31 October. Admission £4.00, children free.

Directions: Signposted from the main A701 Edinburgh - Moffat Road, immediately north of Broughton village.

· *Macmillan Cancer Support: Borders General Hospital*

THE SCHOOLHOUSE
Skirling by Biggar ML12 6HD
Mike and Annie Thompson
T: 01899 860396 E: info@schoolhouseflowers.co.uk
W: www.schoolhouseflowers.co.uk

A developing and informal village garden extending to about half an acre. Home to a seasonal cut flower business with a secluded cutting garden with raised beds filled with colourful and unusual annuals. There are lawns with herbaceous borders, a productive kitchen garden, young orchard with beehive and a recently created wildlife pond. Featured in *Scotland on Sunday*.

Open: Sunday 19 July, 2pm - 5pm, admission £4.00, children free. Homemade teas are available at the village hall nearby.

Peeblesshire & Tweeddale

Directions: Take the A701 or A702 and follow road signs to *Skirling*. The garden is directly opposite the village green.

· *Skirling Village Hall*

WEST LINTON VILLAGE GARDENS
West Linton EH46 7EL
West Linton Village Gardeners
T: 01968 660669 E: j.bracken101@gmail.com

....

A varied and interesting selection of gardens including two new gardens and three that were last opened in 2017. Included is a walled Manse garden in a beautiful riverside setting. Main features amongst all the gardens are large herbaceous borders, greenhouses full of pelargoniums and show begonias, alpine planting and vegetable beds. In addition, there are two new gardens with the main features being an extensive woodland walk, a wildlife pond and a collection of hostas. Also, an immaculately maintained lawn and good selection of sweet peas.

Open: Sunday 2 August, 2pm - 5pm, admission £5.00, children free. Tickets, teas and plants are sold at the Graham Institute in the centre of the village, which will be signposted.

Directions: About 15 miles south west of Edinburgh, take the A701 or the A702 and follow signs. Bus 101 or 102 to Gordon Arms Hotel.

· *Ben Walton Trust & Borders General Hospital, Margaret Kerr Unit*

The Pines, photo by Kathy Henry

PERTH & KINROSS

Scotland's Gardens Scheme 2020 Guidebook is sponsored by INVESTEC WEALTH & INVESTMENT

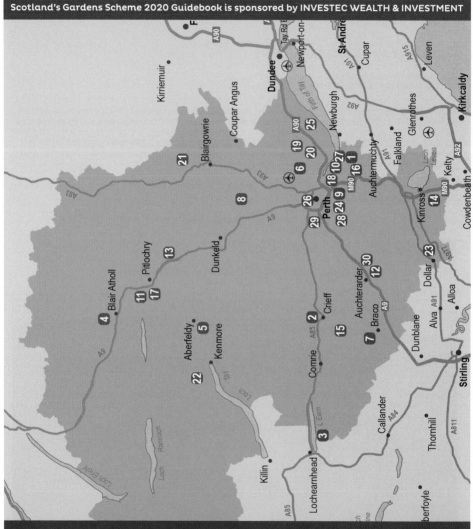

1. 7 Drum Gate	12. Cloan	22. Glenlyon House
2. Allotment Assoc. of Crieff	13. Craigowan	23. Hollytree Lodge
3. Ardvorlich	14. Dowhill	24. Kilgraston School
4. Blair Castle Gardens	15. Drummond Castle Gardens	25. Megginch Castle
5. Bolfracks	16. Eastbank Cottage	26. Parkhead House
6. Bonhard House	17. Explorers Garden	27. Pitcurran House
7. Braco Castle	18. Fehmarn	28. Rossie Gardens
8. Bradystone House	19. Fingask Castle	29. The Bield at Blackruthven
9. Bridge of Earn Village	20. Glendoick	30. The Old Farmhouse
10. Carey House	21. Glenericht House	
11. Carig Dhubh	Arboretum	

Perth & Kinross

OUR VOLUNTEER ORGANISERS

District Organiser:	Margaret Gimblett	Fehmarn, Bridge of Earn PH2 9AH
Area Organisers:	Henrietta Harland	Easter Carmichael Cottage, Forgandenny Road, Bridge of Earn PH2 9EZ
	Elizabeth Mitchell	Woodlee, 28 St Mary's Drive, Perth PH2 7BY
	Lizzie Montgomery	Burleigh House, Milnathort, Kinross KY13 9SR
	Judy Norwell	Dura Den, 20 Pitcullen Terrace, Perth PH2 7EQ
	Richenda Pearson	Spinneyburn, Rumbling Bridge, KY13 0PY
	Kareen Robertson	2 The Orchard, Bridge of Earn, Perthshire PH2 9DX
	Clarinda Snowball	The Limes, Dallerie, Crieff PH7 4JH
	Fiona Stewart	7 Craigend Cottages, Craigend, PH2 8PX
	Heather Wood	Mill of Forneth, Forneth, Blairgowrie PH10 6SP
District Photographers:	Mike Bell	
	Carolyn Bell	6 Strathearn Terrace, Perth PH2 0LS
	David Hay	21A, Robertson Crescent, Pitlochry PH16 5HD
	Mike Nicoll	
Treasurer:	Michael Tinson	Parkhead House, Burghmuir Road, Perth PH1 1JF

GARDENS OPEN ON A SPECIFIC DATE

Cloan, by Auchterarder	Sunday, 16 February
Kilgraston School, Bridge of Earn	Sunday, 23 February
Megginch Castle, Errol	Sunday, 19 April
Fingask Castle, Rait	Sunday, 3 May
Dowhill, Cleish	Sunday, 10 May
Dowhill, Cleish	Sunday, 17 May
Bolfracks, Aberfeldy	Saturday/Sunday/Monday, 23/24/25 May
Braco Castle, Braco	Saturday/Sunday/Monday, 23/24/25 May
Rossie Gardens, Forgandenny	Saturday/Sunday, 23/24 May
Cloan, by Auchterarder	Saturday/Sunday, 23/24 May
Fehmarn, Bridge of Earn	Saturday/Sunday, 23/24 May
Carey House, Abernethy	Sunday/Monday, 24/25 May
Eastbank Cottage, Perth Road, Abernethy	Sunday/Monday, 24/25 May
Explorers Garden, Port Na Craig, Pitlochry	Sunday, 7 June
Cloan, by Auchterarder	Sunday, 7 June
Bridge of Earn Village, Dunbarney Church Hall, Manse Road	Sunday, 14 June
Blair Castle Gardens, Blair Atholl	Saturday, 27 June
The Bield at Blackruthven, Blackruthven House, Tibbermore	Saturday, 27 June
Allotment Association of Crieff, Turretbank Road Crieff	Saturday, 11 July
Drummond Castle Gardens, Muthill, Crieff	Sunday, 2 August
Dowhill, Cleish	Sunday, 9 August
Cloan, by Auchterarder	Sunday, 16 August
Dowhill, Cleish	Sunday, 16 August

Perth & Kinross

GARDENS OPEN REGULARLY

Braco Castle, Braco	15 February - 31 October
Bolfracks, Aberfeldy	1 April - 31 October
Glendoick, Glencarse, Perthshire	1 April - 31 May
Ardvorlich, Lochearnhead	1 May - 31 May

GARDENS OPEN BY ARRANGEMENT

Glenericht House Arboretum, Blairgowrie	1 January - 31 December
Fingask Castle, Rait	27 January - 5 March (Mondays & Thursdays)
Eastbank Cottage, Perth Road, Abernethy	1 April - 30 June
Bonhard House, Perth	1 April - 31 October
Hollytree Lodge, Muckhart, Dollar	1 April - 31 October
Glenlyon House, Fortingall	1 April - 30 September
The Old Farmhouse, Dunning Road	1 April - 31 July
Craigowan, Ballinluig	10 April - 31 July
Pitcurran House, Abernethy	1 May - 1 September
Parkhead House, Parkhead Gardens, Burghmuir Road, Perth	1 May - 30 September
7 Drum Gate, Abernethy, Perthshire	1 May - 30 June
Carig Dhubh, Bonskeid, Pitlochry	1 May - 30 September
Carey House, Abernethy	15 May - 15 July
Bradystone House, Murthly	2 June - 8 August

Perth & Kinross

7 DRUM GATE
Abernethy, Perthshire PH2 9SA
Helen Morrison
E: hmorrison559@gmail.com

What started out in 2004 as just under an acre of bare earth has now turned into an attractive garden split into extensive herbaceous borders, large lawn areas and a young woodland with metasequoias, tulip tree, rhododendrons and wonderful views across the Tay Valley and upwards to the Ochils. The garden continues to develop and mature with earlier planting of topiary and hedging now being able to be sculptured and fruit trees and shrubs bearing produce. Visitors can meander through the garden, pausing in the children's Hideaway Cottage to listen and observe the many species of birds attracted to the garden. Work is ongoing but this is a rare example of what can be achieved from a blank canvas given vision, determination and plenty of time and patience.

Open: by arrangement 1 May - 30 June, admission by donation.

Directions: Seven miles south of Perth. Leave the M90 at Junction 9 and follow signs for *Abernethy, Newburgh* and *Cupar* on the A912 for approximately five miles. Garden Owner will give detailed directions on request.

· *Search and Rescue Dog Association Scotland (SCIO)*

7 Drum Gate

Perth & Kinross

2

ALLOTMENT ASSOCIATION OF CRIEFF
Turretbank Road Crieff PH7 4AR
The Allotmenteers
E: crieffplots@gmail.com
....

The Allotment Association of Crieff (AAC) is set high up above the River Turret with stunning panoramic views of Glen Turret and towards St Fillans. The AAC is only seven years old and previously the ground was used for grazing horses and sheep. Without vehicular access the Allotmenteers had to manually create this little bit of paradise which was a huge task. It is without doubt one of the most scenic locations of any allotment association in Scotland. We invite guests to wander round and enjoy the 30 allotments which produce a huge variety of vegetables, fruit and flowers. Without mains water or electricity and subject to high winds and cold winter temperatures the allotments face special challenges, but none the less the products range from asparagus to grapes and specialist raspberries, along with the more usual veg and fruit.

Open: Saturday 11 July, 1pm - 5pm, admission £5.00, children free.

Directions: Leaving Crieff on the A85 take the right turn towards Glenturret Distillery then turn immediately left up a track. You will see a small parking area and the path to the allotments which will be signposted. It is uphill and is not wheelchair accessible. Parking is available on Turretbank Road and is signposted. To access the allotments cross the A85 to the beginning of the path and follow the signs.

· *Local Charities*

3

ARDVORLICH
Lochearnhead FK19 8QE
Mr and Mrs Sandy Stewart
T: 01567 830218
....

Beautiful hill garden featuring over 170 different species of rhododendrons and many hybrids, grown in a glorious setting of oaks and birches on either side of the Ardvorlich Burn. The paths are quite steep and rough in places and boots are advisable, especially when wet.

Open: 1 May - 31 May, 9am - dusk, admission £5.00, children free.

Directions: On South Loch Earn Road three miles from Lochearnhead, five miles from St Fillans.

· *The Gurkha Welfare Trust*

4

BLAIR CASTLE GARDENS
Blair Atholl PH18 5TL
Blair Charitable Trust
T: 01796 481207 E: office@blair-castle.co.uk
W: www.blair-castle.co.uk
....

Blair Castle stands as the focal point in a designed landscape of some 2,500 acres within a Highland estate. Hercules Garden is a walled enclosure of about nine acres recently restored to its original 18th-century design with landscaped ponds, a Chinese bridge, contemporary plantings, vegetables and an orchard of more than 100 fruit trees. The glory of this garden in summer is the herbaceous border, which runs along the 275 yard south-facing wall. A delightful sculpture trail incorporates contemporary and 18th-century sculpture as well as eight new works, letter-carving on stone from the *Memorial and Commemorative Arts* charity's 'Art and Memory Collection'. Diana's Grove is a magnificent stand of tall trees including grand fir, Douglas fir, larch and wellingtonia running along the Banvie Burn, with the 12th-century ruins of St Bride's Church on the far bank.

Perth & Kinross

Open: Saturday 27 June, 9:30am - 4:30pm, admission details can be found on the garden's website.

Directions: Off A9, follow signs to *Blair Castle, Blair Atholl.*

· *Donation to SGS Beneficiaries*

BOLFRACKS
Aberfeldy PH15 2EX
The Douglas Hutchison Trust
T: 01887 820344 E: info@bolfracks.com

Special three-acre garden with wonderful views overlooking the Tay Valley. Burn garden with rhododendrons, azaleas, primulas and meconopsis in a woodland garden setting. Walled garden with shrubs, herbaceous borders and rose 'rooms' with old-fashioned roses. There is also a beautiful rose and clematis walk. Peony beds are underplanted with tulips and Japanese anemone. The garden has a great selection of bulbs in spring and good autumn colour.

Open: 1 April - 31 October, including the May Weekend Festival, 10am - 6pm. Admission £5.00, children free.

Directions: Two miles west of Aberfeldy on A827. White gates and lodge are on the left. Look out for the brown tourist signs.

· *Donation to SGS Beneficiaries*

BONHARD HOUSE
Perth PH2 7PQ
Stephen and Charlotte Hay
T: 07990 574570 E: stephenjohnhay@me.com

Traditional 19th-century garden of five acres approached through an avenue of magnificent oaks. Mature trees, six classified by the National Tree Register as 'remarkable', including a handsome monkey puzzle, sequoias, Douglas fir and a variety of hollies. Grassy paths wind around ponds, rockeries, shrubbery and smaller trees, providing some splendid perspectives. Rhododendron and azalea beds. Pinetum on a knoll behind the house containing 25 species, beehives and productive kitchen garden. Shifting of garden emphasis to habitat. Possible sighting of red squirrels and green and greater-spotted woodpeckers.

Open: by arrangement 1 April - 31 October, admission £4.00, children free. Sensible shoes should be worn. Tea and cake by arrangement.

Directions: On A94 just under a mile north of Perth take right turn, signed *Murrayshall Hotel.* After approximately one mile take entrance right marked *Bonhard House* at a sharp left turn. From Balbeggie turn left, signposted for *Bonhard*, one mile north of Scone. Turn right in a half a mile, pass any sign for *Bonhard Nursery*, and enter drive at sharp right turn.

· *Freedom from Fistula Foundation*

Perth & Kinross

BRACO CASTLE
Braco FK15 9LA
Mr and Mrs M van Ballegooijen
T: 01786 880437

A 19th-century landscaped garden with a plethora of wonderful and interesting trees, shrubs, bulbs and plants. An old garden for all seasons that has been extensively expanded over the last 27 years. The partly walled garden is approached on a rhododendron and tree-lined path featuring an ornamental pond. Spectacular spring bulbs, exuberant shrub and herbaceous borders, and many ornamental trees are all enhanced by the spectacular views across the park to the Ochils. From snowdrops through to vibrant autumn colour this garden is a gem. Look out for the embothrium in June, hoheria in August, eucryphia in September and an interesting collection of rhododendrons and azaleas with long flowering season.

Open: 15 February - 31 October, 10am - 5pm and May Festival Weekend, 23 - 25 May, 10am - 5pm, admission £4.00, children free. No dogs allowed.

Directions: Take a one-and-a-half-mile drive from the gates at the north end of Braco Village, just west of the bridge on the A822. Parking at the castle is welcome.

· *The Woodland Trust Scotland*

BRADYSTONE HOUSE
Murthly PH1 4EW
Mrs James Lumsden
T: 01738 710308 E: pclumsden@me.com

This cottage garden was converted from a derelict farm steading to create a unique courtyard garden that bursts with colour throughout the season. It has been imaginatively planted by Patricia and her gardener Scott and has recently undergone some exciting changes. There is a woodland walk with interesting trees underplanted with shrubs, that leads to a duck pond where ducks and hens roam freely. There is also a small productive kitchen garden. A real gem of a garden; visitors who are fortunate enough to meet the owner and Scott will be impressed by their enthusiasm and knowledge.

Open: by arrangement 2 June - 8 August, admission £5.00, children free. Please note that the garden is only open for group visits.

Directions: From south/north follow A9 to Bankfoot, then signs to *Murthly*. At crossroads in Murthly take private road to Bradystone.

· *Scotland's Charity Air Ambulance*

BRIDGE OF EARN VILLAGE
Dunbarney Church Hall, Manse Road, Bridge of Earn PH2 9DY
The Gardeners of Bridge of Earn

6 Balmanno Park NEW PH2 9RJ (Ian and Val Davidson): This garden is an unexpected hidden gem where flowers, fruit and vegetables are cleverly blended together.   Some planters and homemade wooden barrows full of plants provide plenty of summer colour.
Craigievairn Heughfield Road, PH2 9BG (George Watson): This small garden is well-stocked with fruit trees, shrubs, roses, perennials and annuals and an established vegetable plot. It is a haven for wildlife with a beaver run to the burn in the wild section of the garden.
Earnbank NEW Back Street, PH2 9XA (Mr and Mrs McGrath): Earnbank is a complex of retirement housing. The communal grounds and gardens back onto the River Earn with views to Moncrieffe Hill. Terraces are planted up with flowers, shrubs and some vegetables. There is a grove of

Perth & Kinross

manicured laurel under-planted with bulbs and seeds, many mature trees and a number of dwarf apple trees. A scenic mural fence hides a range of garden equipment. The grounds are a haven for wildlife including squirrels, many birds, kingfishers, swans and beavers.

Fehmarn NEW PH2 9AH (Mr and Mrs Gimblett): A big 'small garden' with woodland, water, rocks and a cottage garden to the front. Shady and very sunny borders with more trees and lawn to the back. Tucked away in a corner, a tiny but productive fruit and vegetable garden. All looked after and loved by two 'oldies', passionate chief gardener, Margaret, and her husband, Iain, the head groundsman.

Heughfield House Walled Garden Heughfield House, Heughfield Road, PH2 9BH (Ian Cuthbert Imrie): This garden is like a painting, contrast, colour, light, dark, composition, perspective, all come into play. Deliberately designed for birds and wildlife this beautiful garden is full of clipped box in a formal garden at the front with unusual shrubs and shade loving plants in the main garden. The gardens surround a pagoda-style summer house. The house is one of the oldest in the village and has a thatched roof.

Open: Sunday 14 June, 1pm - 5pm, admission £5.00, children free. Tickets and teas (an additional £3 per person) will be available at the church hall.

Directions: From the north and south, take the exit on the M90 for Bridge of Earn and follow the road into the village. Go straight ahead at the mini-roundabout and through the village. Pass Dunbarney Primary School on your left and then turn left into Manse Road. The church and church hall are on your right towards the end of Manse Road with parking available past the church on your right-hand side.

· *Dunbarney and Forgandenny Parish Church*

Heughfield House Walled Garden, Bridge of Earn Village

Perth & Kinross

 CAREY HOUSE
Abernethy PH2 9LN
Caroline and Alan Boyle
T: 01738 851190 E: carolinepboyle@hotmail.com

Set amid panoramic views of the Ochils this is a ceramicist's garden developed from rough pasture and fields of brambles over the past nine years. Pots and sculptures feature on a trail which wanders through distinct areas: orchard, herb garden, shrubbery, cottage garden, lawns, pond, rose garden, summerhouse and studio plus lots of places for sitting and contemplating. Plants from the garden will be for sale.

Open: Sunday/Monday, 24/25 May, 10am - 4pm for the May Weekend Festival. Also open by arrangement 15 May - 15 July. Admission £5.00, children free. Not suitable for wheelchairs. However, partial access is possible by arrangement.

Directions: Abernethy is seven miles south of Perth. Leave M90 at Junction 9 and follow signs for Abernethy on A912. Garden Owner will provide detailed directions on request. Bus stops at top of lane - it is a mile walk from here on a quiet track.

· *The Woodland Trust Scotland*

 CARIG DHUBH
Bonskeid, Pitlochry PH16 5NP
Jane and Niall Graham-Campbell
T: 01796 473469 E: niallgc@btinternet.com

'I don't know how Niall and Jane manage to grow their splendid meconopsis on the sand and rock of their garden but they do, most successfully.' In this stunning situation, when not admiring the views, you will find wonderful primulas, cardiocrinum and meconopsis, all interspersed between beautiful shrubs and other herbaceous plants. Look up and in July you will see roses flowering 40 feet up in the tree. This is a gem of a garden and you will be welcomed by Niall and Jane Graham-Campbell with all their expert knowledge.

Open: by arrangement 1 May - 30 September, admission £5.00, children free.

Directions: Take the old A9 between Pitlochry and Killiecrankie, turn west on the Tummel Bridge Road B8019, Carig Dhubh is three-quarters of a mile on north side of the road.

· *Earl Haig Fund Poppy Scotland*

 CLOAN
by Auchterarder PH3 1PP
Neil Mitchison
T: 01764 664907 E: niall@fastmail.co.uk

Two acres of wild garden, with a wide variety of rhododendrons and azaleas, and an impressive collection of trees, including metasequoia, cryptomeria, *Acer cappadocicum*, *Sequoia sempervirens*, *Quercus robur* 'Filicifolia', liriodendron, several Japanese maples, magnificent beech and Scots pines trees, and extensive yew topiary; also an acre of walled garden with embothriums, *Acer griseum*, liquid amber, several sorbus varieties, parrotia and a large herbaceous border. Fine views of Strathearn from the front of the house.

Open: Sunday 16 February, 10am - 3pm for Snowdrops and Winter Walks. Saturday/Sunday, 23/24 May, 11am - 5pm for the May Weekend Festival. Sunday 7 June and Sunday 16 August, 11am - 5pm. Admission £4.00, children free.

Perth & Kinross

Directions: From A823, just south of A9, follow small road heading north east, signposted *Duchally*. Continue for approximately two-and-a-half miles, turn right at sign *Coulshill*. Continue just under half a mile. Entrance through stone pillars on right.

· **Tiphereth Limited: Camphill Scotland**

CRAIGOWAN
Ballinluig PH9 0NE
Ian and Christine Jones
T: 01796 482244 E: i.q.jones@btinternet.com

This is a specialist garden with a major collection of rhododendrons put together over the last 40 years; initially, mainly species from Glendoick following the plant hunting and discoveries of Peter Cox and the late Sir Peter Hutchison and others. In the last 20 years there have been added noteworthy hybrids sourced from Glendoick and the major English nurseries. Each year further additions are made and earlier introductions which have outgrown their original or secondary planting spot are moved to new locations. With growth rates tending to increase this is a major exercise but the result is a constantly changing garden and more plants are developing into a spectacular presentation. Other plant types include magnolias, ornamental acers and a collection of unusual trees. There are areas of more formal beds where there is a large collection of meconopsis, lilies including cardiocrinum with roughly a hundred flowering each year. The rhododendron flowering period lasts from January to August but the best months are April, May and June. There is adjoining woodland which is being replanted with trees free of disease risk and with the larger rhododendrons which have outgrown the more formal areas. In June and July two large herbaceous borders give summer colour and interest.

Open: by arrangement 10 April - 31 July, admission £5.00, children free.

Directions: From north or south A9 to Ballinluig junction. Follow sign for *Tulliemet* and *Dalcapon*. Pass the filling station and Red Brolly Cafe. Turn right following the *Tulliemet/Dalcapon* sign; this is a steep narrow road so take care. About a half mile up the road take a left turning with fields on either side and Craigowan is the first house on the left about a half mile along. Park on paviours adjoining house.

· **LUPUS UK**

DOWHILL
Cleish KY4 0HZ
Mrs Colin Maitland Dougall
T: 01577 850207 E: pippamd@icloud.com

This will be the last time that the garden opens so please come along and see its magnificent trees, woodland walks, ponds, poppies and swathes of primulas. For more information on the garden read *Scotland for Gardeners* by Kenneth Cox.

Open: Sunday 10 May & Sunday 17 May, 2pm - 5pm. Also open Sunday 9 August & Sunday 16 August, 2pm - 5pm. Admission £5.00, children free.

Directions: Three-quarters of a mile from M90, exit 5. Follow B9097 towards Crook of Devon, the entrance is between the trees on left.

· **MND Scotland**

Perth & Kinross

15 **DRUMMOND CASTLE GARDENS**
Muthill, Crieff PH7 4HN
Grimsthorpe & Drummond Castle Trust Ltd
T: 01764 681433
W: www.drummondcastlegardens.co.uk

Activities and events for a great family day out. The gardens of Drummond Castle were originally laid out in 1630 by John Drummond, second Earl of Perth. In 1830 the parterre was changed to an Italian style. One of the most interesting features is the multi-faceted sundial designed by John Mylne, Master Mason to Charles I. The formal garden is said to be one of the finest in Europe and is the largest of its type in Scotland.

Open: Sunday 2 August, 1pm - 5pm, admission details can be found on the garden's website.

Directions: Entrance two miles south of Crieff on Muthill road (A822).

· *BLESMA*

16 **EASTBANK COTTAGE**
Perth Road, Abernethy PH2 9LR
Mike and Elsa Thompson
T: 01738 850539 E: mikestuartthompson@hotmail.com

Traditional Scottish cottage, a third-of-an-acre garden, walled and bounded by a small burn to the east. Erythroniums, varieties of wood anemones, trillium, a fine display of clematis, rhododendrons and azaleas. Altogether a little haven in the country.

Open: Sunday/Monday, 24/25 May, 10am - 4pm for the May Weekend Festival. Also open by arrangement 1 April - 30 June. Admission by donation.

Directions: When coming from Perth, drive to the Abernethy *30 mph* sign. A layby is on the left. The gate has the property name on it. Bus 36 stops very close.

· *All proceeds to SGS Beneficiaries*

'Do you love your
garden? Why not open
it in 2021?'

Perth & Kinross

EXPLORERS GARDEN
Port Na Craig, Pitlochry PH16 5DR
Pitlochry Festival Theatre
T: 01796 484626
W: www.explorersgarden.com

This six-acre woodland garden celebrates the Scottish plant hunters who risked their lives in search of new plants. The Explorers Garden is divided into geographic areas, each containing examples of the plants collected from that corner of the globe. Set in beautiful Highland Perthshire countryside, the garden is known for its meconopsis collection, stunning vistas and interesting sculptures and structures. Each year a photographic exhibition is held in the David Douglas Pavilion.
National Plant Collection: *Meconopsis.*

Open: Sunday 7 June, 10am - 4:30pm, admission £5.00, children free. Concessions £4.00

Directions: Take the A9 to Pitlochry town, then follow signs to *Pitlochry Festival Theatre.*

· *Acting for Others*

Explorers Garden

Perth & Kinross

FEHMARN
Bridge of Earn PH2 9AH
Mr and Mrs Gimblett
T: 01738 813653 E: gimblettsmill@aol.com

A big 'small garden' with woodland, water, rocks and a cottage garden to the front. Shady and very sunny borders with more trees and lawn to the back. Tucked away, a tiny but productive fruit and vegetable garden. All looked after and loved by two 'oldies', passionate chief gardener, Margaret, and her husband, Iain, head groundsman.

Open: Saturday/Sunday, 23/24 May, 11am - 4pm for the May Weekend Festival, admission £3.00, children free.

Directions: From the north and south, take the exit on the M90 for Bridge of Earn and follow the road into the village. Go ahead at the mini-roundabout and take the first right into Old Edinburgh Road. At the T junction turn right and go straight on for about half a mile. Turn right by a group of bungalows. Fehmarn is first on the right.

· *Prostate Cancer UK*

Fehmarn

Perth & Kinross

19

FINGASK CASTLE
Rait PH2 7SA
Mr and Mrs Andrew Murray Threipland
T: 01821 670777 ext 2 E: andrew@fingaskcastle.com
W: www.fingaskcastle.com

Scotland's funniest garden! *Alice in Wonderland* topiary staggers across the lawn, bumping into stone globes, marble balls and statues from three centuries. Historical and literary figures are scattered among pleasure gardens first laid out in the 18th century. Both Bonnie Prince Charlie and his father are said to have approached the castle from the longer yew parade, the Kings Walk. There is a marked 15-minute walk down the steep dell to a medieval wishing well (St Peter's), over a Chinese bridge crossing the Fingask Burn via the Iron Age Fort to Fingask Loch and Sir Stuart's House, back along another path to the orchard car park (wellies recommended). There are large drifts of snowdrops, daffodils and flowering shrubs depending on the season.
Champion Trees: *Pinus wallichiana* (Japanese maple).

Open: by arrangement 27 January - 5 March (Mondays & Thursdays) for Snowdrops and Winter Walks. Also open Sunday 3 May, 1:30pm - 4:30pm. Admission £3.00, children free (27 January - 5 March) and £4.00, children free (Sunday 3 May). Homemade teas and children's activities on 3 May only.

Directions: Half-way between Perth and Dundee. From the A90 follow signs to *Rait* until small crossroad, turn right and follow signs to *Fingask*.

· *All Saints Episcopal Church: Glencarse & Fingask Follies*

20

GLENDOICK
Glencarse, Perthshire PH2 7NS
Cox Family
T: 01738 860260 E: manager@glendoick.com
W: www.glendoick.com

Glendoick's gardens and garden centre with its award-winning café is the ideal spring day out in April and May. Why not visit Branklyn too, nearby. 2019 sees Glendoick celebrate 100 years since Euan Cox returned from Burma with the first rhododendron seeds to be grown and planted in the gardens. Glendoick Gardens were included in the *Independent on Sunday* survey of Europe's top 50 Gardens and boasts a unique collection of plants from three generations of Cox plant-hunting expeditions in China and the Himalaya. Enjoy one of the finest collections of rhododendrons and azaleas, primulas, meconopsis and other acid-loving plants in the woodland garden and the gardens surrounding the house. Many of the rhododendron and azalea species and hybrids have been introduced from the wild or bred by the Cox family and the gardens boast a vast range of plants from as far afield as Chile, Tasmania and Tibet. There are fine waterfall views in the woodland gardens. The award-winning Glendoick Garden Centre has one of Scotland's best selections of plants including their world-famous rhododendrons and azaleas as well as a gift shop and café.
National Plant Collection: *Rhododendron* sect. *Pogonanthum*, subsect. *Uniflora*, subsect. *Campylogyna* & subsect. *Glauca* and Cox hybrids.

Open: 1 April - 31 May, 10am - 4pm, admission £5.00, children free. Refreshments for groups should be pre-booked - for group bookings contact Jane Cox by email: jane@glendoick.com. See Glendoick website for details of guided tours by Ken Cox in May. The woodland garden is not easily accessible to wheelchairs but some of the gardens by the house are. Toilets and refreshments at the garden centre only.

Directions: Follow brown signs to *Glendoick Garden Centre* off A90 Perth - Dundee road. Gardens are a half mile behind the Garden Centre. After buying tickets at the Garden Centre, please drive up and park at gardens (free parking).

· *Donation to SGS Beneficiaries*

Perth & Kinross

GLENERICHT HOUSE ARBORETUM
Blairgowrie PH10 7JD
Mrs Mary McCosh
T: 01250 872092 E: m.mccosh123@gmail.com

Spectacular collection of Victorian-planted trees and shrubs which are centred around a Grade 'A' listed suspension bridge (1846). Ninety-two tree varieties, mostly conifers including a top Douglas fir which is 171 feet and still growing, also a collection of younger trees. In May you will be able to view the wonderful daffodils and the rhododendrons in flower.

Open: by arrangement 1 January - 31 December, admission £4.00, children free. Honesty box in car parking area close to the river bridge.

Directions: Off the A93, the Lodge House is four miles north of Blairgowrie on the right-hand side A93 when coming from Blairgowrie. Follow the avenue towards the bridge and the parking area is beside the river.

· *Sands*

GLENLYON HOUSE
Fortingall PH15 2LN
Mr and Mrs Iain Wotherspoon
T: 07974 350533 E: thewotherspoons@ednet.co.uk

Interesting garden framed by hedges, with colourful herbaceous borders and fruit trees underplanted with perennials and annuals. There is a kitchen and cutting garden as well as a wildlife pond.

Open: by arrangement 1 April - 30 September, admission £5.00, children free.

Directions: Take the A827 to Aberfeldy, then B846 to Coshieville then turn off for Glen Lyon.

· *Fortingall Parish Church*

HOLLYTREE LODGE
Muckhart, Dollar FK14 7JW
Liz and Peter Wyatt
T: 07973 374687 E: elizwyatt @aol.com

A tranquil one-acre garden, divided by internal hedges into 'rooms' as featured in *Country Homes & Interiors* in January 2018. Highlights include a small Japanese garden, mini orchard, naturalised spring bulbs and wildflowers, rill and wildlife pond, mixed herbaceous borders, a good collection of rhododendrons and azaleas, a variety of unusual trees and shrubs, snow gum, *Metasequoia glyptostroboides*, Persian ironwood and acers, many producing spectacular autumn colours. Our aim is to garden with nature complementing our beekeeping interests.

Open: 1 April - 31 October, admission £5.00, children free. Please call or email to arrange a visit. Groups welcome.

Directions: Approximately 100 yards from the A91 (between Dollar and Milnathort) down the small lane directly opposite the entrance to the Inn at Muckhart.

· *Coronation Hall, Muckhart*

Perth & Kinross

KILGRASTON SCHOOL
Bridge of Earn PH2 9BQ
Kilgraston School
T: 01738 812257 E: marketing@kilgraston.com
W: www.kilgraston.com

Enjoy the carpet of snowdrops, admire the ancient yews, towering wellingtonias, and the resident red squirrels, whilst exploring the pathways and woodlands within the extensive grounds of this 19th-century house. Formerly home to the Grant family, it has been a girls' boarding school since 1930. Statues and sculptures, some by renowned architect Hew Lorimer, dot the landscape, as well as a great children's play area. Inside the school, take in an excellent display of pupil artwork.

Open: Sunday 23 February, 1:30pm - 4:30pm for Snowdrops and Winter Walks, admission £4.00, children free.

Directions: Bridge of Earn is three miles south of Perth on the A912. *Kilgraston School* is well signposted from the main road. Maps are available at the school website.

· *Glenfarg Riding For The Disabled Association Group*

MEGGINCH CASTLE
Errol PH2 7SW
Giles Herdman and Catherine Drummond-Herdman
T: 01821 642222 E: info@megginch.com
W: megginchcastle.com

Come and wander through our hosts of golden daffodils under the ancient trees and avenues of Megginch. Head through the charming, cobbled courtyard into the walled garden where there is a collection of daffodils from the renowned collectors, Duncan and Kate Donald from Croft 16 Daffodils. In the orchard, have a chat with Gavin and his bees, walk back past some of the apple and pear trees that make up our two National Collections, to a warming cup of tea and home-baking under the tallest yew trees in Scotland.
The Scavenger Hunt and secret chocolate Easter eggs, will keep all ages busy on their walk round!
National Plant Collection: Scottish cider apples, Scottish Heritage apples and pears.
Champion Trees: *Acer palmatum.*

Open: Sunday 19 April, 2pm - 5pm, admission £5.00, children free.

Directions: Ten miles from Perth and Dundee directly off the A90, Perth-bound carriageway, 600 yards after the Errol/Rait flyover, on the left hand side, 300 yards after *Beware Pedestrians Crossing* sign.

· *The Inspiration Orchestra*

Perth & Kinross

26 PARKHEAD HOUSE
Parkhead Gardens, Burghmuir Road, Perth PH1 1RB
Mr and Mrs M S Tinson
T: 01738 625983 M:07748 186 815 E: maddy.tinson@gmail.com
W: www.parkheadgardens.com

Parkhead is an old farmhouse sited within an acre of beautiful gardens. Mature trees include an outstanding 300-year-old Spanish chestnut. This hidden gem is a garden for all seasons. Gentle terracing and meandering paths lead you past a large variety of unusual and interesting plants and shrubs. If you seek colour and inspiration come and see this garden.
National Plant Collection: *Lilium* (Mylnefield lilies).

Open: by arrangement 1 May - 30 September, admission £5.00, children free.

Directions: Parkhead Gardens is on a small lane off the west end of Burghmuir Road in Perth. More detailed directions on request.

· *Plant Heritage*

27 PITCURRAN HOUSE
Abernethy PH2 9LH
The Hon Ranald and Mrs Noel-Paton
T: 01738 850933 E: patricianp@pitcurran.com

This end-of-village garden was created 16 years ago. It includes an interesting combination of trees, rare shrubs and herbaceous plants including azaleas, rhododendrons, tree peonies, trilliums and veratrum. Also a rose pergola, eucryphias and a large west-facing hydrangea border for the later summer. Above the pond there is a good collection of pink and white barked birches and an embryonic arboretum.

Open: by arrangement 1 May - 1 September, admission £5.00, children free.

Directions: South east of Perth. From M90 (exit nine) take A912 towards Glenfarg, go left at roundabout onto A913 to Abernethy. Pitcurran House is at the far eastern end of the village. Buses run through Abernethy from Perth and surrounding districts.

· *Juvenile Diabetes Research Foundation Limited*

28 ROSSIE GARDENS
Forgandenny PH2 9EH
Mr and Mrs David B Nichol
T: 01738 812265 E: judynichol@rossiehouse.co.uk
W: www.rossiegardens.com

This romantic garden has been establishing itself since 1657. It is a magical mystery tour of endless paths meandering under magnificent trees, unusual shrubs with a plethora of woodland bulbs and plants at your feet. Lift the branches of a *Hamamelis mollis* to find the startled heron take off from the pond and look up to the massive trunk of the *Abies alba* 100 feet up. From snowdrops to hellebores then trillium and bluebells, flowering shrubs and roses. The garden is at its best in May. The sculptures are by David Annand and Nigel Ross. Look out for the ten-foot teapot and the yew table ready for the Mad Hatter's tea party!

Open: Saturday/Sunday, 23/24 May, 11am - 5pm for the May Weekend Festival, admission by donation. Suggested donation of £5 per person in honesty box, children free.

Perth & Kinross

Directions: Forgandenny is on the B935 between Bridge of Earn and Dunning.

· *Canine Partners*

THE BIELD AT BLACKRUTHVEN
Blackruthven House, Tibbermore PH1 1PY
The Bield Christian Co Ltd
T: 01738 583238 E: info@bieldatblackruthven.org.uk

The Bield is set in extensive grounds with well maintained lawns, hedges, flower meadow and specimen trees. A labyrinth is cut into the grass of the old orchard and there is a wheelchair-friendly labyrinth. Traditional walled garden with colourful, richly stocked borders and lawns, plus cut-flower garden, Healing Garden, glasshouse, trained fruit trees and organic vegetable plot. Walk through extensive woodland and visit the old curling pond. Southton Smallholding is a social enterprise ten minutes walk away, featuring vegetable plots, polytunnels and a number of animals (not staffed on the day).

Open: Saturday 27 June, 2pm - 5pm, admission £5.00, children free.

Directions: From Dundee or Edinburgh, follow signs for *Glasgow, Stirling* and *Crianlarich* which lead onto the Perth bypass. Head west on the A85 signed to *Crieff/Crianlarich* to West Huntingtower. Turn left at the crossroads to *Madderty/Tibbermore*. Entrance is left after a half-mile passing the gate lodge on your right. Parking signed to right at the steading.

· *Southton Smallholding*

THE OLD FARMHOUSE
Dunning Road PH3 1DU
Jane and Nigel Gallier
T: 01764 662471 E: thegalliers@msn.com

A garden of approximately one acre with herbaceous borders, a gravel garden, vegetable garden, trained fruit trees in half-wine barrels, wild areas under-planted with bulbs, and woodland areas with other areas still being developed. As you approach the house look out for our kamikaze hens and the fantailed doves taunting the local sparrow hawk in their netted area. The garden is not always immaculate; a well-ordered winter garden and a floriferous summer garden.

Open: by arrangement 1 April - 31 July, admission £5.00, children free. Open from 10.30 am to 4.30 pm

Directions: From the A9, halfway along the A824 between Auchterarder and Aberuthven take the B8062 at Grand Eagles and head towards Dunning. We are on the left just before the A9 bridge.

· *ABF The Soldiers' Charity*

RENFREWSHIRE

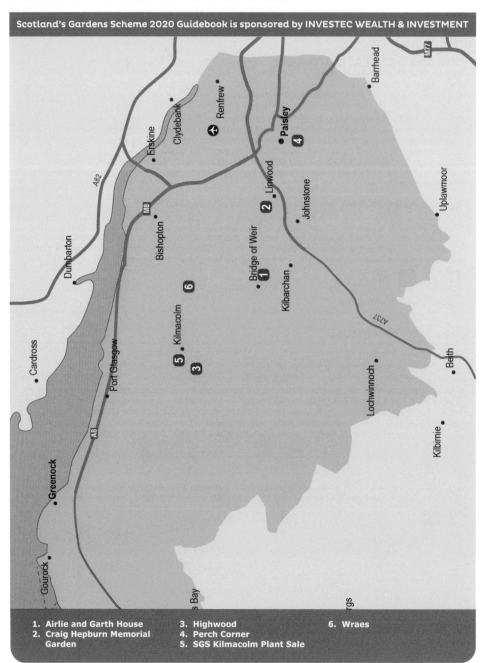

Scotland's Gardens Scheme 2020 Guidebook is sponsored by INVESTEC WEALTH & INVESTMENT

1. Airlie and Garth House
2. Craig Hepburn Memorial Garden
3. Highwood
4. Perch Corner
5. SGS Kilmacolm Plant Sale
6. Wraes

Renfrewshire

OUR VOLUNTEER ORGANISERS

District Organiser:	Alexandra MacMillan	Langside Farm, Kilmacolm, PA13 4SA E: renfrewshire@scotlandsgardens.org
Area Organisers:	Helen Hunter	2 Bay Street, Fairlie KA29 0AL
	Barbara McLean	49 Middlepenny Road, Langbank, PA14 6XE
	Jill Thompson	
Treasurer:	Jean Gillan	Bogriggs Cottage, Carlung, West Kilbride KA23 9PS

GARDENS OPEN ON A SPECIFIC DATE

SGS Kilmacolm Plant Sale, outside Kilmacolm Library	Saturday, 25 April
Highwood, off Lochwinnoch Road, Kilmacolm	Sunday, 10 May
Perch Corner, 25 Stanely Crescent, Paisley	Sunday, 17 May
Wraes, Corseliehill Road, nr Houston	Sunday, 7 June
Airlie and Garth House, Bridge of Weir	Sunday, 14 June
Craig Hepburn Memorial Garden, Stirling Drive, Linwood	Tuesday/Wednesday, 23/24 June

Renfrewshire

AIRLIE AND GARTH HOUSE
Bridge of Weir PA11 3EU
Helen Crichton and Ann Campbell

Airlie Prieston Road, Bridge of Weir PA11 3AN (Helen Crichton): This three-quarter-of-an-acre sheltered walled garden, created over a period of over 50 years by the present owner, is divided up into a series of 'rooms' by hedging, steps and trees. The large herbaceous borders are always full of colour and include many old favourites, phlomis, ligularia, thalictrum, peonies, etc. A tiny fish pond with fountain gives added interest to the paved sunken garden. The white border makes a change from the vibrant violet coloured lace cap hydrangea and vivid red camelia. Roses and clematis climb on the house and garden walls. There is a hobbit house hidden in the trees in one corner.

Garth House Bankend Road, Bridge of Weir PA11 3EU (Ann Campbell): The south facing rear garden is packed with hostas, rhododendrons, alstroemerias, hellebores, brunneras and a wide range of shrubs and climbers, planted to create sheltered, enclosed seating areas. The front garden includes a densely planted 30 yard long herbaceous border (20 years in the making) and offers a panoramic view of the Kilpatrick Hills. There is a small woodland area with six white stemmed Jacquemontii silver birches, a pond (with frogs and lilies) and a small stream. A traditional Victorian greenhouse surrounded by a cutting garden for annuals and peonies. Herbs and soft fruit are also nurtured. Box, yew and hebe balls throughout the garden, mainly grown from cuttings. Children are welcome to climb into the treehouse, swing on the swing or strap into a harness and attempt the climbing wall (under supervision). Final challenge, find the 1940s air raid shelter and seven much loved compost heaps!

Open: Sunday 14 June, 2pm - 5pm, admission £4.00, children free. Maps will be issued on the day. Teas at Garth House, plant sale at Airlie.

Directions: Take the A761 into Bridge of Weir, at the junction take the turning onto Prieston Road for Airlie or Kilbarchan Road for Garth House. Follow the *SGS* signs

· **Humanist Society Scotland: Street Care Project & Multiple Sclerosis Society**

CRAIG HEPBURN MEMORIAL GARDEN
Stirling Drive, Linwood PA3 3NB
Linwood High School
T: 01505 336146 E: craighepburnmemorialgarden@yahoo.co.uk
W: facebook.com/welovegardening14/

The Craig Hepburn Memorial Garden and Outdoor Learning Centre is located in Linwood High School. Our original garden with an outdoor classroom has been expanded to include community raised beds, an orchard, greenhouse and presentation area. We work with all years in the school reconnecting them to the natural world whether it is through growing in our organic garden, encouraging biodiversity or learning about sustainability.

Open: Tuesday 23 June 4pm - 6pm and Wednesday 24 June 3pm - 6pm, admission £3.50, children free. 'How-to' classes and planting seeds.

Directions: Exit the M8 at St James Interchange and take the A737. Take the exit for Linwood onto the A761, follow to Clippens Road and then Stirling Drive. Accessible by McGill buses.

· **Teenage Cancer Trust**

Renfrewshire

Airlie

HIGHWOOD
off Lochwinnoch Road, Kilmacolm PA13 4TF
Dr Jill Morgan

A beautiful woodland walk around 50 acres of native bluebells, primroses and wild garlic in a delightful setting bordering the Green Water river with tumbling waterfalls. Great outdoor space for children to run and explore and splash in the burn (under supervision). A haven of tranquility only three miles from the centre of Kilmacolm.

Open: Sunday 10 May, 2pm - 5pm, admission £4.00, children free. Stout footwear is recommended as the footpath is uneven and can be muddy in inclement weather. Dogs are welcome on a lead. Fantastic opportunity for lovers of wildflowers and photography.

Directions: Take the B786 Lochwinnoch road out of Kilmacolm and continue for approximately two miles. From Lochwinnoch take the B786 Kilmacolm road for approximately six miles. Then follow the yellow *SGS* signs.

· *Orkidstudio*

Renfrewshire

PERCH CORNER
25 Stanely Crescent, Paisley PA2 9LF
Bob and Elaine Moffett

Perch Corner is a large south-facing garden extending to over half an acre with formal areas and woodland paths. The garden overlooks Stanely Reservoir and beyond to the Gleniffer Braes. Planting consists of a vibrant array of mature shrubs and rare trees, which are more often found in extensive west coast gardens, including a range of magnolias, camelias, rhododendrons, azaleas and acers. Specimens include *Davidia Involucrata*, tulipa, copper beeches and cornus. Children are welcome to explore in the woodland area and garden

Open: Sunday 17 May, 2pm - 5pm, admission £4.00, children free.

Directions: From the M8 take exit 28a and follow signs for *RAH Hospital.* Continue on Corsebar Road past the hospital to Moredun Road. Right onto Stanely Road, first right to Stanely Avenue. Continue and bear left at the postbox. Look for the *SGS* signs. From the south, take the B775 down Gleniffer Braes. First left after the Jet petrol station onto Stanely Avenue then as above. From Barrhead take the B774 to Paisley, left at the Splash carwash onto Glenburn Road. Follow Glenburn Road to the end, turn right onto Gleniffer Road, then as above.

· *Parkinsons UK*

SGS KILMACOLM PLANT SALE
outside Kilmacolm Library, Kilmacolm PA13 4LE
SGS Kilmacolm Plant Sale

Spring plant sale in the centre of Kilmacolm.

Open: Saturday 25 April, 10am - noon, admission by donation.

Directions: The plant sale will be held at the Cross outside the Library and Cargill Centre. Accessible by McGill buses.

· *Pancreatic Cancer Scotland*

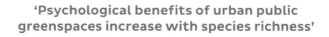

'Psychological benefits of urban public greenspaces increase with species richness'

Renfrewshire

WRAES
Corseliehill Road, nr Houston PA6 7HU
Tim and Jo Mack

Tranquil seven-acre garden developed since 2012, with far reaching rural views. Only surviving historic 1860 wood planted by Lady Anne Spiers of Houston House for the Wraes, currently undergoing renovation with extensive new tree planting. Formal garden with raised herbaceous borders, woodland walk with 100 different rhododendron species and hybrids. Pond, burnside and cliffside walks, peaceful woodland walk with plentiful seating areas to relax and enjoy the views and tranquility. Croquet lawn. A great space for children to run and explore (under supervision). NEW FOR 2020 - apple and pear orchard and wildflower meadow.

Open: Sunday 7 June, 2pm - 5pm, admission £4.00, children free.

Directions: From Houston follow Barochan Road towards Langbank B789 for about a mile, turn left down Corseliehill Road. From Kilmacolm leave the village on Houston Road, past the golf course, turn left down Corseliehill Road for about a mile. Follow the yellow *SGS* signs.

· *Breast Cancer Care*

Wraes

ROXBURGHSHIRE

Scotland's Gardens Scheme 2020 Guidebook is sponsored by INVESTEC WEALTH & INVESTMENT

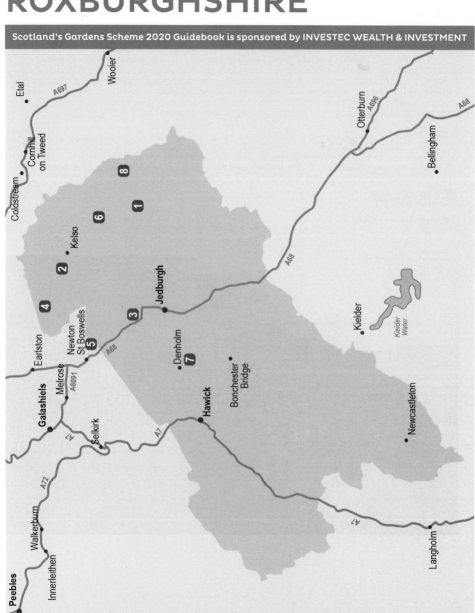

1. **Corbet Tower**
2. **Floors Castle**
3. **Monteviot**

4. **Smailholm Village**
5. **Stable House**
6. **Thirlestane**

7. **West Leas**
8. **Yetholm Village Gardens**

Roxburghshire

OUR VOLUNTEER ORGANISERS

District Organiser:	Sally Yonge	Newtonlees House, Kelso TD5 7SZ E: roxburghshire@scotlandsgardens.org
Area Organiser:	Julie Golding	5 Manorhill Farm Cottages, Makerstoun, TD5 7PA
Treasurer:	Peter Yellowlees	19 Frogston Road West, Edinburgh EH10 7AB

GARDENS OPEN ON A SPECIFIC DATE

West Leas, Bonchester Bridge	Sunday, 7 June
Smailholm Village Gardens, Smailholm Village Hall, Smailholm	Sunday, 21 June
Corbet Tower, Morebattle, near Kelso	Saturday, 27 June
Yetholm Village Gardens, Town Yetholm	Sunday, 5 July
West Leas, Bonchester Bridge	Sunday, 2 August

GARDENS OPEN REGULARLY

Monteviot, Jedburgh	1 April - 31 October
Floors Castle, Kelso	12 April - 30 September
Stable House, Maxton, St Boswells, Melrose	1 May - 31 October (Mondays only)
Floors Castle, Kelso	1 October - 31 October (Saturdays & Sundays)

GARDENS OPEN BY ARRANGEMENT

West Leas, Bonchester Bridge	1 January - 31 December
Thirlestane, Kelso	31 March - 31 October
Stable House, Maxton, St Boswells, Melrose	1 May - 31 October

Roxburghshire

 CORBET TOWER
Morebattle, near Kelso TD5 8AQ
Simon and Bridget Fraser

Charming Scottish Victorian garden set in parklands in the foothills of the Cheviots. The established garden includes a formal box parterre rose garden with old fashioned roses, a well stocked traditional walled, vegetable and cutting garden, terraced lawns around the Victorian house and medieval peel tower. The gardens are approached via an attractive woodland walk with lime avenue.

Open: Saturday 27 June, 2pm - 5pm, admission £5.00, children free.

Directions: From A68 north of Jedburgh take A698 for Kelso. At Kalemouth (Teviot Smokery) follow B6401 to Morebattle, then road marked Hownam to Corbet Tower.

· *Cheviot Churches: Church of Scotland: Morebattle*

 FLOORS CASTLE
Kelso TD5 7SF
The Duke of Roxburghe
T: 01573 223333
W: www.floorscastle.com

The gardens are situated within the grounds of Floors Castle. Meander through to the formal Millennium Parterre and soak up the spectacular visions of colour, texture and the most delicious scents around the four herbaceous borders in one of the finest Victorian kitchen gardens in Scotland. Perennial gardens, fruit cage, Tapestry Garden and glasshouse access. Terrace Cafe, Castle Kitchen Deli shop and play area. Explore the grounds, which offer woodland and riverside walks from Easter to October.

Open: 12 April - 30 September, 10:30am - 5pm. Also open 1 October - 31 October (Saturdays & Sundays), 10:30am - 5pm. Admission details can be found on the garden's website, along with further information about special events.

Directions: Floors Castle can be reached by following the A6089 from Edinburgh; the B6397 from Earlston; or the A698 from Coldstream. Go through Kelso, up Roxburgh Street to the Golden Gates.

· *Donation to SGS Beneficiaries*

'Creating an inspiring, rewarding
and enjoyable experience for
volunteers and visitors alike'

Roxburghshire

MONTEVIOT
Jedburgh TD8 6UQ
Marquis and Marchioness of Lothian
T: 01835 830380
W: www.monteviot.com
....

A series of differing gardens including a herb garden, rose garden, water garden linked by bridges, and river garden with herbaceous and shrub borders of foliage plants. The Garden of Persistent Imagination has been recently created and planted with rose and clematis avenues leading to a Moonstone Gate.

Open: 1 April - 31 October, noon - 5pm, admission £5.00, children free.

Directions: Turn off A68, three miles north of Jedburgh on to B6400. After one mile turn right.

· Donation to SGS Beneficiaries

Floors Castle, photo by Pete Seaward

'Gardening teaches us
patience and appreciation
for the natural world'

Roxburghshire

 SMAILHOLM VILLAGE GARDENS
Smailholm Village Hall, Smailholm TD5 7PH
The Gardeners of Smailholm
W: www.smailholm-village.org.uk

This small rural village, centred around an ancient church and a historic 'farm town', boasts a number of gardens of the cottage variety with varying degrees of formality and maturity. They range from the ancient to new 'works in progress' and offer a combination of traditional and contemporary approaches - often in a single garden! While not having a formal group, the villagers embrace gardening and are at present planting the verges and returning the green spaces around the church to wildflowers. The village hall is famed for its teas, especially fine cakes and superb plant sales. All of the open gardens are within an easy walk of the hall, from which tickets can be obtained. Access to gardens is generally good, with most gardens being wheelchair friendly.

Open: Sunday 21 June, noon - 5pm, admission £5.00, children free. Tickets, route maps and refreshments available from the village hall.

Directions: Smailholm is a small village between Earlston and Kelso on the B6397. From the centre of the village take the Gattonside road and then after 100 yards turn right into the village hall car park.

· Smailholm Village Hall Committee

 STABLE HOUSE
Maxton, St Boswells, Melrose TD6 0EX
Ian Dalziel
T: 01835 824262 E: imd4@mac.com

An enclosed private garden built around converted stables with a sunny courtyard. The garden extends to over half an acre and includes mixed borders in sun and shade, a wildflower meadow, a plant house and a new hot border.

Open: 1 May - 31 October (Mondays only), 2pm - 5pm. Also open by arrangement 1 May - 31 October. Admission £4.00, children free. Please call or email to arrange a visit.

Directions: Two minutes from A68 on A699 to Kelso.

· Royal Blind

 THIRLESTANE
Kelso TD5 8PD
Catherine Ross and John Wylie
T: 01573 420487

Thirlestane is a large, informal garden, with some rough ground and long grass. It previously opened as one of the Yetholm gardens, but since then a nine-acre wood has been planted. This young woodland has a wide mix of trees, including some specimen trees. A spiral mount gives views of the Cheviot hills. There are two ponds and a burn. An orchard has about 50 varieties of apples and other fruit trees. Beech hedges enclose prairie planting in a formal setting. There is an enclosed flower garden, raised beds for vegetables and colour-themed planting.

Open: by arrangement 31 March - 31 October, admission £4.00, children free.

Roxburghshire

Directions: Thirlestane is near Yetholm, not to be confused with Thirlestane, Lauder. Do not follow SatNav, it will try to take you to Lochside. From Kelso, take the B6352 towards Yetholm for about six miles. Continue past a cottage on the edge of the road. Thirlestane is next on the left, opposite the road to Lochside. From Yetholm, take the road to Kelso for about two miles. After a very sharp corner, Thirlestane is on the right.

· *Macmillan Cancer Support*

7 WEST LEAS
Bonchester Bridge TD9 8TD
Mr and Mrs Robert Laidlaw
T: 01450 860711 E: ann@johnlaidlawandson.co.uk

The visitor to West Leas can share in the exciting and dramatic project on a grand scale still in the making. At its core is a passion for plants allied to a love and understanding of the land in which they are set. Collections of perennials and shrubs, many in temporary holding quarters, lighten up the landscape to magical effect. New lily pond and woodland planting added in 2019.

Open: Sunday 7 June and Sunday 2 August, 2pm - 5pm. Also open by arrangement 1 January - 31 December, admission £4.00, children free.   Teas for the specific date openings will be served in Bedrule Village Hall, Bonchester Bridge, Hawick TD9 8TE

Directions: Signposted off the Jedburgh/Bonchester Bridge Road.

· *Macmillan Cancer Support: Borders Appeal*

8 YETHOLM VILLAGE GARDENS
Town Yetholm TD5 8RL
The Gardeners of Yetholm Village

The villages of Town Yetholm and Kirk Yetholm are situated at the north end of the Pennine Way, close to the Bowmont Water in the dramatic setting of the foothills of the Cheviots. A variety of gardens will be open, each with their own unique features and style, reflecting distinctive horticultural interests. The Yew Tree Allotments running along the High Street, Town Yetholm, will open again, providing an ever popular feature with their unique water collection and distribution system. The short walking distance between the majority of the gardens provides magnificent views of the surrounding landscape to include Staerough and The Curr which straddle both the Bowmont and Halterburn Valleys where evidence of ancient settlements remains.

Open: Sunday 5 July, 1pm - 5:30pm, admission £5.00, children free.   Attractions include the ever popular music, local wood-turning products at Almond Cottage, home-baking and produce stall. An excellent plant stall supported by Newton Don Nursery is also planned for the afternoon. Tickets for entrance to all the gardens on sale in the Wauchope Hall, east end of the High Street, Town Yetholm. Cream Teas £3.00

Directions: Equidistant between Edinburgh and Newcastle and south of Kelso in the Scottish Borders. Take the B6352 to Town Yetholm. Ample parking is available along the High Street.

· *Border Group Of Riding For The Disabled (SCIO)*

STIRLINGSHIRE

Scotland's Gardens Scheme 2020 Guidebook is sponsored by INVESTEC WEALTH & INVESTMENT

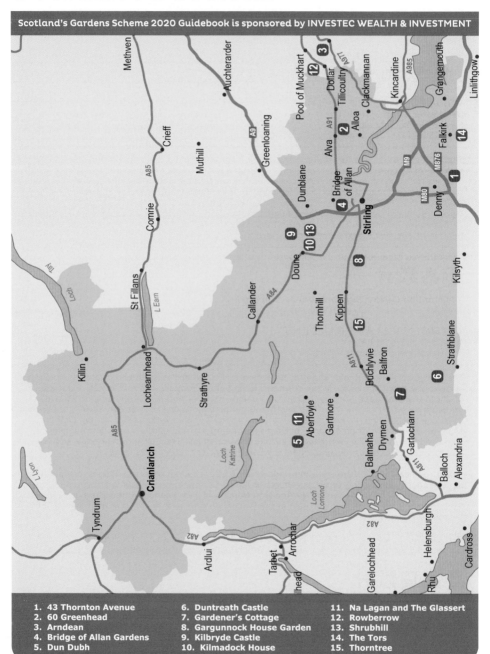

1. 43 Thornton Avenue
2. 60 Greenhead
3. Arndean
4. Bridge of Allan Gardens
5. Dun Dubh
6. Duntreath Castle
7. Gardener's Cottage
8. Gargunnock House Garden
9. Kilbryde Castle
10. Kilmadock House
11. Na Lagan and The Glassert
12. Rowberrow
13. Shrubhill
14. The Tors
15. Thorntree

Stirlingshire

OUR VOLUNTEER ORGANISERS

District Organiser:	Mandy Readman	Hutcheson Farm, Auchinlay Road, Dunblane FK15 9JS
		E: stirlingshire@scotlandsgardens.org
Area Organisers:	Clare Giles	Carselea Farm, Sommers Lane, by Stirling FK9 4UP
	Teresa Hill	11 Clifford Road, Stirling, FK8 2AQ
	Maurie Jessett	The Walled Garden, Lanrick, Doune FK16 6HJ
	Miranda Jones	122 High Street, Dunblane FK15 0ER
	Morna Knottenbelt	Gardener's Cottage, Ballochruin Rd, Killearn G63 9QB
	Rosemary Leckie	16 Chalton Road, Bridge of Allan FK9 4DX
	Ian Lumsden	The Myretoun, Menstrie, FK11 7EB
	Iain Morrison	Clifford House, Balkerach Street, Doune FK16 6DE
	Ann Shaw	Plaka, 5 Pendreich Road, Bridge of Allan FK9 4LY
District Photographer:	Des Coll	27 Meadow View, Cumbernauld G67 2BZ
Treasurer:	David Ashton	Westmore Shiel, Cauldhame, Kippen FK8 3JB

GARDENS OPEN ON A SPECIFIC DATE

Kilmadock House, Stirling Road, Doune	Sunday, 10 May
Na Lagan and The Glassert, Lochard Road, Aberfoyle	Saturday, 16 May
Bridge of Allan Gardens, Bridge of Allan	Sunday, 17 May
Duntreath Castle, Blanefield	Saturday/Sunday/Monday, 23/24/25 May
Kilbryde Castle, Dunblane	Saturday/Sunday/Monday, 23/24/25 May
Shrubhill, Dunblane	Saturday/Sunday, 23/24 May
43 Thornton Avenue, Bonnybridge	Sunday, 24 May
Gargunnock House Garden, Gargunnock	Monday, 25 May
Rowberrow, 18 Castle Road, Dollar	Sunday, 14 June
Thorntree, Arnprior	Sunday, 21 June
43 Thornton Avenue, Bonnybridge	Sunday, 19 July
The Tors, 2 Slamannan Road, Falkirk	Sunday, 26 July
60 Greenhead, Alva, Clackmannanshire	Sunday, 2 August
43 Thornton Avenue, Bonnybridge	Sunday, 27 September

GARDENS OPEN REGULARLY

Gargunnock House Garden, Gargunnock	8 February - 15 March &
	16 March - 25 September (not Sats & Suns)
Kilbryde Castle, Dunblane	8 February - 15 March

GARDENS OPEN BY ARRANGEMENT

Rowberrow, 18 Castle Road, Dollar	1 February - 31 December
Duntreath Castle, Blanefield	1 February - 30 November
Kilbryde Castle, Dunblane	16 March - 30 September
Dun Dubh, Kinlochard Road, Aberfoyle	20 April - 12 June & 7 Sept - 30 October
The Tors, 2 Slamannan Road, Falkirk	1 May - 30 September
Arndean, by Dollar	12 May - 8 June
Gardener's Cottage Walled Garden, Ballochruin Road, Killearn	15 June - 15 October

Stirlingshire

43 THORNTON AVENUE
Bonnybridge FK4 1AR
Tom Williamson and David Gallacher
T: 07821 406232

This astonishing hidden garden sits almost in the shadow of the Antonine Wall. There are over 680 named plants which are mostly herbaceous. More than 230 are grown in pots, along with seasonal bedding providing a wonderful display of plants from spring bulbs through to autumn colour. Awash with bees and butterflies, and our resident doves and robins, it allows people to see what can be achieved in a small suburban garden and within a tight budget. 2019 was a great year, not only was the garden featured on *The Beechgrove Garden* in July, but also won *Best Overall Garden* by Falkirk Council. It also featured in *Country Lifestyle Scotland* as well as helping to promote Scotland's Gardens Scheme and encourage people to take up gardening in a small space.

Open: Sunday 24 May, 1pm - 4:30pm for the May Weekend Festival. Also open Sunday 19 July, 1pm - 4:30pm. And open Sunday 27 September, 1pm - 4:30pm. Admission £3.00, children free. Homemade teas on 19 July only.

Directions: Signposted from the A803. Bus from Glasgow. Please park with consideration for other houses in the area.

· *Forth Valley Sensory Centre & LSA: (Lyn's Small Animal Rehoming)*

60 GREENHEAD
Alva, Clackmannanshire FK12 5HH
Lynn Cameron

A delightful hidden garden in Alva behind the primary school. Divided into 'rooms' with themes, two being Mediterranean and Oriental, there is extensive planting and clever use of pots throughout. Recycled materials are much in evidence, especially in the 'cosy' corner with a fireplace. There is a wide variety of shrubs, perennials and annuals as well as vegetables and fruit. There is a pond and a small wildlife area. An inspiration for those trying to garden in a small space.

Open: Sunday 2 August, 2pm - 5pm, admission £3.00, children free. There may be plants for sale.

Directions: Signposted from the A91. Please park with consideration for other houses in the area.

· *Stirling Baptist Church: Christians Against Poverty(CAP) Forth Valley Debt Centre*

ARNDEAN
by Dollar FK14 7NH
Johnny and Katie Stewart
T: 01259 743525 E: johnny@arndean.co.uk

Opening for more than 40 years, this is a beautiful mature garden extending to 15 acres including the woodland walk. There is a formal herbaceous part, a small vegetable garden and an orchard. In addition, there are flowering shrubs, abundant and striking rhododendrons and azaleas as well as many fine specimen trees. There is a tree house for children.

Open: by arrangement 12 May - 8 June, admission £5.00, children free.

Directions: Arndean is well signposted off the A977.

· *Marie Curie*

Stirlingshire

BRIDGE OF ALLAN GARDENS
Bridge of Allan   FK9 4AT
The Gardeners of Bridge of Allan
E: r.leckie44@btinternet.com

Bridge of Allan gardens will once again have a mixture of both small and large gardens and a few new ones, with a good variety of specimen trees and shrubs, some with interesting sculptures. Azaleas, rhododendrons, magnolias, camellias and many other spring blossoms should be in flower. This year the Bridge of Allan allotments are joining us, and some of the owners will be present to talk about their plantings. The allotments produce quantities of vegetables, fruits and flowers despite the lack of electricity and the worry of flooding from the river nearby. There will be further information about the gardens on the website nearer the time.

Open: Sunday 17 May, 1pm - 5pm, admission £5.00, children free. Teas from 1.30pm at St Saviours Church Hall, Keir Street FK9 4AT. Plant stall at the church. Tickets and maps will be available at all gardens and at the hall.

Directions: Gardens will be signposted from the village.

· *St Saviours Episcopal Church: Bridge Of Allan & Artlink Central Ltd*

DUN DUBH
Kinlochard Road, Aberfoyle FK8 3TJ
Callum Pirnie, Head Gardener
T: 01877 382698 E: callumpirnie@gmail.com

A late Victorian garden of six acres undergoing restoration and development. It is set on a series of terraces and slopes, which run down to the shores of Loch Ard, with superb views west to Ben Lomond framed by stands of mature conifers. There is an enclosed, colour-themed formal garden laid out on three terraces and a new Victorian-style glasshouse overlooking a terraced kitchen and fruit garden. The formal paved terrace at the front of the house overlooks a newly developed rock garden and crag while the lower walk running from the boat house to the main lawn gives views across the loch. A developing woodland garden leads on to a formal late summer herbaceous border and terraced heather garden, all of which provide wonderful autumn colour.

Open: by arrangement 20 April - 12 June & 7 September - 30 October, admission £5.00, children free.

Directions: Full directions will be given when contacting the garden. Groups welcome.

· *Help for Heroes*

Stirlingshire

6

DUNTREATH CASTLE
Blanefield G63 9AJ
Sir Archibald and Lady Edmonstone
T: 01360 770215 E: juliet@edmonstone.com
W: www.duntreathcastle.co.uk
....

Extensive gardens with mature and new plantings. Ornamental landscaped lake and bog garden. Sweeping lawns below formal fountain and rose parterre with herbaceous border leading up to an attractive waterfall garden with shrubs and spring plantings. There is a good variety of herbaceous planting round the formal lawns which are overlooked by ornamental shrubs, woodland walk, 15th-century keep and gatehouse chapel.

Open: by arrangement 1 February - 30 November including for Snowdrops and Winter Walks. Also open Saturday/Sunday/Monday, 23/24/25 May, 11am - 4pm for the May Weekend Festival. Admission £5.00, children free. There will be an honesty box available for the May weekend.

Directions: A81 north of Glasgow between Blanefield and Killearn.

· *All proceeds to SGS Beneficiaries*

7

GARDENER'S COTTAGE WALLED GARDEN
Ballochruin Road, Killearn G63 9QB
Derek and Morna Knottenbelt
T: 01360 551682 E: mornaknottenbelt@hotmail.com
....

The walled garden, acquired in 2013 by the present owners, has been planted with extensive herbaceous borders, box hedging, roses and many unusual plants. There is a White Garden, a long shrub border with primulas and gentians and a former fernery with a collection of salvias and peach and pear trees. June is a good time to visit when the roses are in bloom and borders with lupins, peonies and other perennials are in flower. By late summer, the borders have argyranthemums as well as dahlias, Michaelmas daisies, rudbeckias and blue aconitums. There are fine views of the Campsie Hills and the garden is surrounded by the conifers of the Designed Landscape of Carbeth.

Open: by arrangement 15 June - 15 October, admission £5.00, children free. Groups welcome but limited to ten owing to restricted parking.

Directions: Follow SatNav to G63 0LF, which is Carbeth Home Farm. We are the next entrance below the farm. Turn left on to the gravel road and follow yellow *SGS* signs.

· *The British Horse Society*

8

GARGUNNOCK HOUSE GARDEN
Gargunnock FK8 3AZ
The Gargunnock Trustees
T: 01786 860392 E: gargunnockgardens@btinternet.com
....

Large mature garden five miles from Stirling, with a walled garden, well-established house garden, woodland walks with species and hybrid rhododendrons, massed plantings of azaleas and wonderful specimen trees. Snowdrops in February/March are followed by over 40 varieties of daffodils and the glorious displays of azaleas and rhododendrons in May. In autumn, stunning colours develop on the many wonderful trees along the drive to the house. The three-acre walled garden contains perennial borders, cut-flower beds, greenhouses, fruit orchard and newly-planted arboretum of specimen trees.

Stirlingshire

Open: 8 February - 15 March, 11am - 3:30pm including for Snowdrops and Winter Walks. Also open Monday 25 May, 11am - 3:30pm for the May Weekend Festival. And open 16 March - 25 September (not Saturdays & Sundays), 11am - 3:30pm. Admission £4.00, children free.

Directions: Five miles west of Stirling on the A811, follow the yellow *SGS* signs. Car parking is at the entrance by the lodge. Honesty box is in the car park.

· *Gargunnock Community Trust Ltd & Scotland's Charity Air Ambulance*

KILBRYDE CASTLE
Dunblane FK15 9NF
Sir James and Lady Campbell
T: 01786 824897 E: kilbryde1@aol.com
W: www.kilbrydecastle.com

The Kilbryde Castle gardens cover some 12 acres and are situated above the Ardoch Burn and below the castle. The gardens are split into three parts: formal, woodland and wild. Natural planting (azaleas, rhododendrons, camellias and magnolias) is found in the woodland garden. There are glorious snowdrops, spring bulbs, and autumn colour provided by clematis and acers. Some new plantings for additional late summer/autumn colour was added in 2017. Featured in *Scotland on Sunday* in September 2016.

Open: 8 February - 15 March, 11am - 3.30pm for the Snowdrops and Winter Walks. 23 May - 25 May, 11am - 4pm for the May Weekend Festival. Also open by arrangement 16 March - 30 September. Admission £5.00, children free.

Directions: Three miles from Dunblane and Doune, off the A820 between Dunblane and Doune. On Scotland's Gardens Scheme open days the garden is signposted from the A820.

· *Leighton Library Trust*

KILMADOCK HOUSE
Stirling Road, Doune FK16 6AA
Darren Skillan and Senga McColl

A former Parish Manse, Kilmadock House was bought by the current owners in 2011. An already established and beautifully mature three-acre garden it continues to evolve. Under the skilful eye of Jens Nielsen, ably assisted by Robert and Haydden the garden is entering its next exciting stage. A stunning spring garden boasting a collection of rhododendron, both species and hybrid, Japanese acer, hostas and colourful spring bulbs. The pond and stream take centre stage with lawns and mixed borders leading into informal woodland planting. Maturing Wellingtonia, Metasequoia and Davidia sit comfortably within the natural forest backdrop.

Open: Sunday 10 May, 2pm - 5pm, admission £5.00, children free. There will be a small group from the Doune Pipe Band playing.

Directions: The entrance is directly off the A84 and will be well signposted from the village. Please take care when crossing this busy road. Disabled parking only at the house and no parking on the A84. There is parking throughout the village, but please park with consideration for other houses in the area.

· *Kilmadock Development Trust Limited & Doune Pipe Band*

Stirlingshire

11
NA LAGAN AND THE GLASSERT
Lochard Road, Aberfoyle FK8 3TJ
Lord & Lady Forsyth and Mr & Mrs J Cowderoy

Two delightful gardens on the shores of Loch Ard, which have a wonderful display of rhododendrons, azaleas, a large magnolia and many other shrubs. There are woodland areas with some fine specimen trees, Japanese acers, fruit trees and spring bulbs.

Open: Saturday 16 May, 2pm - 5pm, admission £6.00, children free. Some paths are quite steep and stout footwear is recommended. Wheelchair access is very limited in both gardens. Please note this is a Saturday opening.

Directions: From Aberfoyle follow the B829 towards Kinlochard for about three miles, the yellow signs will be in place. Only disabled parking at The Glassert. There is a car park on the opposite side of the road but it is limited and there will be no parking on the road. Where possible, if meeting up with friends, please use the car park in Aberfoyle and 'car share' for the short onward journey.

· *Forth Driving Group RDA SCIO*

12
ROWBERROW
18 Castle Road, Dollar FK14 7BE
Bill and Rosemary Jarvis
T: 01259 742584 E: rjarvis1000@hotmail.com

Hillfoot Harmony invite you to a garden party! We will not only provide an afternoon tea but also sing to you while you view the garden. On the way up to Castle Campbell overlooking Dollar Glen, this colourful garden has several mixed shrub and herbaceous borders, a wildlife pond, two rockeries, alpine troughs, fruit and vegetable gardens, and a mini-orchard. The owner is a plantaholic and likes to collect unusual specimens. Rowberrow was featured on *The Beechgrove Garden* in summer 2011. A wonderful garden to visit at any time of the year.

Open: Sunday 14 June, 2pm - 5pm. Also open by arrangement 1 February - 31 December. Admission £5.00, children free.

Directions: Pass along the burn side in Dollar, turn right at the T-junction, follow signs for *Castle Campbell* and *Dollar Glen*. Park at the bottom of Castle Road or in the Quarry car park just up from the house.

· *Hillfoot Harmony Barbershop Singers*

13
SHRUBHILL
Dunblane FK15 9PA
Tiff and Michaela Wright
E: wrightrascals@btinternet.com

Two acres of mixed, informal planting of some unusual rhododendrons, azaleas, specimen trees and other shrubs. Beautiful all round views particularly over the Carse of Stirling and towards Ben Ledi and Ben Lomond. Herbaceous borders, meconopsis, late spring bulbs, water feature with a wide variety of primulas. Small walled garden predominantly for fruit and a greenhouse with a well-established vine.

Open: Saturday/Sunday, 23/24 May, 2pm - 5pm for the May Weekend Festival, admission £5.00, children free. There may be plants for sale.

Stirlingshire

Directions: Two miles from Keir roundabout on the B824 on the left, just after the *David Stirling Memorial,* follow the signs and parking advice. One mile from the A820 and on the right.

· *The Teapot Trust*

 14

THE TORS
2 Slamannan Road, Falkirk FK1 5LG
Dr and Mrs D M Ramsay
T: 01324 620877 E: dmramsay28@yahoo.co.uk
W: www.torsgarden.co.uk
....

An award-winning Victorian garden of just over one acre with a secret woodland garden to the side and an orchard leading off to a wild area at the rear of the house. Many unusual maple trees, hydrangeas and rhododendrons are the main interest of this garden and two fine avenues of Chinese paperbark maples are especially noteworthy. Featured on *The Beechgrove Garden* for autumn colour in September 2010, but the best time to see this garden is at the end of July or the beginning of August. *Scotland on Sunday* featured the house and garden in an article with many lovely photographs in September 2015.

Open: Sunday 26 July, 2pm - 5:30pm. Also open by arrangement 1 May - 30 September. Admission £4.00, children free.

Directions: The B803 to the south of Falkirk leads to Glenbrae Road. Turn right at the traffic lights into Slamannan Road and The Tors is a Victorian building immediately on the left. The house is within 200 yards of Falkirk High Station.

· *Strathcarron Hospice*

 15

THORNTREE
Arnprior FK8 3EY
Mark and Carol Seymour
T: 01786 870710 E: info@thorntreebarn.co.uk
W: www.thorntreebarn.co.uk
....

This year Thorntree are opening for one day only! The garden continues to evolve and cotoneasters by the saltire beds have been cut back which means the four flower beds are no longer hidden behind a hedge! Also, the view past the summerhouse can be seen and the Annabelle hydrangea has popped up now that there are less branches above it. In September 2019 a new wildflower garden was made around the patio, so by 2020 it should be in flower on the north-facing side of the house. Wildflowers have been sown around the pond and they have germinated already, so exciting!

Open: Sunday 21 June, 2pm - 5pm, admission £5.00, children free. There will be a large plant stall with home-grown plants. The cardiochrinums are in the wooded area and waiting to seed! Tea, coffee and cake if the weather is fine.

Directions: On the A811, to Arnprior, then take the Fintry Road; Thorntree is second on the right.

· *Forth Driving Group RDA SCIO*

WIGTOWNSHIRE

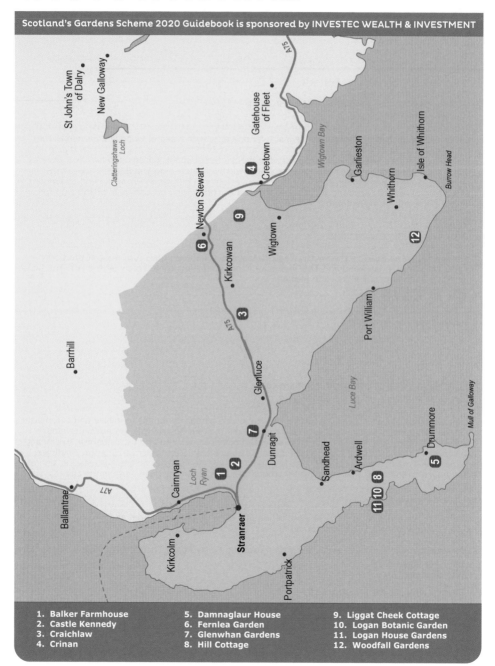

Scotland's Gardens Scheme 2020 Guidebook is sponsored by INVESTEC WEALTH & INVESTMENT

1. Balker Farmhouse
2. Castle Kennedy
3. Craichlaw
4. Crinan
5. Damnaglaur House
6. Fernlea Garden
7. Glenwhan Gardens
8. Hill Cottage
9. Liggat Cheek Cottage
10. Logan Botanic Garden
11. Logan House Gardens
12. Woodfall Gardens

Wigtownshire

OUR VOLUNTEER ORGANISERS

District Organiser:	Ann Watson	Doonholm, Cairnryan Road, Stranraer DG9 8AT E: wigtonwshire@scotlandsgardens.org
Area Organisers:	Eileen Davie	Whitehills House, Minnigaff, Newton Stewart DG8 6SL
	Mary Gladstone	Craichlaw, Kirkcowan, Newton Stewart DG8 0DQ
	Shona Greenhorn	Burbainie, Westwood Avenue, Stranraer DG9 8BT
	Enid Innes	Crinan, Creetown, Newton Stewart DG8 7EP
	Annmaree Mitchell	Cottage 2, Little Float, Sandhead, Stranraer DG9 9LD
	Vicky Roberts	Logan House Gardens, Port Logan DG9 9ND
Treasurer:	George Fleming	Stablesend, Culreoch, Stranraer DG9 8LZ

GARDENS OPEN ON A SPECIFIC DATE

Logan House Gardens, Port Logan, by Stranraer	Sunday, 17 May
Woodfall Gardens, Glasserton	Saturday/Sunday/Monday, 23/24/25 May
Balker Farmhouse, Stranraer	Saturday, 23 May
Logan Botanic Garden, Port Logan, by Stranraer	Sunday, 24 May
Crinan, Creetown	Sunday, 24 May
Castle Kennedy and Gardens, Stranraer	Sunday, 14 June
Woodfall Gardens, Glasserton	Sunday, 21 June

GARDENS OPEN REGULARLY

Glenwhan Gardens, Dunragit, by Stranraer	1 January - 31 December

GARDENS OPEN BY ARRANGEMENT

Craichlaw, Kirkcowan, Newton Stewart	1 January - 31 December
Fernlea Garden, Corvisel Road, Newton Stewart	1 April - 30 September
Liggat Cheek Cottage, Baltersan, Newton Stewart	1 April - 30 September
Hill Cottage, Portlogan, Stranraer	1 April - 31 October
Damnaglaur House, Drummore, Stranraer	1 April - 31 October

Wigtownshire

BALKER FARMHOUSE
Stranraer DG9 8RS
The Earl and Countess of Stair
T: 01581 400225/01776 702024

Balker Farmhouse was restored in 2002 and the garden, formerly a ploughed field, was started in 2003-4 by Davina, Dowager Countess of Stair and Annmaree Mitchell. It is now full of wonderful shrubs and plants for all seasons and is opened in memory of Davina, who died in 2017.

Open: Saturday 23 May, 2pm - 5pm for the May Weekend Festival, admission £4.00, children free.

Directions: One-and-a-half miles off the A75, three miles from Stranraer. Go through the farmyard to the blue gate.

· *Inch Parish Church*

CASTLE KENNEDY AND GARDENS
Stranraer DG9 8SL
The Earl and Countess of Stair
T: 01581 400225
W: www.castlekennedygardens.com

Romantically situated, these famous 75 acres of landscaped gardens are located on an isthmus surrounded by two large natural lochs. At one end the ruined Castle Kennedy overlooks a beautiful herbaceous walled garden with Lochinch Castle at the other end. With over 300 years of planting there is an impressive collection of rare trees, rhododendrons, exotic shrubs and many spectacular Champion Trees. The stunning snowdrop walks, daffodils, spring flowers, rhododendron and magnolia displays and herbaceous borders, make this a 'must visit' garden throughout the year. Champion Trees: 6 British, 11 Scottish and 25 for Dumfries and Galloway.

Open: Sunday 14 June, 10am - 5pm, admission details can be found on the garden's website.

Directions: On the A75, five miles east of Stranraer. The nearest train station is in Stranraer. On a local bus route.

· *Home-Start Wigtownshire*

CRAICHLAW
Kirkcowan, Newton Stewart DG8 0DQ
Mr and Mrs Andrew Gladstone
T: 01671 830208 E: craichlaw@aol.com

Formal garden with herbaceous borders around the house. Set in extensive grounds with lawns, lochs and woodland. A path around the main loch leads to a water garden returning past a recently planted arboretum in the old walled garden. The best times to visit the garden are early February for snowdrops, May to mid-June for the water garden and rhododendrons, and mid-June to August for herbaceous borders.

Open: by arrangement throughout the year, including February through mid-March for Snowdrops and Winter Walks, admission £5.00, children free.

Wigtownshire

Directions: Take the B733 for Kirkcowan off the A75 at the Halfway House eight miles west of Newton Stewart. Craichlaw House is the first turning on the right.

· *All proceeds to SGS Beneficiaries*

4

CRINAN
Creetown DG8 7EP
Mrs Enid Innes

A wonderful ten-acre garden, at its best in May and June with ten lochs. There are many unusual conifers including Wollemi Pine. There are also many different species of oak, birch, chestnut, acer, eucalyptus and many other varieties of hardwoods. The soil is peaty so the rhododendrons, azaleas, camellias and magnolias are star turns. There are substantial collections of viburnums, hydrangeas, pieris and cornus. Around the lochans there are irises, hostas, skunk cabbage and gunnera. The owner has a passion for trees and shrubs.

Open: Sunday 24 May, 2pm - 5pm for the May Weekend Festival, admission £5.00, children free.

Directions: From Creetown take the old station road and keep going up for about a mile until you reach a cattle grid and a timber-clad house, ignore any other turn off.

· *All proceeds to SGS Beneficiaries*

5

DAMNAGLAUR HOUSE
Drummore, Stranraer DG9 9QN
Frances Collins
T: 01776 840636/ 07884 435353

Since moving into Damnaglaur House, in 1991, its owners have totally transformed the garden, putting in a series of 'semi-terraces' and, following the planting of wind-defeating shrubs, they were able to introduce many special herbaceous plants and trees. Just short of half an acre, it slowly evolved into one which feels substantially larger because of its design – the gravel paths weave their way through it towards many hidden corners to come upon countless gems. The views from the garden are stunning, down to Drummore, across Luce Bay and, in the far distance, to the Galloway Hills. An archway, arbour and pergola give extra height for the planting. Seating around the garden gives visitors a chance to sit and enjoy their surroundings, especially close to the pond, with its numerous fish and trickling waterfall.

Open: by arrangement 1 April - 31 October, admission £4.00, children free. Teas available on request.

Directions: From Drummore, follow signs to the *Mull of Galloway* for a mile on B7041 to junction with B7065; Damnaglaur is on the right.

· *British Red Cross: Yemen Appeal*

Wigtownshire

FERNLEA GARDEN
Corvisel Road, Newton Stewart DG8 6LW
Mrs Jenny Gustafson
T: 07909 951 885/ 01671 638273 E: jennygustafson2@hotmail.com

A secluded town garden of a third of an acre. It was created in 2006 to complement a new house. There are many rare and unusual trees and shrubs. Two herbaceous borders, one with hot colours and the other pastels. A Chinese-inspired corner, small pond, fruit trees including a Galloway pippin apple and soft fruit. The upper part of the garden is hidden behind a tall beech hedge, where there is a summer house and adjacent woodland planting.

Open: by arrangement 1 April - 30 September, admission £4.50, children free. Homemade teas can be provided by prior arrangement.

Directions: Turn right at the roundabout on the A75 if coming from Dumfries direction. Go left at the cattle market (opposite Crown Hotel), first through road on the right.

· *Host*

GLENWHAN GARDENS
Dunragit, by Stranraer DG9 8PH
Tess Knott
T: 07787 990702
W: www.glenwhangardens.co.uk

Described as one of the most beautiful gardens in Scotland, Glenwhan Gardens is situated at 300 feet and overlooks Luce Bay and the Mull of Galloway, with clear views to the Isle of Man. Thirty-six years ago there was wild moorland, but now, following considerable dedication and vision, you can see glorious collections of plants from around the world. There is colour in all seasons and the winding paths, well-placed seats, and varied sculptures, set around small lakes, add to the tranquil atmosphere. There is a 17-acre moorland wildflower walk, the chance to see red squirrels and a well-marked Tree Trail.

Open: 1 January - 31 December, 10am - 5pm, admission details can be found on the garden's website.

Directions: Seven miles east of Stranraer, one mile off the A75 at Dunragit (follow brown *VisitScotland* and yellow SGS arrows).

· *WWF-UK*

HILL COTTAGE
Portlogan, Stranraer DG9 9NT
Mrs Mary Shaw
T: 01776 860314/ 07810 541738

Hill Cottage is a half-acre cottage garden sitting amongst glorious scenery with marvellous views over hills and down to the coast. Mainly a cottage garden with a large natural rockery, small pond and vegetable plot.

Open: by arrangement 1 April - 31 October, admission £4.00, children free. Teas available on request.

Wigtownshire

Directions: Turn left from Port Logan, left again onto Killumpha Road about quarter of a mile and it is the second cottage on the right.

· *Blood Bikes Scotland*

LIGGAT CHEEK COTTAGE
Baltersan, Newton Stewart DG8 6AX
Philip and Jennifer Bradley
T: 01671 402639 E: bradley@liggat.plus.com
....

The garden is approximately half an acre and includes a small woodland and shade area with ferns, hostas, trilliums, erythroniums and many other shade-loving plants. The rest of the garden is divided into informal 'rooms' with large borders containing herbaceous perennials, shrubs, conifers, grasses, etc. There is one south-facing bed devoted to less hardy plants including agaves, yuccas, cordylines, aeoniums and tetrapanax. The garden was featured in an episode of *The Beechgrove Garden* on 5 September 2019.

Open: by arrangement 1 April - 30 September, admission £4.00, children free. Teas and plants may be available by prior request.

Directions: From Newton Stewart roundabout (A75) towards Wigtown (A714) *Scotland's National Book Town*. Approximately two miles from the roundabout on the right, above Baltersan Farm on the left.

· *Euan Macdonald Centre for Motor Neurone Disease Research*

LOGAN BOTANIC GARDEN
Port Logan, by Stranraer DG9 9ND
A Regional Garden of the Royal Botanic Garden Edinburgh
T: 01776 860231 E: logan@rbge.org.uk
W: www.rbge.org.uk/logan
....

Logan is a regional garden of the Royal Botanic Garden Edinburgh which celebrates its 350th anniversary in 2020. For more information, visit www.rbge.org.uk/350.
At the south western tip of Scotland lies Logan, which is unrivalled as the country's most exotic garden. With a mild climate washed by the Gulf Stream, a remarkable collection of bizarre and beautiful plants, especially from the southern hemisphere, flourish out of doors. Enjoy the colourful walled garden with its magnificent tree ferns, palms and borders along with the contrasting woodland garden with its unworldly gunnera bog. Visit the Logan Conservatory, which houses a special collection of tender South African species.
National Plant Collection: *Gunnera, Leptospermum*, *Griselinia*, *Clianthus* and *Sutherlandia*.
Champion Trees: *Polylepis* and *Eucalyptus*.

Open: Sunday 24 May, 10am - 5pm, admission details and other opening dates can be found on the garden's website.

Directions: Ten miles south of Stranraer on the A716 then two-and-a-half miles from Ardwell village.

· *Board Of Trustees Of The Royal Botanic Garden Edinburgh*

Wigtownshire

LOGAN HOUSE GARDENS
Port Logan, by Stranraer DG9 9ND
Mr and Mrs Andrew Roberts

A mature woodland garden of 20 acres with fine species of rhododendrons, Champion Trees and plants from the Southern Hemisphere.
Champion Trees: 7 UK and 11 Scottish.

Open: Sunday 17 May, 2pm - 4:30pm, admission £4.00, children free. Well-behaved dogs welcome on leads.

Directions: On the A716, 13 miles south of Stranraer, two-and-a-half miles from Ardwell village.

· *Port Logan Hall*

WOODFALL GARDENS
Glasserton DG8 8LY
Ross and Liz Muir
E: woodfallgardens@btinternet.com
W: www.woodfall-gardens.co.uk

This lovely three-acre 18th-century triple walled garden has been thoughtfully restored to provide year-round interest. It contains many mature trees and shrubs, including some less common species, herbaceous borders and shrub roses which surround the foundations of original greenhouses, grass borders, a parterre, extensive beds of fruit and vegetables, a herb garden and a small woodland walk. This unusual garden is well worth a visit.

Open: Sunday 21 June, 10.30am - 4.30pm and May Weekend Festival, 23 May - 25 May, 10am - 7pm. Admission £5.00, children free; includes self service tea, coffee and biscuits on 21 June only. Please check the garden website for further openings.

Directions: Two miles south west of Whithorn at junction of A746 and A747 (directly behind Glasserton Church).

· *Glasserton and the Isle Of Whithorn Church of Scotland: Glasserton Church & Macmillan Cancer Support*

Logan House Garden

"The Most Outstanding Continuous Care Retirement Community in the UK."

UK OVER 50's HOUSING AWARDS

An integral part of our Retirement Village is Inchmarlo House Care Home which gives confidence to our Home Owners and their families as our nursing, care and security staff are on site 24 hours a day and assistance can be there in minutes.

We also reserve a room in Inchmarlo House for Home Owners who require respite care for short periods. If longer stays are required Home Owners have priority admission.

Since 1986 our policy of providing personalised care has enabled many Home Owners to continue to live in their own homes longer than might be the case elsewhere at considerable financial savings as against moving into a care home.

The Inchmarlo Retirement Village – one of the first and still one of the Best in the UK

"The Best Places to find Your Perfect Retirement Home" – THE SUNDAY TIMES

To find out more call 01330 826242 or email sales.manager@inchmarlo-retirement.co.uk

Then come and see why Inchmarlo is the ideal spot to put down some roots.

INCHMARLO
RETIREMENT VILLAGE

Where Gracious Living Comes Naturally

There are many benefits of joining The Caley...

- Practical **Workshops and Demonstrations** at our Saughton Park base
- Twice monthly free Winter Lecture Series from October to March
- Day Visits to gardens and other places of horticultural interest
- Access to the **Demonstration Allotment** which showcases best practice
- Grow & Learn Awards for individuals with complex learning needs
- Annual Spring Bulb Show with free entry for Caley members

Join Scotland's National Horticultural and Gardening Society today and support the future of horticulture and gardening in Scotland!

Join at www.thecaley.org.uk
Scottish Charity Number SC 006522

The Caley
Royal Caledonian Horticultural Society

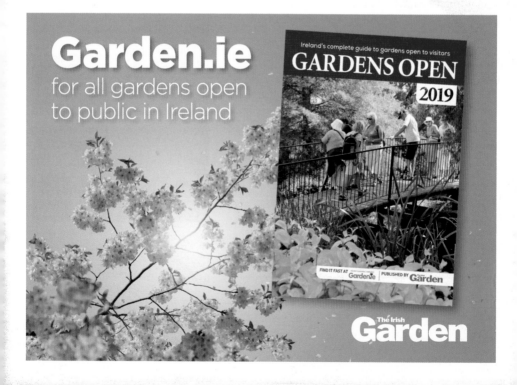

12 months for the price of 9

RHS
Inspiring everyone to grow

Your membership supports
our work as a charity.
Join today.

Introductory offer for new members by annual Direct Debit.
Terms and conditions apply. RHS Registered Charity No. 222879/SC038262

© RHS / Helen Yates

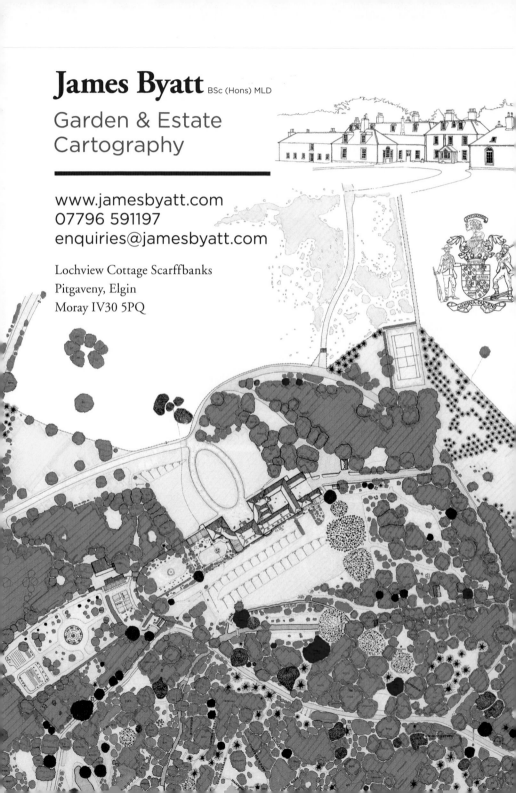

James Byatt BSc (Hons) MLD

Garden & Estate Cartography

www.jamesbyatt.com
07796 591197
enquiries@jamesbyatt.com

Lochview Cottage Scarffbanks
Pitgaveny, Elgin
Moray IV30 5PQ

**Find out more about our full range go online at
www.gardensolutions.info or call 08000 430 450 for a catalogue.**

Garden Solutions

Specialist Compost, Mulch & Soil Conditioner Suppliers

Spending time in your garden can be such a joy: it can transport
you to a blissful oasis and provide a calming experience that can
enhance your health and wellbeing.
With this in mind, we aim to provide the best quality composts
and mulches allowing you to get the best out of your garden by
putting the best in from the start.

Munro
Greenhouses
& Garden Buildings

01786 357 400
info@munrogreenhouses.co.uk
www.munrogreenhouses.co.uk

Scotland's Independent Greenhouse Suppliers

BENNYBEG
PLANT
C E N T R E

Plant Paradise

Muthill Road, Crieff, Perthshire, PH7 4HN
T: 01764 656345
W: www.bennybeg.co.uk

JAMESFIELD
GARDEN
C E N T R E

For all your Garden needs

Abernethy, Perthshire, KY14 6EW
T: 01738 851176
W: www.jamesfieldgardencentre.co.uk

Beautiful
garden planting
By John Gordon BSc (Hons) Dip. Hort. Edin.

My own garden at Torwood (Angus & Dundee) is available to visit on arrangement
and is also open 23/24th May 2–5pm for the May Festival Weekend. Welcome!

• www.gardendisplays.co.uk • email: j.gordon.82@btinternet.com • tel: 07988010418

Celebrating 350 years 1670–2020

Visit four Botanic Gardens to see one of the richest plant collections on Earth

Edinburgh
Arboretum Place and Inverleith Row,
Edinburgh EH3 5LR
Tel 0131 248 2909 | rbge.org.uk
Open every day from 10 am (except 1 January
and 25 December) | Garden is free |
Entry charges apply to Glasshouses

Logan
Port Logan, Stranraer,
Dumfries and Galloway DG9 9ND
Tel 01776 860231 | rbge.org.uk/logan
Open daily 1 March to 15 November
Admission charge applies

Benmore
Dunoon, Argyll PA23 8QU
Tel 01369 706261 | rbge.org.uk/benmore
Open daily 1 March to 31 October
Admission charge applies

Dawyck
Stobo, Scottish Borders EH45 9JU
Tel 01721 760254 | rbge.org.uk/dawyck
Open daily 1 February to 30 November
Admission charge applies

Become a Friend and help us to explore, conserve
and explain the world of plants for a better future.
Call **0131 552 5339** or visit **rbge.org.uk/membership**

**Royal
Botanic Garden
Edinburgh**

Opening beautiful gardens for charity

The National Garden Scheme gives visitors unique access to 3,500 exceptional private gardens in England and Wales, and raises impressive amounts of money for nursing and health charities through admissions, teas and cake.

To find your perfect garden, visit ngs.org.uk

so much more than just a garden centre...

Enjoy a day in West Lothian! with 18 small inspirational themed gardens, the biggest range of garden plants for sale in Scotland and the Orangery tearoom to tempt you, you'll receive a warm welcome!

New Hopetoun Gardens
find us on the A904 between South Queensferry and Linlithgow in West Lothian EH52 6QZ
t: 01506 834433   **w:** www.newhopetoungardens.co.uk
New Hopetoun Gardens - Edinburgh

Dig below
the surface

Explore Scotland's beautiful gardens
and hear their fascinating stories
with Candide's audio tours.

CANDIDE
candidegardening.com/scotland

Visit America's best private gardens through Open Days!

Since 1995, Garden Conservancy Open Days has opened rarely seen private gardens to the public across America.

Preserving, Sharing, and Celebrating America's Gardens

gardenconservancy.org/opendays

Helensbank Garden

A special secret garden - and more!

horticultural courses - garden restoration and design - private venue hire - concert venue

www.helensbank.com
Helensbank@aol.com

Help bees

Help people

Bees for Development is the UK charity helping some of the world's poorest people to create sustainable livelihoods through beekeeping.

Simon Abanyu keeps bees on his mother's farm in Uganda. Since the bees arrived, he and his mother have noticed that their yields of coffee have increased. They earn income also from selling honey, meaning they benefit twice!

UK Charity 1078803

Bees for Development wants to reach more people like Simon: please support this work.

Find out more at
www.beesfordevelopment.org
Bees for Development

info@beesfordevelopment.org | 01600 714848 | 1 Agincourt Street, Monmouth NP25 3DZ UK

GARDENS OPEN ON A SPECIFIC DATE

FEBRUARY

Friday 7 February
Dumfriesshire   Barjarg Tower, Auldgirth

Saturday 8 February
Dumfriesshire   Barjarg Tower, Auldgirth

Sunday 9 February
Dumfriesshire   Barjarg Tower, Auldgirth

Saturday 15 February
Ayrshire & Arran   Blair House, Blair Estate, Dalry, Ayrshire

Sunday 16 February
Dumfriesshire   Craig, Langholm
Perth & Kinross   Cloan, by Auchterarder

Saturday 22 February
East Lothian   Shepherd House, Inveresk, Musselburgh

Sunday 23 February
East Lothian   Shepherd House, Inveresk, Musselburgh
Fife   Lindores House, by Newburgh
Kirkcudbrightshire   Danevale Park, Crossmichael
Peeblesshire & Tweeddale   Kailzie Gardens, Peebles
Perth & Kinross   Kilgraston School, Bridge of Earn

Saturday 29 February
Angus & Dundee   Langley Park Gardens, Montrose

MARCH

Sunday 1 March
Angus & Dundee   Langley Park Gardens, Montrose
Kincardine & Deeside   Ecclesgreig Castle, St Cyrus
Lanarkshire   Cleghorn, Stable House, Cleghorn Farm, Lanark

Sunday 29 March
East Lothian   Winton Castle, Pencaitland
Lanarkshire   Old Farm Cottage, The Ladywell, Nemphlar, Lanark

APRIL

Sunday 5 April
East Lothian   Humbie Dean, Humbie
Lanarkshire   Old Farm Cottage, The Ladywell, Nemphlar, Lanark

Sunday 12 April

Aberdeenshire	Auchmacoy, Ellon
Fife	Cambo Spring Fair, Kingsbarns
Kirkcudbrightshire	3 Millhall, Shore Road, Kirkcudbright

Thursday 16 April

Angus & Dundee	Inchmill Cottage, Glenprosen, near Kirriemuir
Inverness, Ross, Cromarty & Skye	Dundonnell House, Little Loch Broom, Wester Ross

Saturday 18 April

East Lothian	Humbie Dean, Humbie

Sunday 19 April

Aberdeenshire	Westhall Castle, Oyne, Inverurie
Argyll & Lochaber	Benmore Botanic Garden, Benmore, Dunoon
Berwickshire	NEW Harlaw Farmhouse, Eccles near Kelso, Roxburghshire
Dunbartonshire	Kilarden, Rosneath
Perth & Kinross	Megginch Castle, Errol

Saturday 25 April

Argyll & Lochaber	Knock Newhouse, Lochgair
Argyll & Lochaber	Maolachy's Garden, Lochavich, by Kilmelford
East Lothian	Shepherd House, Inveresk, Musselburgh
Renfrewshire	SGS Kilmacolm Plant Sale, outside Kilmacolm Library, Kilmacolm

Sunday 26 April

Argyll & Lochaber	Knock Newhouse, Lochgair
Argyll & Lochaber	Maolachy's Garden, Lochavich, by Kilmelford
East Lothian	Shepherd House, Inveresk, Musselburgh
Fife	South Flisk, Blebo Craigs, Cupar

MAY

Saturday 2 May

Edinburgh, Midlothian & West Lothian	Dr Neil's Garden, Duddingston Village
Fife	The Tower, 1 Northview Terrace, Wormit

Sunday 3 May

Dumfriesshire	Dunesslin, Dunscore
East Lothian	Humbie Dean, Humbie
Edinburgh, Midlothian & West Lothian	Dr Neil's Garden, Duddingston Village
Fife	Earlshall Castle, Leuchars
Glasgow & District	Gartnavel Secret Garden, Gartnavel Royal Hospital, Glasgow
Perth & Kinross	Fingask Castle, Rait

Thursday 7 May

Angus & Dundee	Inchmill Cottage, Glenprosen, near Kirriemuir

Saturday 9 May

Aberdeenshire	Cruickshank Botanic Garden, 23 St Machar Drive, Aberdeen
Edinburgh, Midlothian & West Lothian	Kevock Garden , 16 Kevock Road, Lasswade

Sunday 10 May

Angus & Dundee	Dalfruin, Kirktonhill Road, Kirriemuir
Dumfriesshire	Dalswinton House, Dalswinton

Dunbartonshire	Glenarn, Glenarn Road, Rhu, Helensburgh
Dunbartonshire	High Glenan with Westburn, Helensburgh
East Lothian	Tyninghame House and The Walled Garden, Dunbar
Edinburgh, Midlothian & West Lothian	Kevock Garden , 16 Kevock Road, Lasswade
Edinburgh, Midlothian & West Lothian	Redcroft, 23 Murrayfield Road, Edinburgh
Kirkcudbrightshire	Cally Gardens, Cally Avenue, Gatehouse of Fleet
Perth & Kinross	Dowhill, Cleish
Renfrewshire	Highwood, off Lochwinnoch Road, Kilmacolm
Stirlingshire	NEW Kilmadock House, Stirling Road, Doune

Saturday 16 May

Angus & Dundee	NEW Gardyne Castle, by Forfar
Argyll & Lochaber	Dalnashean, Port Appin, Appin
Argyll & Lochaber	Knock Newhouse, Lochgair
Ayrshire & Arran	Craigengillan Est and Scottish Dark Sky Observatory, Dalmellington
Stirlingshire	NEW Na Lagan and The Glassert, Lochard Road, Aberfoyle

Sunday 17 May

Angus & Dundee	NEW Gardyne Castle, by Forfar
Argyll & Lochaber	Dalnashean, Port Appin, Appin
Argyll & Lochaber	Knock Newhouse, Lochgair
Ayrshire & Arran	Barnweil Garden, Craigie, near Kilmarnock
Dunbartonshire	Ross Priory, Gartocharn
Edinburgh, Midlothian & West Lothian	101 Greenbank Crescent, Edinburgh
Edinburgh, Midlothian & West Lothian	Moray Place and Bank Gardens, Edinburgh
Fife	Balcarres, Colinsburgh
Kincardine & Deeside	Inchmarlo Retirement Village Garden, Inchmarlo, Banchory
Kirkcudbrightshire	NEW Arbigland House, Kirkbean, Dumfries
Peeblesshire & Tweeddale	NEW The Pines, 43, St Ronan's Terrace, Innerleithen
Perth & Kinross	Dowhill, Cleish
Renfrewshire	NEW Perch Corner, 25 Stanely Crescent, Paisley
Stirlingshire	Bridge of Allan Gardens, Bridge of Allan
Wigtownshire	Logan House Gardens, Port Logan, by Stranraer

Wednesday 20 May

Edinburgh, Midlothian & West Lothian	NEW Jupiter Artland & Bonnington House, Wilkieston

Thursday 21 May

Angus & Dundee	Inchmill Cottage, Glenprosen, near Kirriemuir

Friday 22 May

Aberdeenshire	Airdlin Croft, Ythanbank, Ellon

Saturday 23 May

Aberdeenshire	Airdlin Croft, Ythanbank, Ellon
Angus & Dundee	NEW 10 Menzieshill Road, Dundee
Angus & Dundee	NEW Torwood, Milton of Ogilvie, Glenogilvy, Glamis by Forfar
Angus & Dundee	Brechin May Weekend Festival, Locations across Brechin
Argyll & Lochaber	Inveryne Woodland Garden, Kilfinan, Tighnabruaich
Argyll & Lochaber	Maolachy's Garden, Lochavich, by Kilmelford
Argyll & Lochaber	Strachur House Flower & Woodland Gardens, Strachur
Ayrshire & Arran	Glenapp Castle, Ballantrae, Girvan
Ayrshire & Arran	Townend of Kirkwood, Stewarton
Edinburgh, Midlothian & West Lothian	101 Greenbank Crescent, Edinburgh
Fife	Kirklands, Saline
Fife	The Tower, 1 Northview Terrace, Wormit
Lanarkshire	St Patrick's House, Lanark
Perth & Kinross	Bolfracks, Aberfeldy
Perth & Kinross	Braco Castle, Braco

Perth & Kinross	Cloan, by Auchterarder
Perth & Kinross	Fehmarn, Bridge of Earn
Perth & Kinross	Rossie Gardens, Forgandenny
Stirlingshire	Duntreath Castle, Blanefield
Stirlingshire	Kilbryde Castle, Dunblane
Stirlingshire	Shrubhill, Dunblane
Wigtownshire	Balker Farmhouse, Stranraer
Wigtownshire	Woodfall Gardens, Glasserton

Sunday 24 May

Aberdeenshire	Airdlin Croft, Ythanbank, Ellon
Angus & Dundee	NEW 10 Menzieshill Road, Dundee
Angus & Dundee	NEW Torwood, Milton of Ogilvie, Glenogilvy, Glamis by Forfar
Angus & Dundee	Brechin May Weekend Festival, Locations across Brechin
Angus & Dundee	Inchmill Cottage, Glenprosen, near Kirriemuir
Angus & Dundee	The Herbalist's Garden at Logie, Logie House, Kirriemuir
Argyll & Lochaber	Braevallich Farm, by Dalmally
Argyll & Lochaber	Inveryne Woodland Garden, Kilfinan, Tighnabruaich
Argyll & Lochaber	Maolachy's Garden, Lochavich, by Kilmelford
Argyll & Lochaber	Strachur House Flower & Woodland Gardens, Strachur
Ayrshire & Arran	Gardens of Kilmaurs, Kilmaurs
Ayrshire & Arran	Glenapp Castle, Ballantrae, Girvan
Ayrshire & Arran	Kirkmuir Cottage, Stewarton
Ayrshire & Arran	Townend of Kirkwood, Stewarton
Edinburgh, Midlothian & West Lothian	101 Greenbank Crescent, Edinburgh
Edinburgh, Midlothian & West Lothian	Redcroft, 23 Murrayfield Road, Edinburgh
Fife	Kirklands, Saline
Fife	South Flisk, Blebo Craigs, Cupar
Fife	St Fort Woodland Garden, St Fort Farm, Newport-on-Tay
Fife	The Tower, 1 Northview Terrace, Wormit
Inverness, Ross, Cromarty & Skye	NEW White Rose Cottage, Pitcalnie, Tain
Kirkcudbrightshire	Corsock House, Corsock, Castle Douglas
Lanarkshire	Covington House, Covington Road, Thankerton, Biggar
Lanarkshire	Old Farm Cottage, The Ladywell, Nemphlar, Lanark
Lanarkshire	St Patrick's House, Lanark
Lanarkshire	Wellbutts, Elsrickle, by Biggar
Peeblesshire & Tweeddale	Haystoun, Peebles
Perth & Kinross	NEW Carey House, Abernethy
Perth & Kinross	Bolfracks, Aberfeldy
Perth & Kinross	Braco Castle, Braco
Perth & Kinross	Cloan, by Auchterarder
Perth & Kinross	Eastbank Cottage, Perth Road, Abernethy
Perth & Kinross	Fehmarn, Bridge of Earn
Perth & Kinross	Rossie Gardens, Forgandenny
Stirlingshire	43 Thornton Avenue, Bonnybridge
Stirlingshire	Duntreath Castle, Blanefield
Stirlingshire	Kilbryde Castle, Dunblane
Stirlingshire	Shrubhill, Dunblane
Wigtownshire	NEW Crinan, Creetown
Wigtownshire	Logan Botanic Garden, Port Logan, by Stranraer
Wigtownshire	Woodfall Gardens, Glasserton

Monday 25 May

Angus & Dundee	NEW 10 Menzieshill Road, Dundee
Angus & Dundee	Brechin May Weekend Festival, Locations across Brechin
Angus & Dundee	The Herbalist's Garden at Logie, Logie House, Kirriemuir
Ayrshire & Arran	Glenapp Castle, Ballantrae, Girvan
Ayrshire & Arran	Kirkmuir Cottage, Stewarton
Ayrshire & Arran	Townend of Kirkwood, Stewarton
Edinburgh, Midlothian & West Lothian	101 Greenbank Crescent, Edinburgh
Fife	NEW Cambo Farmhouse, Kingsbarns
Fife	South Flisk, Blebo Craigs, Cupar

Fife	The Tower, 1 Northview Terrace, Wormit
Lanarkshire	Covington House, Covington Road, Thankerton, Biggar
Lanarkshire	Old Farm Cottage, The Ladywell, Nemphlar, Lanark
Lanarkshire	Wellbutts, Elsrickle, by Biggar
Perth & Kinross	NEW Carey House, Abernethy
Perth & Kinross	Bolfracks, Aberfeldy
Perth & Kinross	Braco Castle, Braco
Perth & Kinross	Eastbank Cottage, Perth Road, Abernethy
Stirlingshire	Duntreath Castle, Blanefield
Stirlingshire	Gargunnock House Garden, Gargunnock
Stirlingshire	Kilbryde Castle, Dunblane
Wigtownshire	Woodfall Gardens, Glasserton

Thursday 28 May

Inverness, Ross, Cromarty & Skye	Dundonnell House, Little Loch Broom, Wester Ross

Saturday 30 May

Ayrshire & Arran	Netherthird Community Garden, Craigens Road, Cumnock
Caithness, Sutherland, Orkney & Shetland	Amat, Ardgay
Moray & Nairn	10 Stuart Avenue, Ardersier, Inverness
Moray & Nairn	Gordonstoun, Duffus, near Elgin

Sunday 31 May

Argyll & Lochaber	Ardverikie with Aberarder, Kinloch Laggan, Newtonmore
Argyll & Lochaber	Fasnacloich, Appin
Caithness, Sutherland, Orkney & Shetland	Amat, Ardgay
Dumfriesshire	Cowhill Tower, Holywood
East Lothian	Belhaven House, Edinburgh Road, Belhaven, Dunbar
Edinburgh, Midlothian & West Lothian	14 East Brighton Crescent, Portobello, Edinburgh
Edinburgh, Midlothian & West Lothian	Hunter's Tryst, 95 Oxgangs Road, Edinburgh
Fife	Lindores House, by Newburgh
Fife	St Fort Woodland Garden, St Fort Farm, Newport-on-Tay
Glasgow & District	Kilsyth Gardens, Allanfauld Road, Kilsyth
Kirkcudbrightshire	The Limes, Kirkcudbright
Peeblesshire & Tweeddale	Quercus Garden Plants, Whitmuir Farm, West Linton

JUNE

Tuesday 2 June

Peeblesshire & Tweeddale	Stobo Japanese Water Garden, Home Farm, Stobo
Peeblesshire & Tweeddale	The Potting Shed, Broughton Place, Broughton, Biggar

Wednesday 3 June

Inverness, Ross, Cromarty & Skye	House of Gruinard, Laide, by Achnasheen
Peeblesshire & Tweeddale	Stobo Japanese Water Garden, Home Farm, Stobo

Thursday 4 June

Angus & Dundee	NEW Angus & Dundee Garden Trail, locations across Angus &Dundee
Angus & Dundee	Inchmill Cottage, Glenprosen, near Kirriemuir

Friday 5 June

Aberdeenshire	Airdlin Croft, Ythanbank, Ellon
Angus & Dundee	NEW Angus & Dundee Garden Trail, locations across Angus &Dundee
Inverness, Ross, Cromarty & Skye	Gorthleck House Garden, Stratherrick

Saturday 6 June

Aberdeenshire	Airdlin Croft, Ythanbank, Ellon

Aberdeenshire	Leith Hall Plant Sale, Huntly
Angus & Dundee	NEW Angus & Dundee Garden Trail, locations across Angus &Dundee
Ayrshire & Arran	Holmes Farm, Drybridge, by Irvine
East Lothian	NEW Longwood, Humbie
East Lothian	Humbie Dean, Humbie
Edinburgh, Midlothian & West Lothian	Rivaldsgreen House, 48 Friars Brae, Linlithgow
Fife	Newton Barns and Newton Mains, Auchtermuchty
Glasgow & District	Kew Terrace Gardens: Back to Front, Kew Terrace Lane, Glasgow
Inverness, Ross, Cromarty & Skye	Gorthleck House Garden, Stratherrick
Peeblesshire & Tweeddale	NEW Lamancha Community Hub Plant Sale, Old Moffat Road

Sunday 7 June

Ayrshire & Arran	Holmes Farm, Drybridge, by Irvine
Dumfriesshire	NEW Craigieburn, Craigieburn House, by Moffat
Dumfriesshire	Glenae, Amisfield
Dunbartonshire	Geilston Garden, Main Road, Cardross
East Lothian	Stenton Village, Stenton, Dunbar
Edinburgh, Midlothian & West Lothian	Dean Gardens, Edinburgh
Edinburgh, Midlothian & West Lothian	The Glasshouses at the Royal Botanic Garden Edinburgh, Edinburgh
Fife	Earlshall Castle, Leuchars
Fife	Newton Barns and Newton Mains, Auchtermuchty
Inverness, Ross, Cromarty & Skye	Field House, Belladrum, Beauly
Inverness, Ross, Cromarty & Skye	Gorthleck House Garden, Stratherrick
Kirkcudbrightshire	Seabank, The Merse, Rockcliffe
Perth & Kinross	Cloan, by Auchterarder
Perth & Kinross	Explorers Garden, Port Na Craig, Pitlochry
Renfrewshire	Wraes, Corseliehill Road, nr Houston
Roxburghshire	West Leas, Bonchester Bridge

Tuesday 9 June

| Peeblesshire & Tweeddale | The Potting Shed, Broughton Place, Broughton, Biggar |

Thursday 11 June

| Angus & Dundee | NEW Angus & Dundee Garden Trail, locations across Angus &Dundee |

Friday 12 June

Angus & Dundee	NEW Angus & Dundee Garden Trail, locations across Angus &Dundee
Kirkcudbrightshire	Threave Garden, Castle Douglas
Peeblesshire & Tweeddale	NEW Prieston House, Melrose

Saturday 13 June

Aberdeenshire	NEW Altries, Maryculter, Aberdeenshire
Angus & Dundee	NEW Angus & Dundee Garden Trail, locations across Angus &Dundee
Argyll & Lochaber	NEW Argyll Plant Sale, Kilmore Village Hall, near Oban
East Lothian	Dirleton Village, Dirleton
Edinburgh, Midlothian & West Lothian	89 Ravenscroft Street, Edinburgh
Kirkcudbrightshire	Threave Garden, Castle Douglas

Sunday 14 June

Dumfriesshire	Leap Cottage, West Cluden, Dumfries
Dunbartonshire	High Glenan, Helensburgh
East Lothian	Dirleton Village, Dirleton
Edinburgh, Midlothian & West Lothian	Preston Hall Walled Garden, Pathhead
Fife	NEW Blebo House and Blebo Stables, Cupar
Glasgow & District	NEW The Hidden Gardens, 25 Albert Drive, Glasgow
Inverness, Ross, Cromarty & Skye	Old Allangrange, Munlochy
Kincardine & Deeside	Kincardine Castle, Kincardine O'Neil
Kirkcudbrightshire	Threave Garden, Castle Douglas
Lanarkshire	NEW Meadowhead, Meadowhead, Dolphinton, West Linton

Perth & Kinross	Bridge of Earn Village, Dunbarney Church Hall, Manse Road
Renfrewshire	NEW Airlie and Garth House, Bridge of Weir
Stirlingshire	Rowberrow, 18 Castle Road, Dollar
Wigtownshire	Castle Kennedy and Gardens, Stranraer

Wednesday 17 June

Edinburgh, Midlothian & West Lothian	89 Ravenscroft Street, Edinburgh

Thursday 18 June

Angus & Dundee	NEW Angus & Dundee Garden Trail, locations across Angus &Dundee
Angus & Dundee	Inchmill Cottage, Glenprosen, near Kirriemuir

Friday 19 June

Angus & Dundee	NEW Angus & Dundee Garden Trail, locations across Angus &Dundee

Saturday 20 June

Angus & Dundee	NEW Angus & Dundee Garden Trail, locations across Angus &Dundee
East Lothian	Humbie Dean, Humbie
East Lothian	Inveresk Village, Inveresk, Musselburgh
Edinburgh, Midlothian & West Lothian	89 Ravenscroft Street, Edinburgh
Fife	Blebo Craigs Village Gardens, Blebo Craigs, Cupar
Fife	Helensbank, Kincardine
Peeblesshire & Tweeddale	NEW Prieston House, Melrose

Sunday 21 June

Aberdeenshire	NEW Heatherwick Farm, Kintore, Inverurie
Angus & Dundee	Angus Plant Sale, Logie Walled Garden, Kirriemuir
Ayrshire & Arran	Barrmill Community Garden, Barrmill Park and Gardens
East Lothian	Inveresk Village, Inveresk, Musselburgh
Edinburgh, Midlothian & West Lothian	NEW 2 Pentland Crescent, Edinburgh
Edinburgh, Midlothian & West Lothian	Even More Gardens of the Lower New Town, Edinburgh
Fife	Blebo Craigs Village Gardens, Blebo Craigs, Cupar
Fife	Hidden Gardens of Newburgh, Newburgh
Glasgow & District	The Good Life Gardens, Cambuslang, Glasgow
Kincardine & Deeside	Finzean House, Finzean, Banchory
Peeblesshire & Tweeddale	8 Halmyre Mains, West Linton
Roxburghshire	NEW Smailholm Village Gardens, Smailholm Village Hall, Smailholm
Stirlingshire	Thorntree, Arnprior
Wigtownshire	Woodfall Gardens, Glasserton

Tuesday 23 June

Renfrewshire	Craig Hepburn Memorial Garden, Stirling Drive, Linwood

Wednesday 24 June

Renfrewshire	Craig Hepburn Memorial Garden, Stirling Drive, Linwood

Thursday 25 June

Angus & Dundee	NEW Angus & Dundee Garden Trail, locations across Angus &Dundee

Friday 26 June

Angus & Dundee	NEW Angus & Dundee Garden Trail, locations across Angus &Dundee

Saturday 27 June

Angus & Dundee	NEW Angus & Dundee Garden Trail, locations across Angus &Dundee
Argyll & Lochaber	Maolachy's Garden, Lochavich, by Kilmelford
Fife	The Tower, 1 Northview Terrace, Wormit

Moray & Nairn	Haugh Garden, College of Roseisle
Perth & Kinross	Blair Castle Gardens, Blair Atholl
Perth & Kinross	The Bield at Blackruthven, Blackruthven House, Tibbermore
Roxburghshire	Corbet Tower, Morebattle, near Kelso

Sunday 28 June

Aberdeenshire	NEW Heatherwick Farm, Kintore, Inverurie
Argyll & Lochaber	Maolachy's Garden, Lochavich, by Kilmelford
Berwickshire	Netherbyres, Eyemouth
Dunbartonshire	NEW 4 Cairndhu Gardens and Brandon Grove, Helensburgh
East Lothian	Tyninghame House and The Walled Garden, Dunbar
Edinburgh, Midlothian & West Lothian	5 Greenbank Crescent, Edinburgh
Fife	46 South Street, St Andrews
Fife	Backhouse at Rossie Estate, by Collessie
Glasgow & District	NEW Strathbungo and Langside Gardens, March Street, Glasgow
Inverness, Ross, Cromarty & Skye	House of Aigas and Field Centre, by Beauly
Lanarkshire	Covington House, Covington Road, Thankerton, Biggar
Moray & Nairn	NEW No 3 Mains of Burgie, by Forres, Moray

Tuesday 30 June

Ayrshire & Arran	Dougarie, Isle of Arran
Peeblesshire & Tweeddale	The Potting Shed, Broughton Place, Broughton, Biggar

JULY

Friday 3 July

Caithness, Sutherland, Orkney & Shetland	The Castle and Gardens of Mey, Mey

Saturday 4 July

Angus & Dundee	Arbroath Collection of Gardens, Locations across Arbroath
Ayrshire & Arran	The Gardens of Fenwick, Fenwick
Edinburgh, Midlothian & West Lothian	4 Harelaw Road, Edinburgh
Glasgow & District	Milton Community Garden, Liddesdale Square, Milton, Glasgow

Sunday 5 July

Berwickshire	Lennel Bank, Coldstream
East Lothian	Humbie Dean, Humbie
East Lothian	Longniddry Gardens, Longniddry
Edinburgh, Midlothian & West Lothian	NEW Meadow Place, 19 Meadow Place
Glasgow & District	NEW Duchess of Montrose Memorial Garden, 8 Aboukir St, Glasgow
Kirkcudbrightshire	Southwick House, Southwick
Peeblesshire & Tweeddale	Glen House, Glen Estate, Innerleithen
Roxburghshire	Yetholm Village Gardens, Town Yetholm

Tuesday 7 July

Peeblesshire & Tweeddale	The Potting Shed, Broughton Place, Broughton, Biggar

Saturday 11 July

Perth & Kinross	Allotment Association of Crieff, Turretbank Road Crieff

Sunday 12 July

Berwickshire	Coldstream Open Gardens, High Street, Coldstream
East Lothian	Gifford Village and Broadwoodside, Gifford
Glasgow & District	Woodbourne House, Seven Sisters, Lenzie, Glasgow
Kincardine & Deeside	Douneside House, Tarland
Lanarkshire	Dippoolbank Cottage, Carnwath

Thursday 16 July
Angus & Dundee   Inchmill Cottage, Glenprosen, near Kirriemuir

Friday 17 July
Caithness, Sutherland, Orkney & Shetland   The Castle and Gardens of Mey, Mey

Saturday 18 July
Ayrshire & Arran   Whitewin House, Golf Course Road, Girvan
Caithness, Sutherland, Orkney & Shetland   Skelbo House, Skelbo, Dornoch
Fife   Crail: Gardens in the Burgh, 2 Castle Street, Crail
Fife   Dalgety Bay Gardens, Dalgety Bay
Inverness, Ross, Cromarty & Skye   2 Durnamuck, Little Loch Broom, Wester Ross
Moray & Nairn   Gordon Castle Walled Garden, Fochabers, Moray

Sunday 19 July
Ayrshire & Arran   Whitewin House, Golf Course Road, Girvan
Berwickshire   Marlfield and Ruthven Gardens, Coldstream
Dumfriesshire   Westwater Farm, Langholm
Fife   Crail: Gardens in the Burgh, 2 Castle Street, Crail
Fife   Dalgety Bay Gardens, Dalgety Bay
Glasgow & District   Kamares, 18 Broom Road, Newton Mearns, Glasgow
Kirkcudbrightshire   Dalbeattie Community Allotments Association, Port Road, Dalbeattie
Peeblesshire & Tweeddale   The Schoolhouse, Skirling by Biggar
Stirlingshire   43 Thornton Avenue, Bonnybridge

Saturday 25 July
Ayrshire & Arran   Whitewin House, Golf Course Road, Girvan
Edinburgh, Midlothian & West Lothian   NEW The Archivists' Garden, 2 Princes Street, Edinburgh
Moray & Nairn   Haugh Garden, College of Roseisle

Sunday 26 July
Angus & Dundee   Brechin Gardens in Summer, Locations across Brechin
Ayrshire & Arran   Whitewin House, Golf Course Road, Girvan
Dumfriesshire   NEW Craigieburn, Craigieburn House, by Moffat
Edinburgh, Midlothian & West Lothian   NEW Newhaven Heritage Community Garden, Edinburgh
Edinburgh, Midlothian & West Lothian   Craigentinny Telferton Allotments, Telferton Road, Edinburgh
Glasgow & District   The Gardens of Kilmardinny Crescent, Bearsden, Glasgow
Inverness, Ross, Cromarty & Skye   House of Aigas and Field Centre, by Beauly
Kirkcudbrightshire   Crofts, Kirkpatrick Durham, Castle Douglas
Lanarkshire   Wellbutts, Elsrickle, by Biggar
Moray & Nairn   Glenrinnes Lodge, Dufftown, Keith, Banffshire
Stirlingshire   The Tors, 2 Slamannan Road, Falkirk

AUGUST
....

Saturday 1 August
Ayrshire & Arran   Whitewin House, Golf Course Road, Girvan
East Lothian   Greywalls, Gullane
Fife   Willowhill, Forgan, Newport-on-Tay

Sunday 2 August
Angus & Dundee   Montrose Gardens, Various locations across Montrose
Ayrshire & Arran   Whitewin House, Golf Course Road, Girvan
Caithness, Sutherland, Orkney & Shetland   Langwell, Berriedale
Fife   Wormistoune House, Crail
Kincardine & Deeside   Glenbervie House, Drumlithie, Stonehaven
Kirkcudbrightshire   Cally Gardens, Cally Avenue, Gatehouse of Fleet
Lanarkshire   NEW Bothwell Village Gardens, Bothwell

Moray & Nairn   NEW Glebe House, Main Street, Urquhart
Peeblesshire & Tweeddale   West Linton Village Gardens, West Linton
Perth & Kinross   Drummond Castle Gardens, Muthill, Crieff
Roxburghshire   West Leas, Bonchester Bridge
Stirlingshire   60 Greenhead, Alva, Clackmannanshire

Saturday 8 August
Ayrshire & Arran   Whitewin House, Golf Course Road, Girvan
Fife   Willowhill, Forgan, Newport-on-Tay

Sunday 9 August
Ayrshire & Arran   Whitewin House, Golf Course Road, Girvan
Dumfriesshire   Dalswinton Mill, Dalswinton, Dumfries
Dumfriesshire   Shawhead, 7 Vendace Drive, Lochmaben
Inverness, Ross, Cromarty & Skye   Kiltarlity Gardens, Kiltarlity, Beauly
Kincardine & Deeside   Clayfolds, Bridge of Muchalls, Stonehaven
Kirkcudbrightshire   Kings Grange House, Castle Douglas
Lanarkshire   The Walled Garden, Shieldhill, Quothquan, Biggar
Peeblesshire & Tweeddale   NEW The Pines, 43, St Ronan's Terrace, Innerleithen
Perth & Kinross   Dowhill, Cleish

Thursday 13 August
Angus & Dundee   Inchmill Cottage, Glenprosen, near Kirriemuir

Friday 14 August
Caithness, Sutherland, Orkney & Shetland   The Castle and Gardens of Mey, Mey
Dumfriesshire   Dalswinton Mill, Dalswinton, Dumfries

Saturday 15 August
Fife   The Tower, 1 Northview Terrace, Wormit
Fife   Willowhill, Forgan, Newport-on-Tay

Sunday 16 August
East Lothian   Humbie Dean, Humbie
Inverness, Ross, Cromarty & Skye   Kilcoy Castle, Redcastle, by Muir of Ord
Peeblesshire & Tweeddale   Gattonside Village Gardens, Gattonside
Perth & Kinross   Cloan, by Auchterarder
Perth & Kinross   Dowhill, Cleish

Thursday 20 August
Inverness, Ross, Cromarty & Skye   Dundonnell House, Little Loch Broom, Wester Ross

Friday 21 August
Dumfriesshire   Dalswinton Mill, Dalswinton, Dumfries

Saturday 22 August
Fife   Willowhill, Forgan, Newport-on-Tay

Sunday 23 August
Aberdeenshire   Tarland Community Garden, Aboyne
Ayrshire & Arran   NEW Underwood House, Craigie, Ayrshire
Glasgow & District   Horatio's Gardens, Queen Elizabeth University Hospital, Glasgow
Inverness, Ross, Cromarty & Skye   2 Durnamuck, Little Loch Broom, Wester Ross

Friday 28 August
Dumfriesshire   Dalswinton Mill, Dalswinton, Dumfries

Saturday 29 August
Edinburgh, Midlothian & West Lothian   NEW Newhaven Heritage Community Garden, Newhaven Main St
Fife   Willowhill, Forgan, Newport-on-Tay

Sunday 30 August
Glasgow & District   Gartnavel Secret Garden, Gartnavel Royal Hospital, Glasgow
Inverness, Ross, Cromarty & Skye   Old Allangrange, Munlochy
Kirkcudbrightshire   3 Millhall, Shore Road, Kirkcudbright

SEPTEMBER
....

Wednesday 2 September
Peeblesshire & Tweeddale   Laidlawstiel House, Clovenfords, Galashiels

Thursday 3 September
Peeblesshire & Tweeddale   Laidlawstiel House, Clovenfords, Galashiels

Sunday 6 September
Dunbartonshire   James Street Community Garden Plant Sale, Helensburgh
Peeblesshire & Tweeddale   Kailzie Gardens, Peebles

Thursday 17 September
Angus & Dundee   Inchmill Cottage, Glenprosen, near Kirriemuir

Saturday 26 September
Moray & Nairn   10 Stuart Avenue, Ardersier, Inverness

Sunday 27 September
Stirlingshire   43 Thornton Avenue, Bonnybridge

OCTOBER
....

Saturday 3 October
Angus & Dundee   Hospitalfield Gardens, Hospitalfield House, Westway, Arbroath

Sunday 4 October
Fife   Hill of Tarvit Plant Sale and Autumn Fair, Hill of Tarvit, Cupar

Sunday 11 October
Peeblesshire & Tweeddale   Dawyck Botanic Garden, Stobo

Saturday 17 October
Angus & Dundee   12 Glamis Drive, Dundee

Sunday 18 October
Angus & Dundee   12 Glamis Drive, Dundee

INDEX OF GARDENS

ORDER YOUR 90ᵀᴴ ANNIVERSARY ISSUE GUIDEBOOK FOR 2021

The first Scotland's Gardens Scheme Guidebook was created in 1931, and it has become the 'go to' guide for garden visitors in Scotland ever since. So, don't go without your copy in 2021!

Order now and your copy will be posted to you on publication Fill in the form below and send to: Scotland's Gardens Scheme, 23 Castle Street, Edinburgh EH2 3DN

' The daffodil-coloured tome of horticultural promise'

Joanna, Edinburgh Garden Diary

'Supporting your community through local charities'

Scotland's GARDENS Scheme
OPEN FOR CHARITY

Please send me _____ copy / copies of our Guidebook for 2021, price £5.00 plus £2.00 UK p&p, as soon as it is available.

I enclose a cheque / postal order made payable to Scotland's Gardens Scheme.

Name _____

Address _____

_____

Postcode _____

WELCOMING YOU IN 2021

Scotland's Gardens Scheme, 23 Castle Street, Edinburgh EH2 3DN
Copies of our Guidebook may also be purchased on our website: **scotlandsgardens.org**

OUR DISTRICTS BY GEOGRAPHICAL AREA